Philosophy and Science
in the Scottish Enlightenment

Philosophy and Science
in the Scottish Enlightenment

Essays edited by
PETER JONES

JOHN DONALD PUBLISHERS LTD
EDINBURGH

ISBN 0 85976 225 4

The publishers acknowledge the financial assistance of the Scottish Arts Council in the publication of this volume.

Typesetting by Quorn Selective Repro Ltd, Loughborough.
Printed in Great Britain by Bell & Bain Ltd., Glasgow.

PREFACE

This collection of essays is based on seminars and lectures given during 1986 as part of the Institute Project Scottish Enlightenment 'IPSE 86'. The topography of the intellectual and social landscape is being extensively studied and the maps need to be carefully re-drawn on different scales and varying projections. For these reasons, among others, none of the authors attempts a synoptic view of the Scottish Enlightenment. They address some of the lesser-known aspects of the period which help us to grasp its intellectual complexity and, by implication, raise questions about the achievements of our own times. I am most grateful to the contributors for their help in bringing together their findings, and to all of the large number of participants in the project who made it such a rewarding and significant event.

Peter Jones
Director
Institute for Advanced Studies in the Humanities
University of Edinburgh

THE CONTRIBUTORS

Alexander Broadie
Department of Philosophy, University of Glasgow

Arthur Donovan
U.S. Merchant Marine Academy, Kings Point, New York

David V. Fenby
Department of Chemistry, University of Otago

Peter Jones
Institute for Advanced Studies in the Humanities, University of Edinburgh

Thomas A. Markus
Department of Architecture and Building Science, University of Strathclyde

James Moore
Department of Political Science, Concordia University

Andrew S. Skinner
Department of Political Economy, University of Glasgow

Charles W. J. Withers
The College of St. Paul and St. Mary, Cheltenham

Robert Wokler
Department of Government, University of Manchester

Paul Wood
Department of History, Queen's University, Kingston

CONTENTS

Page

Preface   v
List of Contributors   vi
Introduction
    Peter Jones   1
1. Thomas Reid and his pre-Reformation Scottish precursors
    Alexander Broadie   6
2. Natural Law and the Pyrrhonian Controversy
    James Moore   20
3. Science and the Aberdeen Enlightenment
    Paul Wood   39
4. Chemical Reactivity and Heat in the Eighteenth Century
    David V. Fenby   67
5. The Chemical Revolution and the Enlightenment — and
    a Proposal for the Study of Scientific Change
    Arthur Donovan   87
6. Improvement and Enlightenment: Agriculture and Natural
    History in the Work of the Rev. Dr. John Walker (1731–1803)
    Charles W. J. Withers   102
7. Sir James Steuart: Economic Theory and Policy
    Andrew S. Skinner   117
8. Apes and Races in the Scottish Enlightenment: Monboddo
    and Kames on the Nature of Man
    Robert Wokler   145
9. Buildings and the Ordering of Minds and Bodies
    Thomas A. Markus   169
    Index   225

INTRODUCTION

Peter Jones

In the Spring of 1982 I submitted a proposal to the Principal of Edinburgh University, Dr (later Sir) John Burnett, suggesting that the Institute for Advanced Studies in the Humanities devote a six-month period to a multi-disciplinary analysis and celebration of the Scottish Enlightenment. The Summer of 1986 was set aside for the events, and preparations were made to involve as broad a section of the community as possible. The Edinburgh International Festival agreed to adopt the Institute's theme as its own, and the City of Edinburgh likewise organised events associated with the Scottish Enlightenment. The merest summary of the main events must suffice as a record of what happened under the umbrella of the project known as 'IPSE' (Institute Project Scottish Enlightenment). 225 IPSE lectures and seminars were attended by over 8000 people, in venues ranging from the Royal Society of Edinburgh — which had to close its doors because of the crowds — and the Royal Museum of Scotland, to Edinburgh University Library and Pollock Halls. Six IPSE International Conferences brought over 400 overseas delegates to Edinburgh, to participate in debate and investigation; forty IPSE International Fellows were elected to the Institute for periods of up to six months, to pursue research into all aspects of the Scottish Enlightenment. 20,000 Visitors went to the IPSE exhibition, 'A Hotbed of Genius', held in the Queen Street galleries of the Royal Museum of Scotland, and opened by the Honourable Lord Cameron before distinguished guests. The accompanying book, *A Hotbed of Genius* (ed. D. Daiches, P. Jones and J. Jones, Edinburgh University Press), reprinted to meet heavy demand. IPSE commissioned three concerts for the Festival, devised by Dr David Johnson, and held in The Queen's Hall and in St Cecilia's Hall; and IPSE also commissioned a new adaptation for the stage, by Dr Roger Savage, of Hume's *Dialogues Concerning Natural Religion*. Those performances were also held in St Cecilia's Hall.

As part of the University project, a major exhibition of Scottish painting was held in the Upper Library of the University, and in harmony with the IPSE theme, the National Galleries showed Tassie

Medallions. The Royal Botanic Garden celebrated the work of Dr John Hope, and the National Museums of Scotland mounted an exhibition which touched on several aspects of the Enlightenment, under the title 'The Enterprising Scot'. To ensure that visitors spread the word, the Scottish Post Office issued a special aerogramme to commemorate the Scottish Enlightenment, designed in consultation with the IPSE team.

The declared aims of IPSE were 'to generate greater awareness and deeper understanding of Scotland's intellectual and cultural heritage'. The community at large has certainly now heard of the Scottish Enlightenment, and genuine interest in its characters and legacy were expressed by many people. The harmonious relations between the University, the City and National Museums, Galleries and Libraries, the Edinburgh International Festival, and commercial sponsors have been signally strengthened. A large number of scholars have been able to explore new avenues and to exchange ideas with scholars from other fields; historians and philosophers, chemists and geologists, lawyers and doctors were able to work together and challenge each other's perspective.

In spite of increasing study of the Scottish Enlightenment, our understanding of that great period remains uneven and patchy. Detailed work on Hume and Smith, for example, has not been matched by equally extensive and incisive work on Ferguson or Hutcheson; writers such as Kames or Robertson, Blair or Monboddo, have been studied only by isolated scholars, whose interpretations need both challenge and supplementation. Historians of science and of law, of theology and of the arts, still have much to do. It is therefore premature to attempt a synoptic view of the period, although previous attempts are now seen to be distorted: the scientific dimensions are almost always omitted, the philosophical dimensions are almost always garbled, the theological dimensions are almost always misunderstood. A disproportionate amount of time has been given to those now regarded as the intellectual leaders of the period and, as social historians have rightly pointed out, too little attention to the contemporary understanding of or reaction to the ideas of the intelligentsia; furthermore, relatively little notice has been taken of the knowledge, interests, beliefs and values of the greater bulk of the population, whose acquaintance with intellectual theory was often distant. It is, of course, a difficult matter to establish the influence of ideas, especially as they become diffused and transformed; along with his goals and capacities, facts and fears, prayers and prejudices can all affect the emphasis an individual gives to ideas.

To achieve a better understanding of the past a pooling of resources is needed: we need all of the skills nowadays unequally distributed among currently separate 'disciplines'. Philosophers typically judge the merit of a thinker by reference to the fruitful opportunities he affords later generations to use or develop his ideas; this selective emphasis frequently overlooks contemporary interpretations of what was going on, and distorts the tenor of the work taken as a whole. The philosopher must learn to listen to the social historian, who studies contemporary responses and influences, however idiosyncratic. In his turn the social historian must listen to philosophers and historians of science, and learn that thinkers need assessment in terms of the coherence of arguments, their presuppositions and their logical and practical implications. Literary scholars, for their part, must likewise become more intellectually alert to the scientific and political concerns of the day; students of economics and medicine, to cite just two final examples, must take into account factors that would strike many today as outside those domains.

, The goal of pooling such resources should not be mistaken. There is no such thing as a 'total picture': a complete, exhaustive, non-selective account, reflecting and requiring no interpretation, and immune from subsequent revision. All historical judgments are selective, and are thereby evaluative, reflecting what someone deems to be worth attention; all are made from a viewpoint which can change, and can be challenged, and which always needs interpretation. What can be done, however, with enormous benefit, is to gather together and juxtapose accounts from different viewpoints, and as occasion warrants, overlay them, like filters of different colours. We can locate our targets by means of different co-ordinates, remembering always that the scale, the focus, the vocabulary and the methods, are results of judgment and interpretation. An apparently common concern to establish what happened, when, where, how, and why must not be allowed to mask fundamental differences in the knowledge, interests and perspectives of the questioners. As a point of method we should remember, also, that time and distance flatten out the topography, disguising what were very real obstacles to those on the ground; neither the times, nor the findings of the Scottish Enlightenment, were as bland as they can be made to sound. Moreover, the self-appointed spokesmen of an age are rarely representative of it, and their narratives are often unacceptable, even if known, to their contemporaries. Finally, we do well to remind ourselves that the groupings, emphases, metaphors we use for making sense of the past, will be found wanting by our successors.

The character of an age, then, is not fully grasped by exclusive attention to the few individuals celebrated by those who come later.

Accordingly in this book familiar thinkers such as Hume and Smith are set on one side, and attention is given instead to Kames and Monboddo, Sir James Steuart and Dr John Walker. No attempt is made, by any of the contributors, to define the Scottish Enlightenment, or to generalise from what has been studied; a synoptic view is carefully avoided because the implications of these new studies are by no means clear. Although enough has already been done to displace earlier comprehensive accounts, too little has been revised to provide even a unitary line or theme. But whilst a transitional stage in intellectual or historical re-appraisal is, by definition, disorienting, the fundamental questions of method and interpretation which come to the surface ensure that enquiry and discussion are especially invigorating. In fact, agreement is emerging that detailed contextual analysis is required in all domains.

In describing the vigorous intellectual activity taking place in Scotland around 1500, Dr Broadie draws parallels between the work of pre-Reformation philosophers and that of Thomas Reid, whom he calls 'the greatest epistemologist of the Scottish Enlightenment'. Even if the earlier period was little known by the later, and was rooted in alien traditions, perhaps the periodic occurrence of intellectual vitality argues for deep-seated capacities, kept alive in hitherto unrecognised ways. An increasing number of scholars now accepts that, in Professor Moore's words, 'there is no single, undifferentiated, univocal context which will make' intelligible the work of any major thinker. His own essay traces attempts by exiled French Protestants to counter the sceptical and, as they saw it, atheistic claims by their fellow Huguenot Pierre Bayle (1647–1706). Bayle profoundly influenced both Scottish philosophers, such as Hume, and their French contemporaries such as Voltaire and Diderot. By analysing the appeals of the disputants to natural law doctrine, Professor Moore fills in some of the background against which the later Scottish thinkers must be understood.

Professor Wood discusses the extensive scientific work undertaken in Aberdeen into the 'science of nature'. The Scottish Enlightenment was not limited to Edinburgh or the concerns of those who lived there; the 'science of man', which interested the citizens of the capital, must be juxtaposed with contrasting emphases in other centres. He traces the fortunes of Marischal and King's Colleges, and suggests that forward-looking innovative ideas need adequate financial support as well as effective publicity. The next three papers further supplement our understanding of scientific work of the period. Professor Fenby surveys the developing theories of reactivity and heat from Newton to Lavoisier, and draws out the implications of these theories for geology and industry. Professor Donovan looks at the work of Lavoisier in greater detail, and proposes a method for studying scientific change modelled on methods in the arts. Dr Withers describes the work of the Rev. Dr Andrew Walker who, in 1779, was the first person to give lectures on agriculture in an English-speaking University.

Professor Skinner describes the unduly neglected economic theories of Sir James Steuart. Steuart adopted a broadly historical approach to his claims, grounded on his extensive travels throughout Europe. He emphasised diversity and change among inter-dependent economic and social phenomena, and developed a view of an exchange economy. Whilst he would have agreed with Smith's later view that government must intervene when markets fail, he was himself unclear how such failure was to be quickly discerned. Professor Skinner suggests that whereas Smith formulated a system which met the needs of later ages he could not foresee, Steuart sought to tackle the problems of his own day; modern commentators need to examine Steuart without preconceptions derived from Smith.

Dr Wokler argues that original thinkers, typically, 'march into battle backwards'. In other words, they normally define their own positions and goals in relation to currently influential doctrines, and later readers are likely to misunderstand their work if they ignore such implicit references. Dr Wokler looks at the theses of two scholars of the Enlightenment who are nowadays frequently overlooked, Lord Monboddo and Lord Kames. Both adhered to the current demand for a theory of human nature, but unlike his fellow Scots, Monboddo took Buffon — whom he initially misunderstood — as his main inspiration, and not Montesquieu. But in his speculations on man's links with the 'orang-utans', and on the origins of language, Monboddo marks the end of one strand of scientific thinking. Kames's speculations, by contrast, helped to launch a second tradition which, in other hands, became the modern discipline of physical anthropology.

Professor Markus observes that in the architecture and planning of the Scottish Enlightenment, as in its social and political philosophy, there is a tension between revolutionary and traditional strands: a continuation of classical style, on the one hand, together with new notions of achieving order in the functional programmes of buildings, on the other. He explores the ways in which different groups of people perceived and used hospitals, prisons and asylums, and suggests that these reveal their attitudes towards the exercise of power.

1
THOMAS REID AND HIS PRE-REFORMATION SCOTTISH PRECURSORS

Alexander Broadie

In this essay I shall argue for two theses. The first is that the Enlightenment is not unique within the Scottish cultural experience, for a similar intellectual flourish had occurred in the decades around 1500. I shall argue that knowledge of that earlier achievement can help us illumine certain problems about the Enlightenment itself. The second thesis is that a crucial philosophical doctrine of the earlier period re-emerges in the Enlightenment, specifically in the pages of Thomas Reid. Discussion of the latter thesis will lead me into territory of perennial philosophical interest. The first part of this essay is therefore historical in character and the second half philosophical.

I

The Enlightenment was a spectacular period in the cultural life of Scotland. As if from nothing or at most from very little there appeared across the firmament a galaxy of marvellously gifted Scots whose intellectual vigour was placed to brilliant effect at the services of philosophy, sociology, economics, medicine, chemistry, geology, physics. The list seems endless, a fact which forces upon us a reminder of how great was the number of Scots who were contributing to the enrichment of our culture during the decades on either side of 1750.

Considered purely as a historical phenomenon, the Scottish Enlightenment raises large questions. Certainly many, with a picture of early eighteenth-century Scotland as a poor country situated far from the great cultural centres of Europe, might well be puzzled that the Scottish Enlightenment occurred at all. How, it may be asked, could such a country produce so much from its own scant resources?

As a first step to answering this question it should be said that it makes sense to speak of the intellectual vitality of a people, and in explaining the occurrence of the Scottish Enlightenment it is to that resource in particular that we must attend. Proof that such vitality exists is not provided by pointing to a single display of it, but by pointing to the periodic occurrence of such displays. And in the light of that consideration the point I wish to bring into focus is that two and a half centuries earlier during the decades on either side of 1500 Scots were enjoying a similar cultural heyday. They were listened to, read, and quoted with respect in the great universities of Europe; and in Scotland itself the students of the three pre-Reformation universities could study the seven liberal arts at as high a standard as was available anywhere in Europe. I believe that that earlier period was hardly, if at all, less spectacular than the Enlightenment itself.

It is not in doubt that the Enlightenment in Scotland was in certain respects unique. The point to be made however is that in other respects it was not. And especially if we think of the Enlightenment as a period when a number of marvellously gifted Scottish thinkers were mounting a sustained display of the highest intellectual quality, then the Enlightenment was not unique. And this fact seems to me one important context within which to place the achievements of the Enlightenment, and it provides some grounds for explaining how the Scottish Enlightenment was even possible.

I shall not argue that the Scottish Enlightenment began two hundred and fifty years before everyone now thinks it did. For it is plain that the Scottish cultural scene did suddenly flower in the 1720s. The change from the much lower-key cultural scene was sufficiently abrupt to justify us in thinking of the 1720s as a time when a fresh start was being made. Neither shall I argue that the brilliant achievements of the early 1500s constituted an earlier Enlightenment. The Enlightenment was a new departure on a grand scale, for subjects were not just being greatly expanded, some were practically being created. But in the case of the earlier period there was no such grand departure. In Mair's time the achievements, though considerable, are much better characterised as further developments occurring within a well-established intellectual context. We witness in Mair's day the final and glorious flourish of an old order. In the case of the Enlightenment we witness no such thing.

II

I should like now to put flesh on these bones by going into detail about the achievements of some of the Scots writing in the period from the 1490s to the 1530s. It will be observed that then, at least as much as now, scholars did not remain in one place but moved rather freely from university to university. In particular it was the norm for Scots teaching in Scotland to have spent time at one or more universities on the Continent. The Continental university which then attracted the greatest number of Scots was that of Paris. The Scottish scholars were immensely enriched by their experiences at Paris, though it has to be said that they amply repaid their debt by the contribution they made to the life of that university.

Our story however might start more appropriately in Aberdeen with James Liddell, a native of that city who is distinguished in the history of this country by being the first Scot to have a book of his printed during his own lifetime.[1] Liddell made his way to Paris where in 1486 he was appointed examiner of the Scottish students working for their B.A. In 1495 he published two books, one on epistemology, *Tractatus Conceptuum et Signorum* (Paris, reprinted 1497), and the other a logical work, *Ars Obligatoria Logicalis* (Paris), giving rules by which a logic student might best avoid logic traps set by the tutor during formal spoken interchange. The latter book is full of interesting material though it is on the former, the epistemological work, that I shall be drawing in establishing philosophical links between the earlier period under discussion and the Enlightenment.

However, right at the heart of Scottish academic life, and in the long term a far more significant figure than James Liddell, was John Mair, often referred to in recent writings as Major because of his own Latinisation of his name as Johannes Maior. I shall continue to call him Mair.[2] He was an East Lothian man, born *c*.1467, who attended school at Haddington, and subsequently spent a year at Cambridge before he matriculated *c*.1492 at the College of Ste Barbe at Paris. He became regent in arts at Paris in 1495. And by 1506 when he graduated as doctor of theology and began to teach theology at the College of Sorbonne, he had already written a number of influential treatises on logic and had in addition started to acquire an immense reputation as a scholar and teacher.

The great Scottish poet Gavin Douglas, then provost of St Giles in Edinburgh, was sent over to attract Mair back to Scotland. That mission failed, but in 1518 Mair did return, to take up the post of principal of Glasgow University, though the post still left him time to teach in arts and theology in the university. Glasgow could at that period, therefore, boast the services of perhaps the best teacher in Europe. His writing also continued apace. He completed his *Historia Maioris Britanniae* in 1521, and other works were then in gestation. In 1522 Mair transferred to the University of St Andrews where he spent three years teaching and writing before his return to Paris. He remained in Paris for about five years, after which he went back to St Andrews where in due course he became dean of the theology faculty and provost of the University's collegiate church of St Salvator's. He continued to teach. His pupils included John Knox, who in a famous phrase said of Mair that his word was then held as an oracle on matters of religion.

Mair died in 1550, leaving to posterity a huge corpus of writings on logic, metaphysics, theology, bible commentary, epistemology, physics, ethics, and history. Many of the books have chatty, indeed gossipy, prefaces. We know therefore a good deal about his life and very much more about his thought. Ample material is therefore available for an intellectual biography of Mair. Such a biography could be an invaluable contribution to our understanding of that pre-Reformation high point in Scottish cultural life.

I should like now to attend to certain of Mair's Scottish pupils. One, David Cranston (*c.*1479–1512), a priest of the Glasgow diocese, published two logic books that repay close study,[3] one on so-called 'insoluble' propositions, that is, propositions, usually with a self-referential element, which give rise to logical puzzles; and the other a treatise on terms, which contains many insightful points on the nature of thought, and upon which I shall draw in the latter part of this paper.

Another Scottish pupil of Mair was Robert Galbraith (*c.*1485–1544) who spent some years at Paris as professor of Roman law at the College of Coqueret before returning to Scotland to take up a post as senator, that is, lawyer member, of the College of Justice in Edinburgh. His murder in a family feud cut short an immensely distinguished career, to which the chief monument now is a massive four-part work on logic which is certainly one of the great classics of late-scholastic logic.[4] Its contents, which are now unknown except to a handful, deserve to be widely disseminated.

A further Scottish pupil of John Mair was the precocious Aberdonian scholar Gilbert Crab (1482–1522) who published commentaries on certain of Aristotle's books while yet an undergraduate. He also wrote a book entitled *Notions*,[5] a tersely expressed and closely argued work on epistemology, on which I shall shortly be drawing.

The subject of notions also held the attention of George Lokert (*c.*1485–1547), a distinguished thinker from Ayr in the south-west of Scotland.[6] His first book indeed was on the topic of notions. George Lokert studied at Paris, rising there to become professor of theology and prior of the Sorbonne. In 1521, on his return to Scotland he became provost of the collegiate church of Crichton and then in the following year rector of St Andrews University, a post he held for three years before returning to Paris to become overseer of the Scots College there. He came back to his native country to take up an appointment at Teviotdale, and then in 1534 was appointed dean of Glasgow, a post he held till his death. Nine of his books are extant. The majority are on logic although, as I have said, he did also write a book on notions; in addition he wrote a treatise on the mathematical theory of proportions, and he published an edition of the physics writings of Buridan, Albert of Saxony, and Thimon. He was, lastly, the author of a treatise on future contingent propositions. That subject had long held the attention of philosophers and theologians, partly because the fact (if it is one) that propositions about future human actions are now true or are now false was thought to raise serious questions about the possibility of human freedom.

A friend and colleague of Lokert's was William Manderston (c.1485–1552), a Lothian man who was an undergraduate at Glasgow before transferring to Paris where he rose to become professor at the College of Ste Barbe and then in 1525 rector of the university. In due course Manderston returned to Scotland, where he was elected rector of St Andrews. He also resumed his teaching career. He had become doctor of medicine in Paris in 1525, to which ten years later he added a doctorate in theology from the Vatican. However, if he wrote on medicine, nothing of that has come down to us. His extant writings are three in number. One is a huge logic work, his *Tripartitum*, another a work on moral philosophy in which are to be found valuable discussions on the will and on the nature of virtue, and finally a treatise on future contingent propositions, a topic on which, as we have observed, George Lokert also wrote a book.

One further philosopher should be mentioned here, Hector Boece from Dundee who in 1497 took up a teaching post in the newly founded University of Aberdeen, and who rose to become the principal of that university. Boece's writings include a history of Scotland which achieved great popularity, and a logic work[7] which, if not nearly so popular, was certainly a good deal closer to the truth. He is particularly interesting on the subject of the nature of valid inference.

The men I have just mentioned were not the only ones making important contributions to the cultural heyday of pre-Reformation Scotland. Many others could be spoken of. But enough has I hope been said to indicate something of the tremendous intellectual vitality in the country during those crucial decades before the Reformation. It seems to me reasonable to hold that the subsequent intellectual flowering in the Enlightenment was a later expression of the same basic spiritual phenomenon, and in a way the fact that the Enlightenment happened becomes less surprising. The country, we might say, had done it before, so why not again?

III

As regards comparisons between the pre-Reformation period and the Enlightenment, questions can be raised not only about similarities at a high level of generality but also about similarities in respect of detailed doctrines. There are important similarities of the latter kind, and for the remainder of this essay I shall focus on one of especial interest. The doctrine at issue was discussed by a number of members of Mair's circle, and it re-emerges in the Enlightenment as one of Reid's most characteristic teachings. The comparison on which I shall focus relates to 'notions' (= *noticiae*). In the philosophical literature of the late-scholastic period 'notion' was a technical term, and in this essay I shall use the term solely in accordance with the sense assigned to it by those philosophers. The medieval and modern uses of 'notion' have a great deal in common, but such links are for present purposes irrelevant.

Let us begin with a familiar fact, namely, that we perceive things by sight, hearing, smell, taste and touch. We see something, say, a table. In some respect we are changed by that experience. There is of course a physiological or neurological story that can be told here. But even if all the relevant physiological changes are specified it is still possible to hold that there is yet another change, and one of a quite different kind, that we undergo when we perceive, namely, the perceiving itself. If a visible object moves across our line of vision we are thereby changed, for something is now true of us that till that moment had not been true of us, for we are now seeing that object. In discussing such experiences the late-scholastic philosophers used a formidable battery of terminology. A crucial term was 'notion'. If a visible object moves across our line of vision we thereupon have a notion of that object. If there is a thunderclap overhead we have a notion of the sound; and so on for all the sensory modalities.

Members of Mair's circle were not in full agreement on the appropriate definition of 'notion'. I shall take first the definition proffered by the Aberdonian Gilbert Crab: 'A notion is a quality inherent in a cognitive faculty, vitally changing that faculty, and representing some thing or things to it'.[8] By speaking about notions as inherent in a cognitive faculty Crab intends thereby, among other things, to deny that they are material. The point is commonly made in a picturesque way by saying that if God removes a notion from a cognitive faculty and places it in a material object, say a stone, then that quality, however it can then be described, cannot truly be called a notion. In having a notion the faculty of cognition is somehow engaged, but stones do not have cognitions of anything.

The notion, as a quality in the cognitive faculty, is said to change that faculty *vitally*. Cognitive dispositions are excluded by this clause. Having perceived something, I might turn to other matters. The notion I had of the thing ceases, but it is not now as though the notion had never existed for it has had a lasting effect, the proof being that the past perception is now available for recall — the notion can be reproduced. Thus the original notion cooperates in the production of a disposition to reproduce notions equiform with the notion that produced the disposition. My perception of this table produces in my cognitive faculty a disposition to form subsequent notions, not of donkeys or mountains, but of tables. Such a disposition is a quality of the cognitive faculty thus disposed. In acquiring the disposition the faculty is thereby changed. But the quality was said not to constitute a *vital* change in the faculty, for the disposition may be dormant; indeed it may be present in the faculty of a comatose person whom we can have no reason to suppose cognisant of anything whatever.

Finally, according to Crab's definition a notion represents a thing or things to a cognitive faculty. Evidently we are dealing with what may be termed a representative theory of cognition. The notion in the cognitive faculty represents to the faculty the object of the notion. Everything perceived is represented in the perceiver. When I perceive this table I have a notion of it. The table can be thought of as naturally representing itself to a cognitive faculty, and in that sense it is said to be a natural sign of itself. But some signs have a signification which is acquired not by nature but by convention. Not only a table but also the utterance 'table' can produce in me a notion of a table. In grasping the signification of the sound 'table' I have the notion of the conventional significate of the sound. The utterance 'table' therefore can give rise to two quite different notions. For the utterance merely *qua* sound gives rise, in the cognitive faculty of the listener, to a notion of the sound. And it also gives rise to the notion of a table. These two notions are as different from each other as are the notions produced by the utterance 'table' *qua* sound and the inscription 'table' *qua* mark on paper.

The notion of the sound or of the inscription, *qua* sound or inscription, was said to be 'non-ultimate' for, as Mair asserts, the person does not rest at that notion but goes on to consider the conventional signification of the sign.[9] The notion of the utterance or inscription in respect of its conventional signification was said to be ultimate, for the mind does rest there.

I stated earlier that there was not full agreement among the members of Mair's circle as to the proper definition of 'notion'. The chief source of conflict concerns the representation of signs in conventional languages. The question to be asked in this context is: can an ultimate notion be produced by every significant term in our language? If Gilbert Crab's definition is correct, then the answer must be 'no'. For a notion is there said to represent a thing or things to a cognitive faculty. I hear the sound 'table' which conventionally signifies tables. Thereupon I form a notion of a table, and that notion is a representative of the thing, and represents the thing via the sound. However, not every term X in our language is such that it makes sense to say of something that it is an X. This is true especially of the terms in which logicians are most interested such as 'every', 'some', 'no', 'and', 'or' and 'if'. Nothing is an every. To say that something is an every, or a some, or an and, etc., is not even to utter a grammatically well formed proposition. Crab asserts that it is difficult to accept that such logical terms can, in respect of their signification, be represented in the cognitive faculty by a notion. But others, in particular George Lokert, took the opposite view. Lokert defines 'notion' in terms of a quality which immediately represents some thing or things or *in some way* to a cognitive faculty.[10] This definition includes the phrase 'in some way' because Lokert holds that the logical terms have signification but do not signify anything. Instead they signify in some way. The way they signify is expounded in terms of their role in valid inferences. Thus we can expound the signification of 'every' by saying that from 'Every A is B' there follows 'This A is B and that A is B, and so on indicating systematically each A'; but from 'This A is B' or any other of the singular propositions we cannot infer 'Every A is B'. We can however infer the universal proposition from the whole conjunction of singular propositions plus the proposition that those are all the As.

Let us for the present accept Lokert's rather wider conception of a notion, and hold with him, and against Crab, that there are notions corresponding to the logical terms in conventional language as well as to other terms which do not signify any thing though they do signify in some way. This will widen the range of examples available to us though it will not affect the fundamental philosophical point I wish to make here. If I hear the term 'table' I thereupon have a notion of a table. I am now interested in the metaphysical question of the precise mode of existence of the notion corresponding to that conventional term. When I hear the word 'table' I understand what I hear. I also form a notion. The crucial point clearly stated by several of our philosophers is that the notion I form is not the cause of the act of understanding, it is identical with the act.[11] To have a notion of something is the same as the grasping of that thing by the cognitive faculty. Notions, we might say, are the cognitive faculty in action. This is true as much of our notion of 'every' as of our notion of 'table'. Furthermore there are complex notions as well as simple ones. On hearing a proposition we can form a notion which corresponds to it, as our notion of a table corresponds to the term 'table'. The notion I form on hearing 'The table is smooth' is my very act of understanding the proposition.

The various definitions of 'notion' all express the fact that notions have a *representative* function. We can now see that that function consists in the act of the cognitive faculty by which what is presented to the cognitive faculty is understood by it. Thus the table is represented in me by my cognitive grasp of it. It is true that I need a notion if I am to understand anything. But this is not because I grasp the notion and then, through the notion as an intermediary, grasp what the notion represents. The cognitive grasp of the thing is not mediated by the notion, for the notion is the very act of cognitive grasping. Now, a representative theory may lead to scepticism, for if we know something only via our knowledge of the thing's representative, how do we know whether that representative in fact represents what it is supposed to? But the pre-Reformation Scots are free from such pressures. For the representative within us of the outside world is not that through whose grasp we know external things, but is instead our unmediated knowing of those things. Thus there are not three elements here, viz. (i) the act of understanding, (ii) the notion which is the immediate object of that act, and (iii) what the notion is a notion of. There are instead just two elements, for it is not the notion that is the immediate object of the act of understanding, the immediate object of that act is the object of the notion under a different description.

For the present this is all I need to say about notions to help me establish an important link between the pre-Reformation Scots and the greatest epistemologist of the Scottish Enlightenment, Thomas Reid. The link I wish to attend to is that between the concept of 'notion' just expounded and Thomas Reid's discussion of the concept of 'idea'.

IV

Thomas Reid was sure that what he had to say about ideas was common sensical. Let us begin by noting a common phrase used of ideas. They are 'in the mind', not external to it. But we should not be misled by this metaphor. Being in the mind is not like being in the brain. For what is in the brain has spatial location, what is in the mind does not. What we learn from the phrase 'in the mind' is not the location but the subject, that is, we learn what it is that has the idea. But there are different ways of being a subject. Is a mind a subject which has an idea as a brick is a subject which has redness? Reid's answer is 'no', for there is a radical difference between minds and bodies. Unlike body, the mind is essentially active: '. . . from its very nature it is a living and active being . . . it is not merely passive as body is'.[12] Reid therefore prefers to speak of the mind as having operations or activities, as opposed to bodies which have properties but not activities.

Might we not say however that the mind can be characteristically mind without being active? For example the mind is said to have ideas. And this might be compared with a brick having a certain colour. Just as the colour is a property of the brick, so the idea is a property of the mind whose idea it is. And if having the colour is not an activity of the brick, then surely having the idea is not an activity of the mind.

But Reid would think this a poor argument. 'Idea', he tells us, signifies the same thing as 'conception' or 'notion'. But to have a conception or notion of something is to conceive that thing. Hence to have an idea of X is to conceive X. To have a distinct idea of X is to conceive X distinctly. To have no idea of X is not to conceive X at all.[13] It follows that to have an idea is for there to be an operation or activity of the mind. In that case it is entirely proper that talk about ideas should be expressed using the active voice of the verb. Reid's position on this matter could hardly be plainer: 'To think of a thing, and to have a thought of it . . . to conceive a thing, and to have a conception, notion, or idea of it, are phrases perfectly synonymous. In these phrases, the thought means nothing but the act of thinking . . . and the conception, notion, or idea, the act of conceiving'.[14]

Two corollaries should be mentioned here. First, we cannot be in doubt that there are ideas, for ideas exist if we think. As Reid puts the matter: 'To think without ideas would be to think without thought'.[15] Secondly, it is wrong to think of ideas as the objects of thought. Thinking has an object since we cannot think without thinking about something. But the object is not an idea, for the idea is the very activity of thinking.

Thus if I am entertaining an idea about John, the object of my thinking is not my idea of John, for I am not thinking about my idea. The object is John.

Hence for Reid there are not three things to consider here, viz. (i) the activity of the cognitive power, (ii) the idea (also called a 'notion') which is the object of that activity, and (iii) what it is that the idea is an idea of. There are instead just two things, (i) the activity of the cognitive power (which can be called 'having an idea'), and (ii) the object of that activity, which is what the idea is an idea of. In this sense of 'idea' an idea represents something to the cognitive faculty, but it does so only in the sense in which the activity by which we apprehend something represents what it is that we apprehend. Hence on this account of the matter there is no room to wonder whether the idea really represents the object it is supposed to represent. For the idea, *qua* representative, is the very act of grasping that object. There appears therefore to be no danger here of scepticism with regard either to the external world or to the world of intelligible objects.

On this account it is hard to see what distinction might be drawn between Reid's account of the nature of ideas and the account discussed earlier in this essay of the pre-Reformation concept of a notion. On this matter, at least, Reid is plainly following in the footsteps of his great pre-Reformation precursors. But as regards motivation a distinction is in order, for there seems not to have been primarily, if at all, a polemical purpose to John Mair's account of 'notion' given in terms of an *actus intelligendi*, an act of understanding. But an important part of Reid's purpose was certainly polemical. This fact might cause surprise, for, as was said earlier, Reid thought his position on ideas common sensical, and it is easy to see why he thought that. But if common sensical, why did he need to state the position at all? Could he not assume universal agreement? But of course we are dealing here with one of the great battlegrounds of philosophy. On a problem of perennial philosophical concern Reid was standing out against what was, in his day at least, the mainstream view.

There is always room for conflicting opinions about the precise meaning of central statements of great philosophers; here our primary concern is with Reid's interpretation of such statements, in particular with his interpretation of John Locke and David Hume. And in that context we must observe that, for Reid, the central flaw in Locke's philosophy was that Locke thought ideas the objects of our thoughts in respect of all the operations of the understanding. Reid places emphasis on Locke's definition of 'idea' as 'whatsoever is the object of understanding when a man thinks' and on 'I have used ['idea'] to express whatever is meant by phantasm, notion, species, or whatever it is which the mind can be employed about in thinking'.[16] Reid saw this account of 'idea' as based on a profound prejudice about knowledge. The prejudice at issue can be called the 'doctrine of cognitive contiguity', and what it states is that things which are in any way at a distance from us can be known only indirectly, for they are known through our knowledge of things which are not at a distance from us but which are instead somehow in contact with us. Two kinds of distance are of especial relevance, distance in time and in space. It has often been thought that memory raises a problem, for past events now remembered no longer exist. Their effects might yet exist but the events themselves do not. And how can we know something if it does not exist? A common view, one which Reid attributed to Locke, was that we have a present idea of the past event, and through our direct knowledge of that idea we have an indirect knowledge of what is no longer present. Present ideas, conceived of as present objects of thought, have the supposed great advantage that the mind is in direct contact with them. Since there is, supposedly, no difficulty attached to our knowing things which are immediately present to us, we can use the presence to us of ideas as a means to explaining how memory is possible. Likewise spatially distant objects are thought by some to present a problem. The sun being so far from us, how can we be in cognitive contact with it? Reid believed Locke felt the force of this problem, and took Locke's solution to be that we are not in direct contact with the sun but with our idea of the sun. The idea being in our mind, and therefore in immediate contact with us, there is no problem attached to explaining how we can know the idea. That idea is additionally a representative, and in certain respects a likeness, of the sun. And these features of the idea permit us, after all, cognitive contact with the sun itself, even though that contact is indirect, mediated by the idea.

It is plain from this that Locke's position on this matter is in sharp contrast to Reid's and to Reid's pre-Reformation precursors. For Locke is insisting that there are three elements to be considered, viz. (i) a cognitive act, (ii) an idea which is the direct object of that cognitive act, and (iii) what it is that the idea is an idea of, in contrast with Reid, Mair and the latter's associates, all of whom rejected the second of these elements. And just as Reid, Mair and associates avoided the scepticism which is implicit in the doctrine that ideas are the direct objects of thought, so the scepticism is implicit in Locke and is explicit in the writings of successors of Locke. For the problem remains that of establishing that the ideas, considered in the Lockean sense, really represent what it is that they are supposed to represent.

This line of scepticism culminates in David Hume's philosophy, according to Reid's interpretation. For Hume whittles Locke's three elements down to two by denying the reality of the third element, viz. what it is that the idea is an idea of. In one respect therefore Hume and Reid are in full agreement, for both think that Locke introduced too many elements. Their mutual disagreement arises over the question of which of Locke's three elements should be discarded. Hume's choice led him to scepticism with regard to the senses. Reid's choice avoids that conclusion, which after all is precisely what he would wish, given that in opting to stand by the dictates of common sense he thinks he has thereby secured for himself the strategic high ground in his debate with those bewitched by the theory of ideas. As for Hume, whoever he could call upon for support in this debate with his greatest critic, he could not call upon John Mair who, as I hope I have established, would assuredly have sided with Reid in this perennial battle. For in Thomas Reid's epistemology the Scottish Enlightenment was, consciously or otherwise, reliving an experience familiar also to Scottish philosophers of two and a half centuries earlier who were then contributing to a high peak in Scottish philosophical life since matched only by the Enlightenment itself.

NOTES

1. See W. Beattie, 'Two notes on fifteenth century printing: I. Jacobus Ledelh', *Edinburgh Bibliog. Soc. Trans.* 3 (1950), 75–7.

2. For details of his life and work see A. Broadie, *The Circle of John Mair* (Oxford, 1985).

3. *Tractatus insolubilium* (Paris, c.1512, reprinted 1512); and *Tractatus terminorum* in *Sequuntur abbreviationes omnium parvorum logicalium collecte a magistro Anthonio Ramirez de Villascusa cum aliquibus divisionibus terminorum eiusdem: necnon cum tractatu terminorum magistri Davidis Cranston ab eodem correcto* (Paris, c.1513).

4. *Quadrupertitum in oppositiones conversiones hypotheticas et modales Magistri Roberti Caubraith omnem ferme difficultatem dialecticam enodans* (Paris, 1510,

reprinted 1516).

5. *Tractatus noticiarum* (Paris, c.1503).

6. For discussion of his life and work see A. Broadie, *George Lokert: Late-Scholastic Logician* (Edinburgh, 1983).

7. *Explicatio quorundam vocabulorum ad cognitionem dialectices conducentium opera Hectoris Boethii philosophi insignis in lucem edita* (Paris, c.1519). Sole extant copy is in Glasgow University Library.

8. *Tractatus Noticiarum fol.*[2ra]

9. *Termini fol.*[7ra], in *Inclitarum artium ac sacre pagine doctoris acutissimi magistri Johannis Maioris . . . Libri quos in artibus in collegio Montis Acuti Parisius regentando compilavit* (Paris, 1506).

10. *Scriptum in materia noticiarum* (Paris, 1514), *sig.*a ii[ra]

11. See, for example, Mair, *Termini* fol.[2rb]; Cranston, *Tractatus Terminorum sig.*b i.

12. *Essays on the Intellectual Powers*, I 1.

13. *Ibid.*

14. *Ibid.*, II 9.

15. *Ibid.*

16. *Ibid.* See Locke, *Essay*, Bk. I, ch. 1.

2
NATURAL LAW AND THE PYRRHONIAN CONTROVERSY

James Moore

On the title page of the Geneva edition of the *Dictionnaire Historique et Critique* of Pierre Bayle[1] the author's fame was memorialized in the following lines of verse:

> Tel fut l'illustre Bayle, honneur des beaux esprits,
> Dont l'élegante plume en récherches fertile,
> Fait douter qui de deux l'emporte dans ces ecrits
> De l'agréeable ou de l'utile.

The great authority of Bayle's scholarship; his relentless questioning of accepted opinion; his paradoxical stance on revealed religion (at once skeptical and fideistic); his disturbing, engaging, style of writing combined to make his literary works (his *Dictionnaire* and the many occasional pieces gathered in his *Oeuvres Diverses*) a presence his contemporaries and successors found it impossible to ignore. The controversies on philosophical subjects which Bayle's work provoked have been documented and described by Richard Popkin in a series of articles written over the past thirty years and collected in part in *The High Road to Pyrrhonism.*[2] More recently, the wider theological, historical and literary context of these debates has been narrated by Pierre Rétat, in his study, *La Dictionnaire de Bayle et la lutte philosophique au dix-huitième siècle.*[3] In this essay, I wish to call attention to a particular dimension of this debate, the attempt to find in the principles of natural law or the study of natural jurisprudence, a response to the Pyrrhonism of Bayle in morals and politics.

The principal protagonists in this controversy were Jean Barbeyrac and Jean Pierre de Crousaz, both Huguenots or French Protestants, driven into exile by the Revocation of the Edict of Nantes in 1685. They were part of a younger generation of refugee scholars profoundly influenced by one of Bayle's most trenchant critics, Jean Le Clerc. Le Clerc (in the words of Pierre Rétat) remained haunted by Bayle and Pyrrhonism, losing no opportunity to attack one or the other. Of all the

20

adversaries of Bayle, it was Le Clerc who made the strongest impression and inspired the following generation of Barbeyrac and Crousaz.[4]

Barbeyrac was born in 1672 and lived as a private scholar in Berlin until 1710. His theological views were considered too unorthodox by the Huguenot community in Berlin for him to hold even an honorific position.[5] His formidable work on Pufendorf's natural jurisprudence prompted an invitation from the College of Lausanne, where he held an appointment as professor of the law of nature and history from 1710 to 1717. In that year he moved to the University of Groeningen in the Netherlands, where he taught until his death in 1744.[6] Barbeyrac's most widely consulted writings were his extensively annotated translations of the writings of Grotius, Cumberland and Pufendorf, especially Pufendorf. Barbeyrac's translations and extensive notes to Pufendorf's larger work *De Jure Naturae et Gentium* and his shorter work *De Officio Hominis et Civis* were thought by many, if not most, who read them, to be as valuable as the texts. The French editions were in turn translated into English and were reprinted many times.[7] There were other editions of Pufendorf's works, annotated in Latin, for students of moral philosophy in Protestant universities across Europe: in Holland, Switzerland, Germany, not least in Scotland, which was very much a part of this European republic of letters.[8] England was different; in part because the common law of England owed little to the Roman or civil law tradition, unlike Scotland; in part because, as Gershom Carmichael of Glasgow liked to say, English universities were less enlightened.[9] But the dominating figure in this diffusion of the natural law tradition in the first half of the eighteenth century was Barbeyrac. Carmichael acknowledged it and endeavoured to correct his errors; Hutcheson's students vindicated him from the charge of complicity with Barbeyrac's views on various subjects; Rousseau was still able to write in the 1750s and '60s of the authority of Barbeyrac which he also deplored but on political grounds peculiar (at the time) to Rousseau himself.[10]

Crousaz (1663–1750) was also a professor, of logic and mathematics as well as moral philosophy, at the College of Lausanne. He corresponded regularly and voluminously with Barbeyrac who invited him to Groeningen in 1726. The most important of Crousaz's publications were *A New Treatise of the Art of Thinking* (translated from the French in 1724) and his *Examen du Pyrrhonisme Ancien et Moderne* (1733).[11]

Barbeyrac and Crousaz both enjoyed a reputation as teachers among Scottish students who studied abroad, although it was not a pedagogical reputation one would want to emulate. In 1724, the Scottish student, Robert Duncan, wrote from Groeningen to the Edinburgh historian,

Charles Mackie, that

> Barbeyrac gives no Colledges this year but on the Law of Nature and
> has only four students which you would not be surprised at if you heard
> him. He gives us for the most part such poor trifles and besides delivers
> in such a rough style and faltering tongue that of the four students he has
> the half are seldome there.[12]

The same Duncan also provided a report on Crousaz's teaching to
Robert Wodrow. It seems that Crousaz, whom Duncan describes as 'a
smooth cunning person', was suspected of Pelagianism by the Cocceian
Professor of Divinity and was obliged to sign the Dutch Articles and
Confession, which he did, while adding *pacis studiosus* to his signature, a
qualification he was later required to erase.[13] Barbeyrac warned Crousaz
to keep his theological views very much to himself, while teaching at
Groeningen:

> Ne songez pas à un Collège sur l'art de prêcher; bornez-vous à votre
> profession; c'est le meilleur moyen d'avoir la paix. Il faudra même éviter
> tout ce qui approche de la théologie. La prudence et la moderation sont
> ici fort nécessaires.[14]

Unfortunately Crousaz could not avoid theological discussion and
found it necessary or at least prudent to leave Holland in 1726. He
never relinquished his interest in theological topics as we will see.

The most distinguished of Bayle scholars has insisted that his
thinking was informed by a Christian fideism, albeit of a heterodox
sort.[15] As Elisabeth Labrousse interprets his writings, Bayle struggled
to find a place in human understanding for the truths revealed to us by
divine grace. The truths of divine revelation were not to be confused
with the limited truths that could be apprehended by human reason.
And the dictates of human reason often proved inapplicable, at least
they were almost always inoperable, in the realm of practice. Elisabeth
Labrousse has distinguished four orders of truth in Bayle's thinking:
truths of fact or history, truths of reason, truths of faith or revelation,
and truths of practice.

This was not the way Bayle would be read, however, by his
rationalist critics. Barbeyrac and Crousaz, together with Bayle's earlier
critics, Jean Le Clerc and Jaques Bernard, perceived only the first and
the last of the four orders of truth distinguished by Labrousse. They
entirely discounted Bayle's protestations of faith. In their eyes, his
assumption of piety was an imposture; he was an atheist, *tout court*.[16]

They also simply ignored that part of Bayle's *Oeuvres Diverses* devoted to the formal exposition of philosophical topics: logic, metaphysics, moral and natural philosophy: the dimension of Bayle's work described by Labrousse as *vérités de raison*. Their disregard of this aspect of Bayle's work may have been better founded; these were lectures Bayle was obliged to present in a syllabus established by others. In his private correspondence of the period (the 1670s) he had already expressed his admiration for modern Pyrrhonians and *esprits forts* as he described them (Montaigne, Charron, La Mothe le Vayer, Naudé).[17] It was this sceptical or Pyrrhonian posture which Barbeyrac and Crousaz isolated for focused critical attention.

Following the lead of Le Clerc, Barbeyrac and Crousaz directed their criticism to Bayle's doubts concerning reason and the natural order of things. Barbeyrac was concerned above all with the practical consequences which must follow from Bayle's questioning of the most certain, obvious and universally accepted maxims of conduct. In May 1706, he wrote to his friend, Pierre Desmaizeaux, who was later to be Bayle's biographer and the editor of his *Oeuvres Diverses*:

> I esteem, as much as anyone, the good qualities and the fine talents of Mr Bayle: I try, as much as possible, to put a good construction on things; and I have no particular reason which engages me to speak for or against this great genius. But I vow to you that when I consider the affectation with which he lets slip no occasion, either in his *Dictionary* or in his later writings, to display, with all his force, all the difficulties that he can imagine in truths that are the most incontestable . . . while a nothing, a bauble, suffices to make him doubt or support his paradoxes, . . . when I know what reflections . . . will present themselves naturally to those who read his works without being warned, . . . when one absorbs early in life a Montaigne, a La Mothe le Vayer, a Sextus Empiricus, etc — authors very useful to those who are on their guard, but very harmful to a young man who reads them without precaution: . . . I do not know how to prevent myself from saying what must be said, that, in spite of everything, I do not have a good opinion of him.[18]

He shared Bayle's concern to promote religious toleration but he considered that Bayle's scepticism offered a most perverse way of reaching this worthwhile objective. In Barbeyrac's view, toleration of different religious beliefs would be achieved only when there was universal acknowledgement of the natural rights of all believers to work up their own rational understanding of God's providence. The Pyrrhonism represented in the writings of Bayle and others amounted to a sustained attack on natural law and natural rights.

In the Prefatory Discourse to his translation of Pufendorf's treatise *Of the Law of Nature and Nations* Barbeyrac outlined clearly and succinctly the opposition between the natural jurisprudence tradition and the tradition of Pyrrhonism. The science of natural jurisprudence comprehended not only morality but also politics and everything relevant to the conduct of men according to their rank and condition. It was a science whose rudiments might be grasped by every man. The commonest experience of life and the slightest exercise of natural reason provided knowledge of the law of nature.

If persons of the lowest rank and most limited capacities might have knowledge of the law of nature, much more might be expected of persons with more extensive advantages of leisure and learning. It should be possible for such men (and also women and children, provided they devoted themselves to this study) to deduce the moral duties of every station of life. Barbeyrac looked forward to

> the possibility of reducing the science of morality to a system as well connected as that of geometry, for example, or mechanics; and founded on as certain principles.[19]

He found in Locke's *Essay Concerning Human Understanding* directions for making morality a science of this kind: moral ideas were mixed modes or combinations of ideas made in the understanding to regulate moral conduct. He welcomed Locke's assurance that such combinations or relations of ideas were not to be confused or perplexed by the difficulty presented by our ignorance of the real essences or substances of persons or things. In moral science one need not inquire into 'the whole nature and abstruse hidden constitution' of human nature or the physical world; it was enough for the mind to work upon or fabricate ideas of its own making. Barbeyrac did not dwell, as Locke did (in Book III, Chapter V, of the *Essay*), upon the arbitrariness of the mind's construction of moral ideas or mixed modes; nor did he emphasize the diversity of moral ideas and of moral language as Locke was disposed to do throughout the *Essay*. While Locke was at pains to avoid identification of morality as described in the *Essay*, with the law of nature as described by anyone, including the author of *Two Treatises of Government* (whoever he might be), Barbeyrac had no qualms or uneasiness about making precisely this identification.

Barbeyrac also took over the theory of Locke that the law of nature obliges us to acknowledge the rights of others to life, liberty and property. These rights followed from the obligation imposed on us by God to preserve ourselves and others when our own preservation comes not in competition. He endorsed Locke's argument that property is a natural right derived not from pacts or agreements (as Grotius and Pufendorf had argued) but from the labour of our body and work of our hands which mixes our bodies with the earth and other things and makes them our own.[20] Locke extended these rights to the property of conscience or the right to hold dissenting beliefs: provided those beliefs were not Catholic, for Catholics would suppress the rights of conscience, and provided they did not entail negation of any belief in God which would nullify the law of nature and natural rights which follow from it.[21] Barbeyrac endorsed the view that it must be left to the conscience or the private judgement of every man — or rather every judicious man — to determine when his rights have been invaded and when he must therefore defend himself and punish the violator of his rights. He was more explicit than Locke ever chose to be that the people who enjoy this right to rebel against tyrants and violators of natural rights do not include all the subjects of the government. They

> do not include the vile populace or the rabble of the country . . . but only the greater and more judicious part of the subjects of all ranks . . . [22]

But such persons have the right to rebel in defence of their religious beliefs:

> the people have as natural and as unquestionable a right to defend their religion by force of arms against a sovereign who endeavours to compel them or forbid them the free exercise of it as to defend their lives, their estates and liberties against a tyrant. This right is even more allowable than any other, inasmuch as it regards the greatest of all interests, and the strongest of all obligations, or rather that which is the foundation and source of all the others: I mean the indispensable necessity that obliges every man to follow the light of his own conscience.[23]

It was this assumed right of rebellion justified by the claims of conscience which was supposed by many at the court of Louis XIV to be the generally established political doctrine of the Huguenots. Elisabeth Labrousse has argued in her recent book, *Une foi, une loi, un roi*, that this belief or rumour was a misapprehension; that from the Edict of Nantes (in 1598) to the Revocation (in 1685), Huguenots were fiercely loyal to the monarch, whom they saw as their protector.[24] But the belief that Huguenots were potentially disloyal persisted: they were implicated in the minds of French Catholics with the Puritan Rebellion in England and the execution of Charles I. The declaration of Oliver Cromwell that he considered himself the Lord Protector of Protestants in other lands did not help to improve the standing of Huguenots in France. From the standpoint of Bossuet and Louis himself, the state was an organic body, a body politic with the King at its head, the Church as its soul; the Huguenots were seen to be an alien presence which threatened the unity and the integrity of the state. They must be, in the fateful words of Jesus as interpreted by St Augustine, 'compelled to come in'.

Both of these extreme political doctrines, as he conceived them, were rejected by Pierre Bayle. In the light of the disruptive consequences of the Calvinist doctrine of a right of rebellion on grounds of conscience, and the oppressive implications of the Catholic doctrine of the organic unity of church and state, Pierre Bayle attempted to point out the folly of imposing the concerns of revealed or even natural religion on the affairs of the mundane world. In language remarkable for its outspokenness, he argued that belief in God was not necessary for orderly living, that societies of atheists could be conducted, and had been conducted, in a more civilized and tolerant manner than societies of believers of whatever persuasion.

In Bayle's view an atheist was someone who denied a particular providence, the efficacy of prayer and the fear of divine punishment. He might or might not acknowledge the existence of a first cause of the universe. In this light there were unlimited numbers of atheists, not only in antiquity and in remote parts of the world, they were everywhere in modern civilized societies. Such persons were neither immoral nor incapable of life in society, they were merely more influenced by the approval and disapproval of other persons than by fear of God.[25] They were moved no doubt by vanity, by love of esteem and by passions of still more doubtful merit or worth. But they were capable of being corrected and instructed. They were also capable of making judgements concerning the usefulness and agreeableness of characters and modes of conduct. And they were capable of a natural honesty or candour.[26] And most important, they were uninfluenced by the socially destructive forces of superstition and idolatry.

It is sometimes said, Bayle remarked, that a society of true believers, especially of true Christians, would be the best that anyone could imagine:

a golden age, a regime of peace, of concord and virtue; no usury, no fraud, no ambition, no avarice, no cabals or factions; charity, chastity, modesty and good faith would prevail in a manner truly marvellous.[27]

One may anticipate that Bayle has some doubts about the possibility of this ideal society of true believers. Such societies may not collapse at once into general anarchy, he acknowledged, but they are not immune from the maladies and disorders that have afflicted all societies: revolutions, civil wars, foreign wars, conquests. Indeed the condition of societies of true believers, especially of true Christians, must always be much worse than other societies. When God instituted the Christian religion, he did so to indicate the way to heaven. His intention was not to leave instructions concerning the government of societies. The true Christian will consider himself a pilgrim, journeying through this earthly life; he will renounce worldly pleasures, riches, glory; he will devote himself to prayer and to acts of charity. To be sure, such a society will soon be conquered by its neighbours. Its members will be sheep in the midst of wolves. There is no assurance that societies of Christians (or of Jews or of Moslems) will be saved by God. Supernatural grace and miracles are not a good foundation for politics. Leave these dogmas, then, to theory, he advises, and practise instead exactly the reverse of the teachings of the Gospel:

> Preserve avarice and ambition in all their vivacity, preventing only theft and fraud; encourage ambition by rewards: promise a pension to inventors of new methods of production and new ways of expanding commerce. Go to the ends of the earth to discover gold; let nothing stand in the way of the accumulation of wealth; accumulate in your own state the riches of other states. You will soon have a treasury capable of maintaining a great navy and a formidable army.[28]

Bayle's political thinking reflected the mercantilist opinion that the power of the state depends upon its capacity to impoverish other states, by trade, by war and by the accumulation of riches, in particular, gold bullion.[29] It also expressed a rigorous Augustinian dualism. On the one hand, there was the heavenly city of the true believer, whose thoughts, passions and style of life are evidently not of this world. On the other hand, there was the earthly city dominated by the thinking, motivation and behaviour of lustful men driven by their mortal appetite for property and power. It was a fashionable dualism in France, in the late seventeenth century. Pierre Nicole made it central to his analysis of 'le grandeur' in his *Essais Morales* (1672); Malebranche invoked this dichotomy between *sociétés de religion* and *sociétés de commerce* in his *Entretiens Metaphysiques* (1688); it appears, not centrally to be sure, but as a recurrent theme in the Chevalier Ramsay's *Essai sur le gouvernement civile* (1720). Whatever devotional content this dichotomy may have retained was basically lost in its translation into English in the ebullient cynicism of Mandeville's *The Fable of the Bees*. But however fashionable and modish and 'modern' this approach to moral and political problems may appear, it is worth underlining that Bayle's moral and political writings (together with other aspects of his thought) were characterized by Bayle's natural law critics as Pyrrhonism, as expressive of an outlook as ancient as the views of Sextus, reiterated by Carnaedes and by Philus in Cicero's *De Republica*.

The most direct critique of this dimension of Bayle's moral and political thinking was provided not by Barbeyrac but by Jean Pierre de Crousaz in his *Examen du Pyrrhonisme Ancien et Moderne*, 1733. Barbeyrac greeted the publication of this work in a lengthy review, in which he advertised it as a signal victory in debate for reason and natural law against the ever increasing forces of Pyrrhonism:

> Never has this sect made more progress than in our own time; although, it seems, never have there been more able men who are ready to combat it . . . It will surprise no one (he continued) that the works of Mr Bayle must form the object of any book which examines modern Pyrhonnism conjoined with the ancient variants.[30]

Crousaz was also a natural lawyer in his moral and political philosophy, but his understanding of the law of nature was quite different from Barbeyrac's. He had nothing to say of natural rights and obligations and he considered talk of contracts, especially tacit contracts, to be irrelevant for morals and politics.[31] He thought that one conceives ideas of virtue and duty in the same way one conceives ideas of beauty and of geometrical form. Ideas are thoughts. The activity of thinking generates such ideas. They are not innate; we are not born with a great many ideas; but we are born with a disposition to be self-conscious and to proceed from consciousness to ideas of order and symmetry. His ideas of virtue and duty are not dissimilar to those of Malebranche and to Clarke, whom he sometimes quotes. Ideas of virtue and vice are real entities. If there are individuals and even entire nations who appear to be ignorant of the ideas of virtue and duty, it is because of the dullness of the human mind and still more it is because of indolence and sensuality which distracts the mind and renders it incapable of instruction. It proves that the greater part of mankind still stand in need of instruction by clear-headed and charitable tutors. When Clarke demonstrated that it would be as contrary to reason and to the nature of things for the sun and the moon to desert their proper places and relations as for any one of us to desert the station in life to which he has been assigned by divine providence, his reasoning indicated the way to a systematic exposition of moral duties according to the law of nature.[32]

But Mr Bayle wrote, Crousaz tells us, as though no systematic account of morals had ever been presented. Like Horace and Juvenal, he liked to compare the behaviour of men unfavourably with the behaviour of beasts who never harm other beasts of their own species. And when Mr Bayle recommends to us the precepts of Horace, one should not forget, Crousaz reminds us, that Horace was an Epicurean, for whom a life lived among the Gods was a life which achieved the heavenly satisfactions of well-turned verse and requited love. Horace would have done better to fix his mind upon ideas of the natural virtues: on wisdom, on charity, on the pleasures of the mind, and other ideas of that kind.[33] Similarly, Mr Bayle:

> If instead of searching through old secondhand books to find whatever might set religion in opposition to philosophy; if instead of amusing himself with frivolous and superfluous details, the correction of dates and names which no one learns without forgetting them; if instead he had studied Grotius and Pufendorf attentively, there he would have found the right ideas.[34]

He had found the wrong ideas certainly in Horace and in other ancient and modern writers of an Epicurean and skeptical persuasion, who had persuaded him that virtue and vice were to be discovered in judgements concerning the useful and agreeable. And still worse, Bayle supposed that atheists might distinguish not only the useful from the agreeable but might also be capable of a natural honesty or candour. And the same atheists might discover this natural honesty (*honnête naturelle*) in nature itself and not merely in opinion.[35] It was surely contradictory, Crousaz remarked, to think that atheists and pagans might distinguish vice from virtue, discovering virtue even in nature itself, while contending that true moral judgements must be inspired by reading Holy Scripture and by Divine Grace. And Bayle went on to compound the paradox by observing that the vast generality of believers have no idea of virtue (revealed or otherwise). He regularly finds, Crousaz laments, in societies composed of Christians, Jews and Moslems no one but fanatics, persons of such stupidity and feebleness of mind that they cannot distinguish figurative from literal writing, they have no ideas of right and wrong and no capacity to reason from such ideas as they do have. But Crousaz would insist (with Barbeyrac and, behind them both, Jean Le Clerc) that Scripture must always be read and interpreted in the light of natural reason. One must not insist too rigorously on the teachings of the prophets, the disciples, even Jesus himself. One must have in mind natural ideas of the just and the reasonable and adhere to them.[36]

Crousaz proposed, then, a formulation of natural law, albeit different in inception from the treatises of Barbeyrac, Pufendorf and Locke. Like their more elaborate systems of rights and duties, Crousaz proposed in effect a science of the law of nature which might regulate and direct the conduct of rulers as well as citizens and subjects. A ruler sufficiently instructed in the law of nature would never mistake his own will for the law of nature; he would not sacrifice the lives of his subjects to increase his territories; he would not force his subjects to live in poverty, so that he might indulge himself and his court in every pleasure and luxury. He would be

> A frugal ruler, one who is averse to luxury and debauchery, who is attentive to the well being of his subjects, who is law abiding and resolved that his subjects should obey the law . . . who keeps his word . . . Would such a ruler not be secure against violent uprisings? Would he lack allies? And would one say that such a ruler should exchange a large part of his piety for a large dose of injustice and of knavery?[37]

Not if one has been properly instructed in the principles of natural law:

> Qu'on lise attentivement un Cours de Droit Naturel, on trouvera des Principes qui lèvent toutes les Difficultés.[38]

This was also what Barbeyrac meant when he pronounced that politics as well as physics could be made a science capable of demonstration:

> It is certain, that Politicks, as well as Physick, is a conjectural science as Mr Bayle expresses himself . . . in his *Reply to the Questions of a Provincial*. But whatever that famous Philosopher says, who, according

to his Custom pretends to gather from thence some Arguments for Scepticism, yet if he would seriously examine true Politicks, he would find that most of its Principles and Maxims have a Certainty in them, which comes very near a Demonstration; and as to those things which look like Problems, their obscurity proceeds rather from the difficulty of Application, Ignorance of some Circumstances, or Want of Attention, than any absolute Impossibility to establish a Rule of Certainty concerning them . . . The Boasting of the Scepticks proceeds from the Observation of the Behaviour of *bad Politicians*, and *ambitious Sovereigns*, and not from the Principles and Maxims which arise from the natural Design of Civil Government, and the public Good, separate from the private Interest of some Persons.[39]

Barbeyrac's language, here, as in many places in his work, cannot fail to evoke a resonance in the ears of any reader of Hume's political essays: notably the pivotal essay 'That Politics may be Reduced to a Science'.[40] It cannot fail to impress itself on one who reads further in Hume's essays, however, that he assumed that the conduct of politicians will be just the reverse of the behaviour assumed by Barbeyrac and Crousaz. Political writers have taken it as a maxim that 'every man ought to be supposed a knave and to have no other end in all his actions than private interest'.[41] Hume has taken over assumptions concerning human nature, concerning the passions and the difficulty of controlling, regulating and checking the passions from Bayle and writers in the Pyrrhonian tradition. He shares at the same time the aspiration of Barbeyrac and Crousaz to regulate the behaviour of knavish, avaricious men by law and regular behaviour in society and politics. Was Hume, then, a natural lawyer, as Duncan Forbes, and some other students of Hume's philosophical politics, have taken him to be?[42] Or is he better understood as a skeptic in his moral and political writings, as Shirley Letwin, Geoffrey Marshall and others have been prepared to argue?[43] In the light of the foregoing I would suggest that while natural jurisprudence was Hume's point of departure in the *Treatise*, Book III, Part II, his discussion eventuates in skepticism, that his thinking was in part at least an outcome of this particular controversy or debate.

A comparison of the range of topics and headings which appear in Book III, Part II of Hume's *Treatise* with a particular English translation of Barbeyrac's edition of Pufendorf (the Spavan abridgement of 1716) reveals a surprising affinity and congruence between the two texts.[44] Although no copy of Pufendorf's work (however annotated or abridged) appears in Hume's library, — a circumstance reported recently with what seemed to me unnecessary or at least misplaced relish —[45] a copy of the Spavan abridgement is housed in the University Library at Edinburgh. And we know that it was available to Scottish readers in the period because Gershom Carmichael of Glasgow denounced the editor Spavan for plundering the notes of Barbeyrac and for using these annotations (along with one or two of Spavan's own) to mislead Scottish students of moral philosophy, who ought to have been learning to correct Pufendorf's natural jurisprudence in the direction of greater reverence for the deity, instead of discovering, through the mediation of Barbeyrac, arguments conducive to skepticism. Carmichael's denunciation of this edition of Pufendorf was first published in 1718, and it was repeated more elaborately and emphatically in 1724, when his book was published in Edinburgh.[46] Among the annotations given prominence in the Spavan edition, it will suffice to mention three remarkable observations of Barbeyrac's, which exhibit how attractive he found the Pyrrhonian persuasion he struggled to refute.

On the very basic question of whether God's government of the state of nature was effective government, as Pufendorf insisted it was, Barbeyrac ultimately expressed some doubt.[47] For if we abstract from revealed religion, from the condition of the soul and from other matters impertinent to natural jurisprudence, the sanctions attached by God as legislator and executor of the laws of nature must be themselves natural and observable in this world. Thus it was sometimes said (by Pufendorf for one) that natural law criminals are punished for their crimes against nature by illness, by accidents and by other evidence of divine providence. But most people, Barbeyrac observed, do not make these connections. It may be the case that God punishes pirates, bullies, murderers, by shipwrecks, broken legs and by death itself; but few believe that God intervenes in these ways. He inferred from these doubts that Locke was right, therefore, to have claimed that in the state of nature each man must have the right to punish natural law criminals. Locke of course did not advertise his amendment of Pufendorf's theory of divine punishment as a skeptical revision, though he allowed that many would consider his theory of the natural right to punish criminals a strange doctrine. It was Barbeyrac who made explicit the skeptical implications of this move for the natural law tradition.

Secondly, Barbeyrac rejected Pufendorf's explanations of the origin of languages, that the meaning of words was fixed by the imposition of signs and attended by pacts, tacit or express. It was more probable that men never met together to agree upon precise significations of words or rules of speech. It came to pass insensibly, and without any reflection; nor was there any tacit agreement properly so called. We may every day discern new words, expressions, and terms of speech to come into use, which put a new sense upon the terms already received.[48]

Thirdly, he acknowledged a parallel problem in the origin of societies. The supposition of Grotius and Pufendorf and even Locke (as Barbeyrac understood him) that men must have formally contracted with one another to live in society was perhaps, he acknowledged, a mistake. Pufendorf and Locke had made insufficient allowance for the rudeness and violence which attended the origin of societies. Crafty and ambitious individuals supported by force may be supposed to have brought men into societies. This was again the sceptical theory of the origin of societies, endorsed by Barbeyrac, to the great disgust of more than one contemporary jurist.[49]

Hume's adherence to the skeptical theory that justice is an artificial virtue, that we have no motive to be just, that the rules of justice are themselves justified by nothing but their utility was one of the aspects of Hume's theory of morals which Hutcheson appears to have seized upon and which Hume defended, in his letter to Hutcheson, of September 17, 1739:

> I have never called justice unnatural, but only artificial. *Atque ipsa utilitas justi prope mater et aequi*, says one of the great moralists of antiquity (Horace). Grotius and Pufendorf, to be consistent, must assert the same.[50]

This statement of Hume's together with others contained in this letter must have severely taxed the benevolence of Hutcheson, who could not have been unaware that the emphasis on the useful and the agreeable in Horace's work was part of a satire on the stoic theory of a life fixed according to reason and the law of nature.[51] Moreover, Grotius had singled out this aphorism of Horace, which Hume quotes, as the *very position* he was arguing against in his Prolegomena to the *Laws of War and Peace*.[52] And we have seen that the reduction of justice and other virtues to consideration of utility and agreeableness was considered (by Crousaz) to be more Pyrrhonian than even Bayle's moral philosophy, which at least continued to find a place (however inconsistently in Crousaz's mind) for natural honesty or frankness.[53]

Hume's conviction (repeated in the second *Inquiry*) that the writers on the law of nature all return at last to the principle of utility is open to a number of possible interpretations.[54] A consideration which may impart some historical plausibility to Hume's claim is the ironical matter of fact that the most distinguished contemporary representative of the natural law tradition, Jean Barbeyrac, had come around, on many disputed questions, to the Pyrrhonian point of view.

The centrality of Barbeyrac's place in the natural law tradition of the early eighteenth century, the ambiguity of his position in debate with Bayle and the Pyrrhonian tradition in morals and politics may provide, then, one of the many contexts or settings in which it may be helpful to read Hume's *Treatise* and his political essays and discourses. The latter require, to be sure, acquaintance with writings of other genres: the political pamphlet literature of the early eighteenth century, the writings of French economic theorists whose work (as Voltaire observed) is not unrelated to the Pyrrhonism of Bayle, and the works of classical republican thinkers of the seventeenth and eighteenth centuries. The task of tracing and locating the contexts of Hume's philosophy is a formidable one as anyone who has attempted it will attest. As all students of Hume's philosophy know, there is no single, undifferentiated, univocal context which will make his work intelligible. The discovery of the various settings, backgrounds, readings, which shed light on one or another aspect of his thinking has been for many of us what appears now to be a life's work, animated happily by the spirit of bonhomie which evidently inspired the subject of our studies. There may be other ways of spending one's life which would be more useful; there is none, I submit, which would be, most of the time at least, more agreeable.

NOTES

I am grateful to Elisabeth Labrousse, Harry Bracken and David Norton for their critical comments on an earlier draft of this paper.

1. 'Such was the illustrious Bayle, the honour of fine minds, Whose elegant pen engaged in fertile research, Makes us doubt which of the two is more characteristic of his work, Its agreeableness or its utility.' These lines were written by an admirer of Bayle's named Mr de la Monnoye. For discussion, see 'La Vie de M. Bayle' by Pierre Desmaizeaux, prefaced to the fourth edition of the *Dictionnaire Historique et Critique* (Amsterdam, 1730), Vol.I, p.cviii.

2. Richard Popkin, *The High Road to Pyrrhonism* (San Diego, Austin Hill Press), 1980.

3. Pierre Rétat, *La Dictionnaire de Bayle et la lutte philosophique au XVIIIᵉ siècle* (Paris, Société d'Edition 'Les Belles Lettres', 1971).

4. *Ibid.*, p.27.

5. Sieglinde Othmer, *Berlin und die Verbeitung des Naturrechts in Europa* (Berlin, Walter de Gruyter, 1970), esp. Ch.2, 'Die untersuchung gegen Jean Barbeyrac, 1699–1701'.

6. Phillipe Meylan, *Jean Barbeyrac et les debuts de l'enseignement du droit dans l'ancienne Academie de Lausanne* (Lausanne, F. Ronge), 1937.

7. Barbeyrac's translation of Pufendorf's *De jure Naturae et Gentium* was first published in 1706; the shorter work, *De Officio Hominis et Civis*, appeared in 1707. I refer in what follows to the fourth edition, in the English translation of Basil Kennet, *Of the Law of Nature and Nations*, published in London in 1729.

8. Horst Denzer, *Moral philosophie und Naturrecht bei Samuel Pufendorf* (München, 1972); Leonard Krieger, *The Politics of Discretion* (Chicago, The University of Chicago Press, 1975). Hans Medick, *Naturzustand and Naturgeschichte der burgerlichen Gesellschaft* (Gottingen, 1973), and Jerome B. Schneewind, 'Pufendorf's Place in the History of Ethics', *Synthèse* (1987) vol.72, pp.123–155 for an incisive analysis of Pufendorf as a moral philosopher.

9. S. Puffendorffii, *De Officio Hominis et Civis, juxta Legem Naturalem, Libri Duo. Supplementis et Observationibus in Academicae Inventutis usam auxit et illustravit Gerschomus Carmichael* Editio Secundae, (Edinburgh, 1724).

10. *Ibid.*, p.xxi; *A Vindication of Mr. Hutcheson from the Calumnious Aspersion of a Late Pamphlet by Several of his Scholars*, Nov., 1738, pp.11, 13; René Dérathé, *Jean Jacques Rousseau et la science politique de son temps* (Paris, Presses Universitaires de France, 1950), pp.89–92.

11. Jacqueline E. de la Harpe, *Jean Pierre de Crousaz (1663–1750) et le Conflit des Idées au Siècle des Lumières* (Berkeley and Los Angeles, University of California Press), 1955.

12. Letter from Robert Duncan to Charles Mackie, 29 February 1724, in: Edinburgh University Library Laing MSS.II, 91. I owe this reference to Istvan Hont.

13. Robert Wodrow, *Analecta, or materials for a history of remarkable providences* . . . (Edinburgh, for the Maitland Club, 1842–43, Vol.III, pp.303–304.

14. Letter from Barbeyrac to Crousaz, 3 June, 1724, in: Bibliothèque Centrale et Universitaire, Lausanne. Ms. Fonds J. P. de Crousaz, Tom.XIV, p.15. See J. E. de la Harpe, *Jean Pierre de Crousaz, op.cit.*, n.12, pp.191.

15. Elisabeth Labrousse, *Pierre Bayle: Tome II Heterodoxie et Rigorisme* (The Hague, Martinus Nijhoff), 1964. It is not surprising perhaps that Barbeyrac and Crousaz should have misapprehended the underlying piety of Bayle's thinking; they brought their own questions and presuppositions to his work, a tendency shared by other readers of Bayle in the eighteenth century and which is perhaps unavoidable in all cases of 'influence'. See *Ibid.*, p.ix and Elisabeth Labrousse, *Pierre Bayle* (Oxford, Oxford U.P., 1983), p.90.

16. This dismissal of Bayle's faith may well have contained, as Elisabeth Labrousse has suggested, an element of *mauvaise foi*. As we will see (above, p.30), Barbeyrac and Crousaz themselves subscribed to the truths of revelation only as those truths were interpreted in the light of reason. It was a source of intermittent aggravation to them that Bayle, more skeptical than they in other respects, should have retained a reputation in some circles of the Reformed as a devout man. Barbeyrac, writing to Le Clerc from Berlin in 1706, thought it strange that the same persons in the Berlin Consistory of the Reformed Church who were most ardent in suppressing Le Clerc's translation of the New Testament were also those who valued most highly the later writings of Bayle, works which, in Barbeyrac's eyes, were more dangerous than those of Hobbes and Spinoza: 'Ce qu'il y a d'étrange, c'est que ceux des autres qui ont paru les plus ardent à le solliciter [the suppression of Le Clerc's work] affectent de faire valoir les derniers ouvrages de Mr. Bayle, plus dangereuses à mon avis, que les livres de Hobbes et de Spinoza'. Letter from Barbeyrac to Le Clerc, 10 April, 1706, in University of Amsterdam Ms. R.K. c.3.

17. Letter from Pierre Bayle to M. Minutoli, 31 January 1673, in: *Oeuvres Diverses de Mr. Pierre Bayle . . .* (The Hague, 1727–31), Vol.IV, pp.535–539. See, however, Elisabeth Labrousse, *Pierre Bayle*, Vol.III, pp.257 ff. for the continuity of rationalist themes in Bayle's moral philosophy.

18. Letter from Barbeyrac to Pierre Desmaizeaux, 22 December 1706, in: British Library Additional Mss.4281, fol.20–21.

19. Jean Barbeyrac, 'An Historical and Critical Account of the Science of Morality and the Progress it has made in the World from the earliest times down to the Publication of this Work', in Pufendorf, *Of the Law of Nature and Nations* (1729), p.4.

20. *Of the Law of Nature and Nations* (1729, Book IV, Ch.IV, Section IV, note 4, p.365.

21. John Locke, *A Letter Concerning Toleration* (London, 1689). The relevant passages are cited by Barbeyrac in *Of the Law of Nature and Nations* (1729), Book VII, Ch.IV, Section XI, note 2, pp.665–666.

22. *Of the Law of Nature and Nations* (1729) Book VII, Ch.VIII, Section VI, n.1, p.720.

23. *Ibid.*, VII, Viii, V, p.719, n.2.

24. Elisabeth Labrousse, *'Une foi, une loi, un roi': la Révocation de l'Édit de Nantes* (Geneva and Paris, Labor et Fides, Payot, 1985).

25. Pierre Bayle, 'Pensées Diverses sur la Comète', in English translation *Miscellaneous Reflections on the Comet* (London, 1708), Vol.I, pp.368–370.

26. Elisabeth Labrousse, *Pierre Bayle*, II, p.91. On Bayle's understanding of atheism, *Ibid.*, pp.103–104.

27. Pierre Bayle, 'Continuation des Pensées Diverses sur la Comète', *Oeuvres Diverses*, III, p.629.

28. *Ibid.*, p.631.

29. See Lionel Rothkrug, *Opposition to Louis XIV: the Political and Social Origins of the Enlightenment* (Princeton University Press, 1964), pp.8ff and Nanerl O. Keohane (*Philosophy and the State in France from the Renaissance to the Enlightenment* (Princeton University Press, 1980).

30. *Bibliothèque raisonnée des ouvrages des savans de l'Europe Jan.*, *Fév.*, *Mar.* 1733, pp.70–110; *Jui.*, *Août*, *Sept.* 1733, pp.36–90. Barbeyrac's authorship of these reviews was communicated in a letter to Crousaz, 20 March, 1734, Bibliothèque centrale et universitaire, Lausanne: Ms. Fonds J. P. de Crousaz, Tom.XIV, p.19.

31. J. P. de Crousaz, *A New Treatise of the Art of Thinking* (London, 1724), p.118.

32. *Examen du Pyrrhonisme Ancien et Moderne* (1733), pp.323, 395, 639 and *A New Treatise of the Art of Thinking*, pp.288–300.

33. *Examen*, p.608.

34. *Examen*, p.616.

35. Pierre Bayle, 'Continuation des Pensées Diverses', *Oeuvres Diverses*, III, p.412: 'Il me paroit évident que des Athées peuvent distinguer entre le bien agréable, le bien utile, et le bien honnête et trouver dans la nature même et non pas dans les opinions de l'homme le fondement de ces trois espèces de bien'.

36. *Examen*, pp.401–404.

37. *Examen*, p.616.

38. *Examen*, p.617.

39. Barbeyrac's remark appears in Pufendorf, *Of the Law of Nature and Nations*, 4th edition (1729) Book I, Part II. Section IV, p.16, n.3. The quotation from Bayle is from 'Responses aux questions d'un Provincial', *Oeuvres Diverses*.

40. David Hume, 'That Politics May be Reduced to a Science', in *Essays Moral Political and Literary*, ed. by T. H. Green and T. H. Grose (London, Longmans, Green and Co., 1875), p.99: 'So great in the face of laws and of particular forms of government, and so little dependence have they on the humours and tempers of men, that consequences almost as certain and general may be deduced from them, as any which the mathematical sciences afford us'.

41. David Hume, 'On the Independency of Parliament', in *Ibid.*, p.117: 'Political writers have established it as a maxim, that, in contriving any system of government and fixing the several checks and controls of the constitution, every man ought to be supposed a *knave*, and to have no other end, in all his actions, than private interest'.

42. Duncan Forbes, *Hume's Philosophical Politics* (Cambridge, Cambridge University Press, 1975), and 'Natural Law and the Scottish Enlightenment', in R. H. Campbell and A. Skinner (eds.), *The Origins and Nature of the Scottish Enlightenment* (Edinburgh, John Donald 1982).

43. Shirley Letwin, *The Pursuit of Certainty* (Cambridge, Cambridge University Press, 1965) and Geoffrey Marshall, 'David Hume and Political Skepticism', *The Political Quarterly* (1954).

44. *Pufendorf's Law of Nature and Nations: Abridg'd from the Original. In which the Author's entire Treatise (de Officio Hominis et Civis) that was by himself design'd as the Epitome of his larger work is taken. The Whole compared with the respective last Editions of Mr Barbeyrac's French Translations, and Illustrated with his Notes.* By J. Spavan, M.A. (London, 1716), 2 volumes, pp.339, 371 and Index.

45. This comment was made for the sole and mischievous purpose of provoking my friend, David Norton. His excellent contribution to Hume scholarship, 'New light on Hume's Library', was presented to the Hume Society at the University of Edinburgh, on August 29th, 1986.

46. S. Puffendorfii, *De Officio Hominis et Civis . . . auxit et illustravit Gerschomus Carmichael* (1724), *op.cit.*, n.10, p.412.

47. *Op. cit.*, n.52; *Pufendorf's Law of Nature and Nations (1716, the Spavan abridgement)*, *Vol.II*, *pp.307ff*. In the 4th edition *Of the Law of Nature and Nations* (1729) this note appears in Book VIII, Ch.III, Section IV, no.3, pp.764–765. Barbeyrac's observations develop remarks made by Jacques Bernard in the *Nouvelles de la République des Lettres*, 1706, p.48 in reply to Bayle's *Réponses aux Questions d'un Provincial*.

48. *Op. cit.* (Spavan abridgement), Vol.II, pp.2–3; *Of the Law of Nature and Nations* (1729), Book IV, Ch.1, Section V, p.311.

49. *Op. cit.* (Spavan abridgement), Vol.II, pp.190–192; *Of the Law of Nature and Nations* (1729), Book VII, Ch.1, Section VI, n.1, pp.629–630.

50. Letter of David Hume to Francis Hutcheson, 17 September 1739, in: *The Letters of David Hume*, ed. by J. Y. T. Greig (Oxford, at the Clarendon Press, 1932), Vol.I, p.33.

51. Samuel Pufendorf took this assertion of Horace's to mean 'that there is no such thing as natural law, but that all law first arose from the Convenience and Profit of Particular States and is incapable of any other Measure'. He added: 'Aristippus too and Pyrrho in Diogenes Laertius Book II and Book IX deliver themselves very grossly concerning the Origin of Just and Unjust'. *Of the Law of Nature and Nations* (1729) Book II, Ch.III, Section X, p.128.

52. Hugo Grotius, *The Rights of War and Peace . . . to which are added all the large notes of Mr. J. Barbeyrac* (London, 1738), Preliminary discourse, section XVII, p.xx.

53. J. P. de Crousaz, *Examen du Pyrrhonisme Ancien et Moderne* (Paris, 1733), p.404–405.

54. Hume, *An Enquiry Concerning the Principles of Morals*, ed. by L. A. Selby-Bigge (Oxford, Clarendon Press, 1902), p.195. For an insightful analysis, see Dario Castaglione, 'Hume's Conventionalism and the Early Modern Natural Law Tradition', a paper written for the 1986 meeting of the Conference for the Study of Political Thought held at the University of Edinburgh, August 25th to 28th, 1986.

3
SCIENCE AND THE ABERDEEN ENLIGHTENMENT

Paul Wood

During the past two decades, the intellectuals and institutions of eighteenth-century Edinburgh have been studied in increasing detail.[1] Yet for all its merits, this rapidly expanding body of literature on the Athens of the North has created a seriously distorted historiographic view of the Scottish Enlightenment as a whole. For although we have a relatively clear picture of the cultural history of Edinburgh in the period, developments in Aberdeen, Glasgow, and St. Andrews are both largely obscure and seen primarily from an Edinburgh perspective. The current bias of research has created the illusion that the Scottish Enlightenment was essentially an Edinburgh affair, and has made Nicholas Phillipson's claim that 'there is an important sense in which the history of the Scottish enlightenment *is* the history of Edinburgh' seem less contentious than it might otherwise appear.[2] While the importance of Edinburgh as a 'hotbed of genius' is undeniable, assertions such as Phillipson's are nevertheless problematic because we simply do not know enough about enlightened côteries elsewhere in Scotland. In order to form a balanced assessment of Edinburgh's role in the Scottish Enlightenment, more work needs to be done on the spread of enlightened ideas and ideals in the other urban centres of eighteenth-century Scotland.[3]

In this essay, I want to take a preliminary look at one such civic context, and examine the role of science in the Aberdeen Enlightenment. I have chosen to concentrate on science for two reasons. First, insufficient attention has hitherto been paid to the part played by science in the Scottish Enlightenment more generally. The scholarly consensus has been that enlightened Scots were preoccupied with the sciences of man rather than those of nature, and the distinctiveness of the Scottish Enlightenment has been defined accordingly.[4] However, this is an extremely partial view, for it overlooks the substantial contributions of men such as Colin Maclaurin and William Cullen to the cultural efflorescence of Scotland's Age of Reason. Moreover, in dealing with thinkers like Thomas Reid or James Hutton, this historiography makes little sense of the relationships between their inquiries into the natural and moral realms, and obscures the interactions of the sciences of man and nature in enlightenment Scotland as a whole. What must be recognized is that science was an integral part of enlightenment culture throughout Europe, and that Maclaurin's natural philosophy and Cullen's physiology were as much elements of the Scottish Enlightenment as the social speculations of David Hume or Adam Smith. In my view, Scotland's enlightenment, like those elsewhere, only becomes fully intelligible once we acknowledge the catalytic role played by the ideology, institutions, and intellectual products of science therein.

A second, related, reason for concentrating on the study of nature is that the few historians who have examined aspects of the Aberdeen Enlightenment have tended to ignore the significance of science within the cultural milieu of eighteenth-century Aberdeen. Because of the presence of savants like Alexander Gerard and James Beattie, Aberdeen is commonly regarded as a centre for philosophical speculation or literary endeavour rather than for the pursuit of natural knowledge. Thus, in a pioneering essay comparing the enlightenments of Aberdeen, Glasgow, and Edinburgh, Roger Emerson has argued that Aberdonians were largely taken up with epistemology, morals, history, and *belles lettres*, and has concluded that 'one looks in vain for significant [published] works on law, medicine, or even politics'.[5] But in fact, there were works of considerable merit on the natural sciences and medicine penned in the eighteenth century by Aberdeen men such as Thomas Reid, John Gregory, and John Stewart.[6] In any case, published works are often a misleading indicator of intellectual interests, and the available archival evidence suggests conclusions at variance with Emerson's portrayal of the Aberdeen enlightenment. Drawing on these little-used archival records, as well as on printed texts, I shall argue in what follows that science figured prominently in the universities and polite societies of enlightened Aberdeen.

I

Let me begin by examining the teaching of science in the Aberdeen colleges. At the time of the Glorious Revolution, Marischal students were taught what was known as 'general physics' in the third year and 'special physics' in the final year of their four-year course. Under the rubric of general physics they reviewed 'all the Hypotheses, both ancient and modern' which had been put forward by natural philosophers, and in special physics the students were 'informed how to explain all the particular phenomena of nature'.[7] In the 1680s the physics lectures were largely Cartesian in orientation, with additional information and ideas taken from leading English virtuosi like Boyle, Wren, Hooke, and Wallis. Beginning in the early 1690s, Newton's theories of gravitation and of light and colours were discussed, and by about 1710 the regents were expounding Newton's system of the world rather than that of Descartes.[8] As for their style of teaching, it would seem that the regents did not include demonstration experiments in their prelections, and they apparently avoided abstruse mathematical technicalities. For even though the students received instruction from the Liddell Professor of Mathematics, this was confined primarily to the rudiments of arithmetic and geometry. It may be that the students were also taught the use of astronomical and surveying instruments by the Mathematics Professor since Liddell had bequeathed such instruments to the university in 1613, but there is no direct evidence to confirm this.[9]

There are signs of growing scientific aspirations, if not activity, on the part of the faculty and its patrons at the turn of the eighteenth century. An abortive attempt was made to found an observatory in the college in the late 1690s, though few details of this scheme have survived.[10] A Chair of Medicine was endowed by the ninth Earl Marischal in 1700, with Patrick Chalmers being appointed its first incumbent. But Chalmers treated his Chair as a sinecure, and failed to provide any form of intellectual leadership.[11] Following the Jacobite rebellion of 1715, however, far-reaching changes began to take place at Marischal. Because of their Jacobite sympathies, all except one of the faculty were deposed in 1717 by a Royal Commission of Visitation, and a number of the men chosen to replace them promoted science within the college. Matthew McKail, who succeeded to the Chair of Medicine in October 1717, seems to have been keenly interested in the physical sciences, and he was apparently one of the architects of the plan formulated in 1726 to begin a course of experimental philosophy. Evidently dissatisfied with his Chair, McKail later switched to the post of Regent in 1729, and unsuccessfully attempted to establish himself as the 'Professor of Natural and Experimental Philosophy'. Apart from these facts about his career, little is known of McKail, and the only hint we have of his theoretical interests is given by the title of a public discourse he gave in 1729 called 'On the connexion and difference betwixt the atomic or Copernican and the Newtonian philosophy'.[12]

There is little doubt that the new Liddell Professor of Mathematics, Colin Maclaurin, raised the standard of mathematics teaching, both in his public lectures and in his private courses. Unlike his predecessors, Maclaurin engaged in original research, and while in Aberdeen he published two papers in the *Philosophical Transactions* along with his first book, the *Geometrica Organica* (1720), and in so doing, established himself as one of Britain's leading mathematicians.[13] Significantly, there is evidence which indicates that Maclaurin was also trying to do work on observational astronomy in Aberdeen, and it may be that his researches ranged more widely through the physical sciences.[14] Maclaurin, it seems, was an effective pedagogue too, for we find him writing to a correspondent in 1719 that he 'had thrice as many Scholars this Year as I had the last', and the college records show that he took an active part in the efforts made to alter the character of the teaching of natural philosophy at Marischal in the immediate post-'15 period.[15] Thus although Maclaurin's tenure of the Liddell Chair was brief (he delivered what were to be his last lectures in May 1721), during his time at Marischal he set a precedent for those who followed him by providing instruction in mathematics which was second to none in Scotland, and he was instrumental in elevating the status of the experimental study of nature within the College.

The appointment of George Turnbull as regent in 1721 also did much to alter the intellectual complexion of Marischal. A graduate of Edinburgh and an early member of the Rankenian Club, Turnbull was familiar with the latest fashionable philosophical currents and, as his correspondence with Lord Molesworth shows, something of a Commonwealthman.[16] Although he was probably no more than a competent expositor of the theories of Newton and other contemporary natural philosophers, Turnbull is nevertheless important in the present context because he was apparently the first regent at Marischal to advance the view that the methods employed in the natural sciences ought to be followed in the moral sciences as well. As natural philosophy proceeded by experiment and analogy in the analysis of the physical world, so too he believed that moral philosophy should be an empirical science of the phenomena and laws of the moral system.

While he acknowledged Bacon as the father of the experimental method, Turnbull's understanding of that method was shaped by Newton's methodological pronouncements in the *Opticks*, and, to a lesser extent, in the *Principia*. In his thesis for the graduating class of 1723, entitled *Of the connexion between natural science and moral philosophy*, Turnbull praised Newton's use of the methods of analysis and synthesis in discovering the law of gravitation and in investigating the properties of light, and he asserted that these methods should be utilized to further the progress of our moral enquiries. To justify this claim Turnbull cited a passage in Query 31 of the 1717 edition of the *Opticks*, where Newton wrote that 'if natural Philosophy in all its Parts, by pursuing this Method [of analysis and synthesis], shall at length be perfected, the Bounds of Moral Philosophy will be also enlarged'.[17] Turnbull thus used Newton to legitimate his own methodological programme for moral philosophy, and we can see in this thesis the origins of the so-called 'Newtonian turn' of British methodological thought.[18] Furthermore this scientistic approach to moral philosophy was later taught in the college by men such as David Fordyce, and it became a distinctive feature of the philosophical tradition at Marischal.[19]

Along with the new personnel came a fundamental change in the curriculum at Marischal, namely the introduction of experimental demonstrations into the teaching of natural philosophy. Following the lead of the universities of Edinburgh and Glasgow, the college made moves to emulate the courses in experimental philosophy which had been offered in London, Cambridge, and Oxford by academics like William Whiston and John Keill, instrument makers such as Francis Hauksbee, and entrepreneurs of science like J. T. Desaguliers.[20] Marischal successfully petitioned the King in 1718 for funds 'for purchasing proper Instruments towards advanceing Experimental Philosophy', and, on the advice of Colin Maclaurin, the college acquired 'A Large Double Air Pump & Apparatus' along with other experimental hardware from Hauksbee in June of that year.[21] Maclaurin seems to have lobbied too for a set of astronomical instruments, as he complained to the Savilian Professor of Geometry at Oxford, Edmund Halley, in December 1720, of 'the want of Instruments [for astronomical observation] which our Colledges are not able or not willing to purchase'.[22] His complaint is suggestive, for it indicates that the instruments which had survived from Liddell's bequest were either completely outmoded or inadequate for the purposes of serious observational astronomy, and that earlier efforts to found an astronomical observatory at Marischal had foundered because of the lack of the requisite apparatus. Moreover, Maclaurin's remarks point to the fact that college finances at this time were in disarray. Repeated appeals to the Crown for financial assistance in the 1720s apparently met with limited success, and this imposed severe limitations on the extent to which the college could acquire scientific hardware for teaching and research.[23]

Even though money was not forthcoming from the King, Marischal's faculty pressed ahead with their intention of remodelling the science curriculum, and in order to solve the problem of financing their scheme they resorted to a public appeal for funds in 1726.[24] In the 'Proposals For setting on Foot a Compleat Course of *Experimental Philosophy* in the

Marischal College of *Aberdeen*', which were printed and distributed at the end of the 1725–26 session, the faculty adverted to the 'Meanness' of the college funds and asked college alumni and 'all Noblemen, Gentlemen and lovers of Learning' to assist in the purchase of 'Entire *Setts* of Instruments necessary in *Astronomy, Mechanicks, Opticks, Chymistry, Hydrostaticks*, and *Anatomy*. . .the *Best Books* which treat of Natural and Experimental Philosophy' and 'Models of the newest *Machines* in Husbandry'. Once obtained, the instruments, books, and models were to be used in a course of experimental philosophy taught during the regular session by the regents in conjunction with the Professors of Mathematics and Medicine, and open to registered students and to all those who subscribed more than one guinea. To make the scheme even more attractive, it was proposed that 'any Contributor when he pleases to come with his Friends shall be attended by some one or other of the Professors, and have any Experiment he desires performed', and the 'Proposals' stressed that 'In explaining the Experiments care will be taken to make every thing as plain and easy as possible, by shunning all difficult and unnecessary Terms of Art, so that even those who have not made progress in *Mathematicks* may understand some of the most useful and pleasant Parts of Natural Philosophy, especially all sorts of *Machines* in *Husbandry* and *Common-Life*'.[25]

To raise the much-needed cash, therefore, the Marischal faculty chose to emphasize the practical utilities of scientific knowledge, especially as applied to agriculture, and to appeal to the improving interests of the landed men of the north-east. The extent to which they succeeded is now difficult to determine. The faculty petitioned the Commissioners of Supply for Aberdeenshire in May 1726 and received a modest sum, and in September of that year a similar petition elicited a grant of £21 from the Town Council of Aberdeen.[26] However, no other record survives of subscriptions being paid to Marischal for the purposes set out in the 'Proposals'. Previous historians have taken this to mean that the scheme was a dismal failure, but circumstantial evidence suggests that further contributions were received. In a letter dating from July 1726 describing the current state of college affairs, mention is made of the fact that Marischal had 'made a small Collection of Instruments for Experimental Philosophy Upon the Charitable Collection of our Friends & Neighbours'.[27] Furthermore, the Faculty Minutes for 1733 show than an 'Instrument Room' containing unspecified scientific apparatus existed in the college, and that a course of experimental philosophy was indeed being given (presumably replacing the 'special physics' section of the magistrand year). Since the construction of a special room for the teaching of experimental philosophy was one of the proposals put forward in 1726, and the course itself was being taught in some form, it seems legitimate to infer that there had been a few private subscribers.[28]

Even if the ambitious plans of 1726 were not fully realised at the time, their importance should not be underestimated, for they reflect Marischal's recognition of the value of the new form of scientific practice popularized in the courses of Desaguliers and others, and the realisation that the college had to offer lectures on experimental philosophy in order to compete with rival institutions like Edinburgh and Glasgow for prospective students. Moreover, at least some of the ideas sketched in the 'Proposals' continued to guide faculty thinking for many years to come. In 1750, for example, the faculty decided to open the course of experimental philosophy then being taught by David Fordyce to the sub-scribers to a fund for instruments, and there do seem to have been a few contributors, although Fordyce reported that 'none of [them] did attend his Lectures'.[29] Seen in the context of these schemes, Patrick Copland's policy of opening his lectures to the public in the late-eighteenth century appears to have some precedent in the college. So too does his extensive use of models in his lectures on practical mechanics, for the 'Proposals' of 1726 acknowledged the pedagogical utility of models, and extant college receipts indicate that models were being used by Copland's predecessor in the Chair of Natural Philosophy, George Skene.[30] Consequently, the 'Proposals' can, I suggest, be read as a manifesto for the place of science within the Marischal curriculum.

At King's College, scientific aspirations and achievements were more modest in the first half of the eighteenth century. Unlike Marischal, King's lacked a Professor of Mathematics until 1703, when Thomas Bower was appointed to the newly founded chair. Much of Bower's time was subsequently occupied with trips to Edinburgh and London to secure an adequate salary, with wrangles over his rights in faculty meetings, and with efforts to move to Marischal, but he did launch a subscription *circa* 1710 in order to purchase instruments for the college.[31] In his 'Proposals for Buying Mathematical Instruments for the use of the King's College of Aberdeen', Bower justified his appeal for money on the grounds that 'A stock of Mathematical Instrument[s] about an University' was of 'publick advantage'. What Bower included under the heading of 'mathematical instruments' is uncertain, but the set of proposals which he drew up implies that he intended to offer a course of experimental philosophy in addition to his mathematics prelections, and that he also wanted to use the instruments for the purposes of research.[32] Bower apparently met with some success in his fundraising activities, as a faculty minute from July 1720 mentions 'Mathematical Instruments. . .purchased with the Money contributed by the Subscribers in Dr. Bowers books'.[33] However, no record seems to survive of the apparatus which Bower acquired for the college, nor is there any sign that he did in fact give a course of experimental philosophy. Moreover, it would seem that the equipment available was still limited, for when the faculty came to purchase further experimental hardware in the late 1730s, they noted that 'the College is at [a] Considerable loss by not having a sett of Mathamatical [*sic*] Instruments compleated'.[34] Thanks to a sizeable bequest earmarked specifically for 'mathematical instruments proper to make physical and mathematical experiments', King's was then able to buy additional equipment, though again we do not know the exact details of what was bought.[35] Presumably the college's instruments were used by Bower's successor Alexander Rait and the King's regents to illustrate their physics lectures with demonstration experiments as was the practice at Marischal and elsewhere, but it is clear that in the first half of the eighteenth century King's did not make a determined effort to remodel the structure and pedagogical style of the science curriculum like its Aberdeen rival.[36]

With the major reforms effected in 1753, the teaching of the natural sciences became more firmly entrenched in the curriculum at both Marischal and King's, and the students at the two colleges now followed degree courses of much the same structure. Under the new academic régime at Marischal, students were expected to undergo more rigorous instruction in mathematics during the first three years of their course, with the Professor carrying them through the elements of algebra and geometry to Newton's method of fluxions and the technicalities of the *Principia*.[37] They were also to be given a course of natural philosophy in their third year covering the standard subjects of mechanics, hydrostatics, pneumatics, optics, and astronomy, along with emergent sciences like magnetism and electricity. However, the most radical alteration of the curriculum affected the second year, for the students were in future to be lectured on natural and civil history. In these lectures they were to be informed about the various classes of natural bodies, the 'uses of these natural bodies, and of the principles of the several arts in life which depend upon, and are employed about them', and about 'the rise and fall of states, and of the great revolutions that have happen'd in the world'.[38] Thus over a third of the reformed curriculum was formally taken up with the sciences of nature, and even in areas like natural theology and metaphysics there was a scientific component since the findings of natural philosophers were to be used to defend religious orthodoxy.[39] Accompanying these changes in the syllabus was a reorganization of the teaching staff, with the adoption of the professorial system and the establishment of chairs in natural philosophy and in civil and natural history, thereby doubling the number of science-related professorships.

Prompted by the actions of their Marischal counterparts, the King's faculty introduced similarly wide-ranging curriculum reforms. After a year of reading Greek, the King's students were to proceed to 'a Course of Mathematics, both speculative and practical, and. . .an Introduction to all the Branches of Natural History'. In their third year the 'Mathematical Course [was] to be carried on, along with a Course of Natural and Experimental Philosophy', and in their final year they were to study 'the Philosophy of the Human Mind and the Sciences that Depend upon it'.[40] Using the manuscripts of Thomas Reid, who was a regent at King's from 1751 to 1764, the scientific components of the curriculum can be further specified. In their mathematics classes, the pupils were lectured first on the elements of geometry and algebra, and then on such subjects as spherical geometry, trigonometry, mathematical astronomy, and fluxions. The practical applications of mathematics in fields like surveying and navigation were also discussed. Reid seems to have spent far less time on civil history than was done at Marischal and concentrated on natural history, prelecting on the classification of the creation, comparative anatomy, and the physiology of plants, animals, and man. Finally, his natural philosophy course covered mechanics, astronomy, cohesion, magnetism, electricity, hydrostatics, pneumatics, and optics.[41] The curriculum as taught by Reid was thus essentially the same as that at Marischal.

However, the curricula at Marischal and King's were far from being identical. Because the faculty retained the regenting system at King's, and each regent was given the freedom to organize his lectures as he saw fit, there was more variation within the courses of natural history and natural philosophy.[42] For example, Thomas Reid's research interests are reflected in the fact that he appears to have spent more time prelecting on the science of optics than his fellow regents, and, unlike the rest of his colleagues, James Dunbar retained the old division between general and special physics in his natural philosophy lectures.[43] Yet despite these individual variations, all of the regents followed the eighteenth-century natural philosophy textbook tradition and taught the same subjects which Reid covered in his prelections. The mathematics course too probably varied slightly, since, with the effective disappearance of the mathematics chair in the 1730s, the level of instruction depended upon each regent's abilities and inclinations.

But the most striking differences in structure and content occur in the natural history courses. For much of the period 1753 to 1800 the King's lectures were much broader in scope than those given at Marischal. Thus Thomas Gordon's prelections delivered in the 1770s began with a description of the solar system, and then proceeded to 'the earth, and its appendages', a category which for Gordon included light, heat, and air, and the vegetable and animal kingdoms.[44] In the 1790s, Robert Eden Scott followed much the same pattern, although his treatment of the earth was much more extensive and he did not include any material on the structure of the solar system.[45] At Marischal, the first Professor of Civil and Natural History, Francis Skene, restricted himself to the various classifications of unorganized matter, vegetables, and animals, which he described in often excruciating detail.[46] Unfortunately the lectures of his successor George Skene have not survived, but the shape of the course given by James Beattie parallels that of Robert Eden Scott's, for Beattie also dealt with what he called 'the history of the terraqueous globe', mineralogy, botany, and zoology.[47] Unlike natural philosophy, there was no well-established textbook tradition in natural history during the eighteenth century, and this probably accounts for the differences between the lectures given in the two colleges. The reasons for the changes at Marischal towards the end of the eighteenth century remain obscure, but it may be that Beattie (and Robert Eden Scott) modelled his course on that given by the Edinburgh Professor of Natural History, John Walker.[48]

The restructuring of the curricula of the two Aberdeen colleges in 1753 thus marks the end of the old scholastic order of learning. The break with tradition is signalled most clearly by the replacement of logic by civil and natural history in the second year of the philosophy course, which reflects the Baconian roots of the reforms, and the avowed aim in both colleges to teach 'those parts of Philosophy, which may qualify Men for the more useful and important Offices of Society'.[49] To the architects of the curricular reforms, knowledge had to be useful, and the utilitarian ideology of early modern science meshed well with their vision of the place of university education in an improving society. However, we should be sensitive to the modalities of utility in this period, for the uses of science were not simply economic. For most of the regents and professors, the primary use of natural knowledge was to demonstrate the being and attributes of God. As Thomas Reid put it in his natural history lectures in the 1750s: '. . . the Noblest Use of this Study [i.e.

natural history], the most Worthy of the Human Mind, and that which gives the highest Relish to it is that it gives the clearest Evidence of the Being the Wisdom and Bounty of the Almighty Maker of all these things who tho he is in himself Invisible yet hath manifested his Wisdom and Goodness and Power in these his works'.[50] Consequently scientific knowledge was presented within a natural theological framework, and, while its practical applications were by no means overlooked, science was chiefly valued as a resource for the defence of religious orthodoxy. Because of these perceived utilities, therefore, science came to displace other, hitherto more important, forms of learning like logic, and to occupy a pre-eminent place within the reformed curricula of Marischal and King's.

Structurally, the curriculum at the two colleges changed little following the 1753 reforms,[51] but further efforts were made to expand the facilities for science. In 1754 the faculty at King's resolved to build a chemical laboratory and dissecting room, and to establish a museum to house natural history specimens, 'Models of the most useful and curious Instruments and Machines', and instruments 'for Surveying, Mensuration, Navigation, Astronomy and Optics'. Despite the limited availability of funds, the faculty decided to select forthwith a set of rooms in the college and to refurnish them as circumstances permitted. The faculty was thus willing to take the initiative, but they did appeal to their alumni and other potential benefactors to 'contribute some proper furniture for such Apartments, and be Assistant in which way as they see most Proper for Promoting so good a Design'.[52] It is unclear at present how far this plan was immediately realized, but we do know that William Ogilvie took an active hand in developing the museum after he began teaching in 1764, so that by 1792 Ogilvie could claim that the museum was furnished 'with a considerable variety of specimens in Natural History, disposed in such a manner that they may be easily exhibited to the Students for their inspection'.[53] Further details about the museum can be gleaned from Francis Douglas's *A General Description of the East Coast of Scotland from Edinburgh to Cullen*, wherein Douglas states that the 'collection of birds, fishes, marbles, spars, etc., etc.' at King's was housed in 'three apartments' which Ogilvie had 'fitted up, and furnished'. According to Douglas, Ogilvie had begun the collection and built it up with 'the assistance of many respectable people in the country around'. Douglas reported further that Ogilvie had every intention of 'enlarging the museum, as new acquisitions come to hand: but without pretending to adorn it with splendid or costly specimens'.[54] From this account, it would seem that

King's in fact owed its natural history collection largely to Ogilvie's initiative, and that he had managed to secure some local support for the venture. What is also evident is that Ogilvie's efforts were constrained by a lack of college funding, a point to which I shall return below.

A second important scheme launched in the 1750s by King's was a complete failure. With the consent of the faculty, the Professor of Medicine, John Gregory, endeavoured to broaden the scope of medical teaching at King's. In 1758 he introduced courses on the theory and practice of medicine and on chemistry taught by himself, and persuaded Dr. David Skene to prelect on anatomy, *materia medica*, and midwifery. But the lure of established medical schools in Edinburgh and elsewhere was too great, and the scheme collapsed after two sessions for lack of students.[55] Another attempt in 1792 by Dr. William Chalmers to begin a series of lectures on anatomy and physiology failed as well because Chalmers could not attract the requisite number of students, and ill-health prevented him from making a determined effort to enlarge the constituency for his planned course.[56] Although the small size of the student body undoubtedly limited the possibilities for innovation, it should be noted that some of the faculty at King's during the latter part of the eighteenth century appear to have resisted proposed improvements, especially if the proposals entailed the expenditure of college funds. A particularly revealing exchange occurred in 1785, when William Ogilvie wanted to purchase books using college money. The faculty minutes record the following response:

> We answer, a botanical garden, buying an apparatus for a course of experimental Philosophy and a variety of models of useful engines, buying an Astronomical apparatus and building an observatory, buying specimens for the musaeum, antiques, medals, statues and pictures, may all be reckoned *academical purposes*, and each will find zealous advocates at one period or another; they ought all therefore to be taken upon the College funds according to this [i.e. Ogilvie's] argument, and poor Sorrel's back must be broken. It has been the wisdom of the society uniformly hitherto, steadily to resist all these tempting plans, and we see no reason for being more compliant in the present instance.[57]

The majority of the King's men were thus hostile to the sorts of schemes Ogilvie promoted within the college, and their attitude contrasts markedly with that prevalent at Marischal. Unlike their colleagues in the new town, the King's faculty were content to conserve and consolidate the college's financial resources, and they made little effort to cultivate alternative sources of funding. Consequently, the natural history museum was, as we have seen, largely reliant on private donations of specimens, and additional scientific apparatus was obtained through benefactions rather than through purchases by the college.[58] While the faculty was willing to innovate in the 1750s, it seems that it became increasingly difficult as the century wore on for men such as William Ogilvie to gain support for their endeavours to improve the facilities for science at King's.

At Marischal, on the other hand, the teaching of the sciences continued to flourish. Soon after the curriculum reforms, money was spent on renewing old instruments and on acquiring new apparatus.[59] The college museum established in the mid-1760s incorporated a natural history collection, which included specimens given by private donors.[60] A botanic garden was functioning by 1786, and the college later hired a lecturer to give botany prelections there.[61] In the 1780s, the energetic Patrick Copland secured grants amounting to £150 from the Trustees of the Board of Manufactures for the purposes of constructing models of machinery to be used in his lectures, and by the time of his death in 1822 he had managed to accumulate some 530 items of equipment.[62] With the backing of the faculty, Copland also succeeded in opening a college observatory in 1781, which was built on a site donated by the Town Council. The observatory boasted an impressive array of instruments, which Copland had obtained from influential patrons like Lord Bute, or purchased through public subscription.[63] In exchange for this support, Copland began in 1785 to teach a course of natural philosophy in the evenings which the public could attend, and the college made special concessions to the Governors of Gordon's Hospital in return for their contribution to the observatory fund.[64]

During the closing decades of the century, the teaching of the natural sciences expanded in other directions as well. Beginning in 1784, chemistry lectures were offered in the college by George French, who was subsequently elected to the newly founded chair of chemistry in 1793.[65] Finally, in the 1790s efforts were made by the Professor of Medicine Dr. William Livingstone to set up a regular series of medical prelections, and thanks to the backing he received from members of the recently formed Aberdeen Medical Society, Livingstone achieved some success.[66] Unlike King's, therefore, Marischal made a determined effort to develop and improve its facilities for the study of the sciences of nature, and began to offer a range of scientific and medical subjects outside the normal arts curriculum. Had men like Thomas Reid and John Gregory remained at King's rather than moving on to prestigious chairs elsewhere, science might have been more effectively promoted within the college. But with their departure in the mid-1760s, the lobbying for change subsided, and, despite the efforts of William Ogilvie, King's declined into a state of intellectual mediocrity, with its faculty dominated by undistinguished members determined to maintain the *status quo*. By contrast, the impetus for innovation remained alive at Marischal, which allowed enterprising men like Patrick Copland to build on the reforms of 1753.

II

Having traced the growth of science within the universities, I turn now to examine the role of science in the polite societies of the Aberdeen Enlightenment. The earliest such society is something of a mystery, for we only know of its existence through a single fragment entitled 'Minutes of a Philosophical Club 1736' which survives among the papers of Thomas Reid. This manuscript apparently records the proceedings of a series of weekly meetings held between 12 January and 9 February 1736, and there are other notes in Reid's hand which suggest that the Club was still active in January 1737.[67] No additional evidence concerning this club seems to be extant, and the minutes give no indication of its membership, though it seems legitimate to assume that Reid was himself a member. Other likely candidates include Reid's close friend, the Marischal Professor of Mathematics John Stewart, and David Fordyce, who later rhapsodized about a philosophical club in his *Dialogues concerning Education*.[68] It may be that the club was in some way associated with Marischal, as Stewart was a faculty member, Reid was college librarian, and Fordyce was a graduate and student of divinity.[69]

Although the known topics canvassed by the club were drawn entirely from moral philosophy, the discussion of 12 January 1736 centred on natural theology. Addressing themselves to the question 'What Things in the Course of Nature may we reasonably ascribe to the continual influence & Operation of God or other active powerful and Invisible beings under him?', the members agreed that it was probable that 'the preservation of Creatures in Being is owing to [God's] continual Influence', and that phenomena which could not be accounted for by the laws of mechanism, such as gravitation, attraction and cohesion, voluntary motion, generation, and instinctive behaviour among animals, were to be ascribed to Divine influence as well.[70] Reid and his fellow discussants thus adopted the Newtonian views of savants such as Samuel Clarke regarding the existence and operation of active principles in the natural order, and in so doing carried on the natural theological tradition nurtured in Aberdeen by George Turnbull among others. Another possible venue for the discussion of natural theology was the Theological Club founded by George Campbell in the early 1740s, but no records of its meetings are seemingly extant.[71]

One of the next societies to be organized in Aberdeen was devoted to the study of medicine. This was a small club formed by David and Andrew Skene, John Ross, Duncan Forbes, Alexander Donaldson, and John Walker in July 1750 for the purposes of 'mutuall Improvement in Physick or any Branch of Knowledge connected therewith'. Apart from two versions of the list of the club's rules, however, we have no information about how long it remained in existence or about the topics surveyed by its members.[72] Yet the formation of this club is significant, for it was perhaps the first formal grouping in Aberdeen to focus exclusively on the natural sciences.

Fortunately we can document more fully the scientific activities of the two most important societies of the Aberdeen Enlightenment, the Gordon's Mill Farming Club and the Aberdeen Philosophical Society. Begun in December 1758, the Farming Club vigorously promoted the cause of agricultural improvement, and it is within the context of this society that we can see the methods and theories of the natural sciences being self-consciously applied to the problems of agriculture. Soon after the club was founded, the Humanist at King's, Thomas Gordon, captured the methodological spirit of their enterprise. He told his fellow club members that 'As agriculture ought to be considered as a noble & important branch of natural Philosophy, it should be pursued in the same method', and he reviewed those aspects of Bacon's exposition of the experimental method which he thought were relevant to their corporate inquiries.[73] In a similar vein, John Gregory argued that agriculture could be established on firm principles 'if Farmers were but so much Philosophers, as from their own experiments to make proper Inductions and. . .if they would borrow from natural Philosophy those Lights which it will afford to Husbandry'.[74] Gregory himself endeavoured to apply scientific theory to agricultural practice in attempting to explicate the nourishment of plants in order to improve cultivation techniques.[75] Thomas Reid was consulted on the mechanical principles underlying the design of agricultural implements, and he also utilized his mathematical skills in devising a rationalized system of book keeping for farmers.[76] The men of the Gordon's Mill Farming Club therefore sought to harness natural knowledge and what they took to be the methods of science to agriculture, and in so doing they kept alive the ideology of improvement which, as we have seen, was already manifest in Aberdeen in the 1720s.

Likewise founded in 1758, the Aberdeen Philosophical Society was *the* major forum of the Aberdeen Enlightenment for the discussion and debate of matters scientific.[77] The Wise Club, as the society was popularly known, does not usually figure in the literature on eighteenth-century scientific institutions, or works on science in the Scottish Enlightenment. Yet the club typifies the way in which provincial philosophical societies combined papers on *belles lettres*, natural philosophy, morals, and social theory in their proceedings, and illustrates how science was a constituent part of enlightenment culture.[78] Rather than reduce the society to a species of literary club in the manner of D. D. McElroy, it is far more instructive to compare it with the French provincial academies so well described by Daniel Roche or with the slightly later English literary and philosophical societies such as the Manchester Lit. and Phil.[79] Viewed from this perspective, the Aberdeen Philosophical Society tells us much about British provincial science in the eighteenth century, and the range of intellectual concerns of enlightened côteries of the period.

The members of the Society came almost exclusively from the faculties of Aberdeen's two colleges, and their scholarly interests were fairly diverse. But it is significant that a large proportion of the most active participants in the club were men who had a strong scientific bent. This group of activists included four of the founders of the society, namely John Gregory, David Skene, John Stewart, and Thomas Reid, as well as such later members as George Skene.[80] Inevitably the preoccupations of these men were reflected in the society's transactions, for during the fifteen years of its existence 21% of the questions proposed for discussion and 17% of the formal discourses delivered dealt with scientific and medical topics.[81] Of the questions proposed, a number were related to agricultural improvement and explored problems which exercized the Gordon's Mill Farming Club, such as the nutrition of plants and the use of manures.[82] Little attention was paid to the philosophical aspects of scientific practice, or to mathematics or chemistry, but the members frequently discussed natural historical and medical questions, and issues in the physical sciences were regularly debated.[83] Astronomy too was a popular subject, and the society was perhaps the first learned body in Britain to prepare for the 1761 transit of Venus, as Robert Trail asked in 1758: 'What are the proper methods of determining the sun's parallax by the transit of Venus over his disk in 1761?'. By contrast, the Royal Society of London did not discuss the matter until June 1760, when it was provoked into action by the receipt of a memoir on the transit by the French astronomer DeLisle.[84] Assisted by 'three or four members of [the] Society', Thomas Reid later observed the transit in June 1761 and reported his findings to a meeting held on 14 July.[85] The society thus occasionally engaged in collaborative scientific research, and because its members were almost all university men it enjoyed the advantage of being able to draw on the resources of the two Aberdeen colleges to support such projects. Moreover, there were precedents for the astronomical work carried out by the club in 1761, as Reid had joined forces with John Stewart to observe an eclipse of the sun which occurred in July 1748, and he may have been involved in a similar exercise in 1737.[86]

Although there were proportionately fewer formal discourses devoted specifically to science and medicine, some of them stand out as being noteworthy contributions to the intellectual life of the society. Prompted in part by the publication in 1756 of Robert Simson's edition of Euclid's *Elements*, Thomas Reid in 1762 critically examined Euclid's definitions and axioms in order to solve the vexed problem of properly defining parallel lines, and John Stewart similarly grappled with the philosophical foundations of mathematics in his discourses for 1762 and 1763. In many ways the most impressive series of papers came from David Skene, who delivered seven discourses on natural history which were mainly taken up with the problem of justifying the use of systematic classification schemes in botany.[87] Natural history was also the subject of discourses by John Gregory, John Ross, and William Ogilvie, and it would seem that the majority of the membership shared an interest in this branch of the sciences.[88]

Along with the society's inclusion of science in its proceedings went a commitment to scientism. In the rules of the society drawn up by its founder members in 1758, we find the following revealing passage:

> The Subject of the Discourses and Questions shall be Philosophical, all Grammatical Historical and Philological Discussions being conceived to be forreign to the Design of this Society. And Philosophical Matters are understood to comprehend Every Principle of Science which may be deduced by Just and Lawfull Induction from the Phenomena either of the human Mind or of the material World; [and] All Observations & Experiments that may furnish Materials for such Induction. . . .[89]

The founders thus wished to limit the society to natural historical and inductive inquiries into the material and moral realms. Their definition of the Wise Club's scope sharply differentiates it from other contemporary and roughly equivalent groupings in Scotland such as the Glasgow Literary Society, and their assertion of the methodological unity of the sciences of man and nature has its roots in the teachings of George Turnbull. As I have already suggested, scientism was a distinctive feature of the philosophical tradition initiated at Marischal by Turnbull, and the Aberdeen Philosophical Society was an important institutional manifestation of that tradition.

With the demise of the society in 1773, the Aberdeen Enlightenment once again became almost exclusively university-based.[90] One grouping which did emerge towards the end of the eighteenth century was the Aberdeen Medical Society, which started life as a student debating club in 1789.[91] Initially the Medical Society had a membership of twelve and met in private homes, but it soon doubled in size, took on non-student members, and began to meet weekly in a classroom at Marischal. The college proved hospitable to the club in other ways, for Dr. William Livingstone, who was appointed Professor of Medicine there in 1793, became its leading patron, and the society eventually held its meetings and established its museum and library in a house owned by him. On the other hand, Livingstone's prickly colleague at Marischal, George French, was openly hostile to the club. But his opposition did not seriously affect its affairs, since other influential Aberdonians, including the Professor of Medicine at King's, William Chalmers, and his successor, Sir Alexander Bannerman, actively supported the society, and hence protected it from the machinations of French.

Modelled on the Edinburgh Medico-Chirurgical Society, the Aberdeen club restricted itself exclusively to medical topics which reflected the concerns of the local students and practitioners. Such a narrowness of focus replicates the growing specialization to be found in the Edinburgh societies of the period, and this fragmentation of intellectual life marks the end of the relatively unified enlightenment culture shared by Scotland's *literati* earlier in the century.[92] The founding of the Aberdeen Medical Society can thus be seen as a sign of similar changes taking place in the north-east. Other significant alterations in the cultural complexion of Aberdeen were occurring too. The generation of university men who had engineered the reforms of 1753 were largely gone. In the mid-1760s John Stewart died, and Thomas Reid and John Gregory departed to pursue their careers in Glasgow and Edinburgh respectively. George Campbell and Alexander Gerard remained, but their circle began to fracture due to the tensions generated by the abortive attempts to unite the two colleges in the 1770s and '80s. After the collapse of the second unification scheme in 1786, William Ogilvie in particular found himself isolated, and at loggerheads with the majority of his colleagues at both

King's and Marischal.[93] Outside the colleges, David Skene had died in 1770, and with him Aberdeen lost its most outstanding naturalist. There was thus in Aberdeen a divided rump of a once coherent group of savants who had promoted enlightened ideas and ideals from the 1730s onwards.

Science too was being transformed. In the late 1780s, the Town Council of Aberdeen began to draw on the expertise of Patrick Copland and his Marischal colleague Robert Hamilton when planning and effecting various civic improvements. The two men were deeply involved in the research on the town's water supply which formed the basis of the Gordon Water Report of 1792, and Copland was also instrumental in standardizing Aberdeen's weights and measures, and refining local bleaching techniques. Whereas improvers had traditionally turned their attention to weights and measures and bleaching, Coplands activities (along with those of Hamilton) as a member of the Town Council Water Committee look forward to large-scale efforts in the Victorian era to apply science to the problems of urban society. With Copland and Hamilton, therefore, we find the ideology of improvement shifting from an agricultural to a civic mode.[94]

In the wake of the French Revolution, natural knowledge was also put to increasingly conservative political uses. Science had always been deployed in the defence of orthodoxy within the universities, but in the highly reactionary climate of the 1790s, this kind of usage was taken to extremes. Following the lead of the Edinburgh Professor of Natural Philosophy, John Robison, British men of science began to equate heterodox scientific views with atheism and political radicalism.[95] An interesting instance of this kind of rhetoric is to be found in Robert Eden Scott's public utterances at King's College in 1798. In an address delivered to the university in that year, Scott attacked the principles of the French Revolution, and censured the 'spirit of innovation' propagated by Condorcet and other political writers in France.[96] Similarly, in his geology prelections read in the autumn of 1798, Scott warned his students that the 'disciples of infidelity' on the continent had launched a sustained assault on natural and revealed religion, utilizing the findings of physics and natural history. Given these challenges to the authority of 'the Scriptural account of the formation of the earth, the general deluge, & the various revolutions which our globe has undergone', Scott therefore believed that it was 'a very proper subject' for his lectures to review the major theories of the earth in order to ascertain whether they gave any support to the cause of irreligion, and hence to the erosion of traditional forms of authority in society. Consequently, his criticisms of the theories of Buffon and Hutton in his prelections were made in the context of his overt fears of the subversive effects of atheism and his rabid anti-Jacobinism. The revolutionary ferment of the 1790s thus had a profound impact on Scott's perception of Buffon's and Hutton's geological systems, and his critique of their ideas displays the same conservative tendencies observable in Scottish intellectual life more generally during the decade of reaction so skilfully orchestrated and exploited by Henry Dundas and his Tory henchmen.[97]

III

To conclude, historians have long accepted that Newton was one of the great patriarchs of the Enlightenment. This being so, it is curious that some scholars have not acknowledged the fact that natural philosophy was an integral part of enlightened culture. As I noted in the introduction, many eminent writers on eighteenth-century Scotland still tend to exclude science from their purview when defining the distinctive characteristics of the Scottish Enlightenment. I have tried to indicate in the main part of this paper the reasons why I think they are wrong to do so. First, the history of Aberdeen's two universities during the eighteenth century illustrates the centrality of scientific knowledge. The introduction of experimental philosophy and natural history, the increase in personnel, the expansion of the instrumental facilities for teaching and research, and the founding of observatories, museums, and botanical gardens constitute the most significant changes in King's and Marischal in this period. Secondly, science also played an important role in the polite societies formed by enlightened Aberdonians, particularly in the heyday of the Gordon's Mill Farming Club and the Aberdeen Philosophical Society. Thirdly, scientism provided an overarching cognitive and ideological structure, linking together the moral and the natural sciences in both the curricula and the clubs. It is for these three reasons, then, that I want to claim that science was at the core of the Aberdeen Enlightenment, and recent work by other scholars suggests that similar conclusions can be drawn regarding the institutional and intellectual centrality of science in the enlightenments of Edinburgh and Glasgow.[98] Hence it is arguable that more attention needs to be paid to the cultural role of natural knowledge if historians are to truly understand the dynamic of the Scottish Enlightenment.

NOTES

The author wishes to thank: the Social Sciences and Humanities Research Council of Canada for financial support; Professor Roger Emerson for his comments on earlier drafts of this essay; the Librarian of Aberdeen University for permission to quote from manuscripts in his care; the Keeper of the Records of Scotland for permission to quote from manuscripts; and Dr. Dorothy Johnston for help with the Aberdeen archives.

1. By far the best introduction to this recent work is Richard B. Sher, *Church and University in the Scottish Enlightenment: The Moderate Literati of Edinburgh* (Princeton, 1985), which contains the most useful and comprehensive bibliographical guide to the literature on the Scottish Enlightenment yet produced.

2. Nicholas Phillipson, 'Towards a Definition of the Scottish Enlightenment', in *City and Society in the 18th Century*, edited by Paul Fritz and David Williams (Toronto, 1973), pp. 125–47 (p. 125).

3. I assume here that the Enlightenment was primarily an urban cultural form. On this point see Roger Emerson, 'The Enlightenment and Social Structures', in *City and Society*, pp. 99–124 (p. 99).

4. Here I echo Roger Emerson; see his 'Natural Philosophy, Scientism and the Problem of the Scottish Enlightenment', *Studies on Voltaire and the Eighteenth Century*, 242 (1986), 243–91. One writer who has acknowledged the importance of science in the Scottish Enlightenment is Anand Chitnis in his *The Scottish Enlightenment: A Social History* (London, 1976).

5. Emerson, 'Enlightenment and Social Structures', p. 112. As Professor Emerson's more recent work indicates, he would no longer characterize the Aberdeen enlightenment in this way.

6. Thomas Reid, 'An Essay on Quantity; occasioned by reading a Treatise, in which Simple and Compound Ratio's are applied to Virtue and Merit'. *Philosophical Transactions of the Royal Society of London*, 45 (1748), 505–20; John Gregory, *A Comparative View of the State and Faculties of Man with Those of the Animal World* (London, 1765); John Stewart, *Sir Isaac Newton's Two Treatises of the Quadrature of Curves, and Analysis by Equations of an Infinite Number of Terms, explained* (London, 1745).

7. R. S. Rait, *The Universities of Aberdeen: A History* (Aberdeen, 1895), p. 289.

8. Christine M. Shepherd, 'Newtonianism in Scottish Universities in the Seventeenth Century', in *The Origins and Nature of the Scottish Enlightenment*, edited by R. H. Campbell and Andrew S. Skinner (Edinburgh, 1982), pp. 62–85 (pp. 66, 78); *idem*, 'Philosophy and Science in the Arts Curriculum of the Scottish Universities in the 17th Century' (unpublished Ph.D. dissertation, University of Edinburgh, 1974), pp. 243–59, 288–93. See also John L. Russell, 'Cosmological Teaching in the Seventeenth-Century Scottish Universities', *Journal for the History of Astronomy*, 5 (1974), 122–32, 145–54.

9. Betty Ponting, 'Mathematics at Aberdeen: Developments, Characters and Events, 1495–1717', *Aberdeen University Review*, 48 (1979–80), 26–35 (p. 27). There were instruments of this kind in the college, as a catalogue from 1670 shows; Ponting, 'Mathematics', p. 30.

10. Between 1697 and 1701 an observatory was built in the north wing of the old college building, but for reasons which remain unclear no instruments were installed in the new structure; see AUL (Aberdeen University Library) MS M. 114, p. 2335, and for financial accounts dating from 1696 and 1699, M. 361/1/1.

11. Rait, *Universities*, pp. 291–92; *Fasti Academiae Mariscallanae Aberdonensis*, edited by Peter John Anderson, 3. vols. (Aberdeen, 1889–98), II, 55.

12. *Fasti*, II, 43, 55; McKail must have agreed to teach part of the proposed course of experimental philosophy, as the published 'Proposals' note that the Professor of Medicine would share in the lecturing; see AUL MS 3017/10/18/2. Moreover, McKail was one of the two university representatives who lobbied the Commissioners of Supply of Aberdeenshire; AUL MS M. 361/1/4.

13. Colin Maclaurin, 'Tractatus de Curvarum Constructione & Mensura; ubi plurimae series Curvarum Infinitae vel rectis mensurantur vel ad simpliciores Curvas reducuntur', and 'Nova Methodus Universalis Curvas Omnes cujuscunque Ordinis Mechanicae describendi sola datorum Angulorum & Rectarum Ope', *Philosophical Transactions of the Royal Society of London*, 30 (1717–19), 803–12, 939–45; *idem, Geometria Organica; sive, descriptio Linearum curvarum universalis* (London, 1720).

14. See Colin Maclaurin to Edmond Halley, 9 December 1720, in *The Collected Letters of Colin Maclaurin*, edited by Stella Mills (Nantwich, 1982), p. 166.

15. Colin Maclaurin to I. Spreull, 30 March 1719, *Collected Letters*, pp. 8–11 (p. 8). For his involvement in the purchase of instruments for the college, see below.

16. For Turnbull's biography, see James McCosh, *The Scottish Philosophy, Biographical, Expository, Critical, from Hutcheson to Hamilton* (London, 1875), pp. 95–106. Turnbull's membership of the Rankenian Club is discussed in M. A. Stewart, 'Berkeley and the Rankenian Club', *Hermathena*, 139 (1985), 25–45 (pp. 31–34). Edited versions of Turnbull's letters to Molesworth are published in *Historical Manuscripts Commission Reports, Various Collections*, 8 (London, 1913), pp. 343–44, 352, 360–61.

17. George Turnbull, *De Scientiae naturalis cum Philosophia morali conjunctione* (Aberdeen, 1723), pp. 3–4; Sir Isaac Newton, *Opticks: or, A Treatise of the Reflections, Refractions, Inflections and Colours of Light*, fourth edition (London, 1730; New York, 1952), p. 405.

18. L. L. Laudan, 'Thomas Reid and the Newtonian Turn of British Methodological Thought', in *The Methodological Heritage of Newton*, edited by Robert E. Butts and John W. Davis (Toronto and Oxford, 1970), pp. 103–31.

19. See, for example, 'A Brief Account of the Nature, Progress and Origin of Philosophy delivered by the late Mr. David Fordyce P. P. Marish. Col. Abdn. to his Scholars before they begun [sic] their Philosophical Course. Anno 1743/4', AUL MS 184, especially fols. 1ʳ-2ᵛ, 22ᵛ-23ᵛ, 26ʳ.

20. On the early courses of experimental philosophy, see M. Rowbottom 'The Teaching of Experimental Philosophy in England, 1700–1730', in *Actes*

du XIᵉ Congrès International d'Histoire des Sciences, 6 vols. (Warsaw, 1968), IV, 46–53.

21. AUL MSS M 361/1/2 and 3, M 361/11/2, and M 387/13/9.

22. Colin Maclaurin to Edmond Halley, 9 December 1720, *Collected Letters*, p. 166.

23. See, for example, the appeal in 1726 for more funds to be used to augment salaries and repair the college buildings: AUL MS 387/10/2. By the late 1730s, the college fabric was in a ruinous state of disrepair. The faculty launched a public appeal for money, to which, significantly, the government contributed little: *Fasti*, I, 423–26.

24. Public subscriptions for funds to purchase scientific instruments had been launched in King's College Aberdeen and Glasgow *c*. 1710, and St. Andrews in 1714. See pp. 45–46 above and note 39; Peter Swinbank, 'Experimental Science in the University of Glasgow at the Time of Joseph Black', in *Joseph Black, 1728–1799: A Commemorative Symposium*, edited by A. D. C. Simpson (Edinburgh, 1982), pp. 23–35 (pp. 30–31); R. G. Cant, *The University of St. Andrews: A Short History* (Edinburgh and London, 1970), p. 83.

25. A copy of the 'Proposals' survives in AUL MS 3017/10/18/2. The text is also printed in *Fasti*, I, pp. 410–11.

26. AUL MS M 361/1/4; *Fasti*, I, 408–10.

27. 'Instructions to Mr Blackwell [the younger] at London', 26 July 1726, AUL MS 387/10/2, fol. 1ᵛ.

28. Entry for 12 June 1733, in 'Minutes of Marischal College 1729–1790', AUL MS M 41, fol 3ᵛ. At this meeting, the faculty agreed to adopt the professorial system, and William Duff was appointed Professor of Natural Philosophy. However, they were forced to reverse their decision in June 1734 because of action by McKail's successor, Francis Skene; see 'Minutes of Marischal', fols. 5ʳ-8ʳ. Another source of funding for the maintenance and purchase of experimental hardware was the gifts made by graduating classes. Contributions were made in 1726, 1727, 1728, 1733, 1744, 1747, 1754, 1755, and 1756; *Fasti*, II, 300–2, 306, 314, 316, 321–23.

29. 'Minutes of Marischal', fol. 34ʳ.

30. On Copland, see above, page 51 and the references cited there. Skene's expenditures are detailed in AUL MS M. 361/1/5, 6, and 10.

31. For details of Bower's chequered career, see 'King's College Minutes 1700–1706', AUL MS K 39, pp. 41–45, 56; 'King's College Minutes 1709–1714', AUL MS K 40, fols 9ʳ and 10ʳ; and AUL MS K 34, p. 72 (a biographical sketch by Thomas Gordon). Archibald Pitcairne actively cultivated interest on Bower's behalf when Bower had designs on the Liddell Chair at Marischal; see Archibald Pitcairne to the Earl of Mar, 16 May 1706, in *The best of our owne: Letters of Archibald Pitcairne, 1652–1713*, edited by W. T. Johnston (Edinburgh, 1979), pp. 43–44.

32. 'Proposals For Buying Mathematical Instruments for the Use of the Kings College of Aberdeen', Scottish Record Office, Mar and Kellie MSS, GD 124/15/966/2. In the 'Proposals' Bower said that he planned to open his course to subscribers. I am grateful to Roger Emerson for drawing Bower's 'Proposals' to my attention, and for suggesting that they date from *c*. 1710.

33. 'King's College Minutes 1716–1722', AUL MS K 41.

34. 'King's College Minutes 1733–1754', AUL MS K 43, p. 62.

35. Cosmo Innes, *Fasti Aberdonenses: Selections from the Records of the University and King's College of Aberdeen, 1494–1854* (Aberdeen, 1854), pp. 206–7.

36. Although Rait was appointed Professor of Mathematics in October 1732, he switched to the post of Regent in 1733 and taught the normal arts curriculum; see Thomas Gordon's remarks in AUL MS K 34, p. 72, and Innes, *Fasti*, pp. lxxxvii, 446. The account books show that Rait was using the college's instruments in his teaching; see the 'Procuration Accounts, 1717–53', AUL MS K 57, accounts for 1743–44, p. 8.

37. [Alexander Gerard], *Plan of Education in the Marischal College and University of Aberdeen, with the Reasons of it* (Aberdeen, 1755), pp. 32–33.

38. [Gerard], *Plan*, pp. 30–31.

39. [Gerard], *Plan*, pp. 26–27.

40. *Abstract of some Statutes and Orders of King's College in Old Aberdeen, M.DCC.LIII. With Additions M.DCC.LIV* (Aberdeen, 1754), p. 13.

41. P. B. Wood, 'Thomas Reid, Natural Philosopher: A Study of Science and Philosophy in the Scottish Enlightenment' (unpublished Ph.D. dissertation, University of Leeds, 1984), pp. 69–74.

42. The King's faculty made a point of the freedom each regent enjoyed in organizing his courses: *Abstract*, p. 19. See also *Abstract*, pp. 11–12, for the faculty's defence of the regenting system.

43. Compare Reid's treatment of optics in his lectures with those of Thomas Gordon and Roderick Macleod: 'Notes of a Course of Lectures delivered at King's College, Aberdeen, during [the] Session 1757–58', AUL MS K 160, pp. 286–324 (the lectures break off incomplete); 'Notes from the Natural Philosophy Course of Thomas Gordon taken by Alexander Thomson', AUL MS K 167, pp. 667 ff; 'Notes on Natural Philosophy by Robert Eden Scott from the Lectures of Roderick Macleod, 1783–84', AUL MS K 173, pp. 101–60. For Dunbar's lectures see AUL MS K 237, especially pp. 7–8.

44. See the notes taken by Alexander Robertson *c*. 1777 in AUL MS K 168.

45. Robert Eden Scott, 'The Elements of General Natural History for the Semi-Class 1795–6', AUL MS K 182.

46. Two sets of notes from Francis Skene's lectures survive: William Patterson, 'An Abridgement of Natural History For the use of the Students in the Marischal College Aberdeen January 1st 1768', AUL MS M. 177, and 'A Concise System of Natural History being yᵉ Substance of a Course of Lectures delivered by Prof. Francis Skene, in yᵉ Marischal College 1775', AUL MS M 208.

47. 'Institutes of Natural History', AUL MS M 189. These notes were taken by William Knight in the 1799–1800 session.

48. Compare the organization of Beattie's and Scott's lectures with that of Walker's natural history course; see John Walker, *Lectures on Geology [sic]*, edited by Harold W. Scott (Chicago and London, 1966). Scott spent a brief period in Edinburgh in the mid-1780s. Significantly, a copy of Walker's lectures survives among the papers of Thomas Gordon and Robert Eden Scott recently discovered in the University of Aberdeen; see AUL MS 3107/6/5.

49. *Abstract*, p. 13; for similar sentiments expressed by the Marischal faculty, see [Gerard], *Plan*, p. 7.

50. AUL MS 2131/6/IV/1. fol. 2^r.

51. It should be noted, however, that at King's College the teaching of astronomy shifted to the magistrand year; see the 'Notes from the Natural Philosophy Course of Thomas Gordon', AUL MS K 167 (in which the astronomy lectures begin on 1 November 1773, that is, the beginning of the session), and Robert Eden Scott's 'Notes on Moral Philosophy and Astronomy. . . .from the lectures of Roderick Macleod', AUL MS K 172 (which date from 1784–85).

52. *Abstract*, pp. 20–21.

53. 'King's College Minutes 1789–1800', AUL MS K 48, fol. 26^r.

54. Douglas's description of the museum is quoted in James W. H. Trail, 'Natural Science in the Aberdeen Universities', in *Studies in the History and Development of the University of Aberdeen: A Quatercentenary Tribute paid by certain of her Professors and of her Devoted Sons*, edited by P. J. Anderson (Aberdeen, 1906), pp. 147–200 (p. 158).

55. AUL MS 3061/25, p. 10; J. M. Bulloch, *A History of the University of Aberdeen, 1495–1895* (Aberdeen, 1895), p. 159.

56. Rait, *Universities*, pp. 206–7. Chalmers announced his lectures and his plan for an anatomical collection and museum at a faculty meeting held on 24 November 1792; see 'King's College Minutes 1789–1800', fols. 32^r–33^r.

57. 'King's College Minutes 1770–1789', AUL MS K 47, p. 183.

58. For the purchase of scientific instruments using donations, see the 'Statistical Account of the University and King's College of Aberdeen', in *The Statistical Account of Scotland 1791–1799*, edited by Sir John Sinclair, 20 vols. (Wakefield, 1983), I, 282.

59. AUL MS M 111, pp. 197–98; M 361/1/5-8; 'Minutes of Marischal College', fol. 50^r.

60. On the origins of Marischal's museum, see the faculty minutes for December 1765 and January 1766, 'Minutes of Marischal College', fol. 65^{r-v}. A brief description of the museum is included in the 'Historical Account and Present State of the Marischal College and University of Aberdeen', in *Statistical Account*, I, 328–29.

61. In 1780 the Rev. Robert Memis of Stonehaven gained the support of the Marischal faculty in his attempt to found a botanical garden, though a minute from 1782 indicates that the garden had yet to be established. Then, in September 1785, the faculty again discussed laying out a botanical garden, noting that the plants had already been obtained from the Royal Botanical Gardens in London and Edinburgh. This time they resolved to act: 'Minutes of Marischal College', fols. 82^v, 88^r, 91^{r-v}. See also Trail, 'Natural Science', pp. 160–61. Marischal College acquired a number of plants from John Hope in 1786; see the list entitled 'Botanical Plants for the College Garden received from Dr Hope Edin^r 1786, AUL MS 3017/10/30.

62. *Fasti*, I, 448, 451–52. On Copland's teaching career more generally, see John S. Reid, 'Patrick Copland 1748–1822: Aspects of His Life and Times at Marischal College', *Aberdeen University Review*, 50 (1984), 359–79.

63. On the observatory, see John S. Reid, 'The Castlehill Observatory, Aberdeen', *Journal of the History of Astronomy*, 13 (1982), 84–96.

64. *Fasti*, I, 448, 450.

65. 'Minutes of Marischal College', fols. 89ᵛ-90ʳ; *Fasti*, I, 461–67; George Campbell to Barbara Black, 1 February 1793, and a statement delivered by George French to the faculty at Marischal, dated 11 November 1793, in 'Dr. George French's Papers 1767–1830', AUL MS 52. See also Alexander Findlay, *The Teaching of Chemistry in the Universities of Aberdeen* (Aberdeen, 1935), pp. 4–16.

66. Ella Hill Burton Rodger, *Aberdeen Doctors at Home and Abroad: The Narrative of a Medical School* (Edinburgh and London, 1893), pp. 61–63.

67. AUL MSS 2131/6/1/17 and 7/V/6. For further details on the Club see Wood, 'Thomas Reid', pp. 43–45.

68. [David Fordyce], *Dialogues Concerning Education* (London, 1745), pp. 63–70.

69. Stewart succeeded Maclaurin as Professor of Mathematics in 1727. Reid was Librarian at Marischal from 1733 to 1736. Fordyce graduated in 1728, and then studied divinity. Ramsay of Ochtertyre states that while he was Librarian, Reid attended some of Fordyce's sermons; see *Scotland and Scotsmen in the Eighteenth Century from the Mss. of John Ramsay*, edited by A. Allardyce, 2 vols. (Edinburgh and London, 1888), I, 294. In a letter to an unidentified London correspondent written *c*. 1737, Reid introduced Fordyce as someone visiting the metropolis to 'See men and things': Reid to ?, *c*, 1737. AUL MS 2131/3/III/7, fol. 1ʳ.

70. AUL MS 2131/6/1/17, fol. 1ʳ.

71. Sir William Forbes, *An Account of the Life and Writings of James Beattie, LL.D.* (London, 1824), pp. 13–14. Among the members of this club was the Hutchinsonian, John Skinner. It is conceivable, therefore, that the validity of natural theology and the theological implications of Newtonianism were debated.

72. AUL MS 37, fol. 1ʳ; see also fol. 167ʳ⁻ᵛ for another draft.

73. 'Minute Book of the farming club at Gordon's Mill 1758', AUL MS 49, pp. 34–35. On the Farming Club, see J. H. Smith, *The Gordon's Mill Farming Club, 1758–1764* (Edinburgh and London, 1962).

74. 'Reflexions on the Principles of Agriculture', AUL MS f. 2206–40, p. 1.

75. Most of Gregory's 'Reflexions' is taken up with this question.

76. 'Minute book of the farming club', pp. 122, 140, 231; W. R. Humphries, 'The Philosopher, The Farmer and Commercial Education', *Scottish Educational Journal*, 14 May 1937, pp. 619–20, 21 May 1937, pp. 661–63 (on Reid's book keeping scheme).

77. On the Aberdeen Philosophical Society see James Valentine, 'A Society of Aberdeen Philosophers One Hundred Years Ago', *Macmillans Magazine*, 8 (1863), 436–44; McCosh, *The Scottish Philosophy*, pp. 227–29; and W. R. Humphries, 'The First Aberdeen Philosophical Society', *Transactions of the Aberdeen Philosophical Society*, 5 (1938), 203–38; Stephen A. Conrad, 'Citizenship and Common Sense: The Problem of Authority in the Social Background and Social Philosophy of the Wise Club of Aberdeen' (unpublished Ph.D. dissertation, Harvard University, 1980). A slightly revised version of Dr. Conrad's dissertation is to be published by the Garland Press.

78. A similar point can be made about the Glasgow Literary Society, which also canvassed a broad range of subjects. Neither of these societies is discussed in James E. McClellan III's *Science Reorganized: Scientific Societies in the Eighteenth Century* (New York, 1985). The distinction McClellan draws between scientific societies and learned societies is unfortunate, for it helps to obscure the place of science in enlightenment culture and tends to marginalize societies like those in Aberdeen and Glasgow.

79. D. D. McElroy, *Scotland's Age of Improvement: A Survey of Eighteenth-Century Literary Clubs and Societies* (Pullman, 1969), pp. 47, 48; Daniel Roche, *Le Siècle des Lumières: Académies et Académiciens Provinciaux, 1680–1789*, 2 vols. (Paris and La Haye, 1978); on the Manchester Literary and Philosophical Society, see Arnold Thackray, 'Natural Knowledge in Cultural Context: The Manchester Model', *American Historical Review*, 79 (1974), 672–709.

80. George Skene was elected a member on 8 September 1761, but was not formally admitted until 9 November 1762. Another figure who was active in the later years of the club was William Traill, who succeeded John Stewart as the Marischal Professor of Mathematics in 1766. Traill proposed a number of questions on scientific topics and discoursed on various mathematical subjects.

81. My calculations are based on an analysis of the minute books of the Society; see AUL MSS 539/1 and 2. The questions proposed for discussion are usefully listed in McCosh, *The Scottish Philosophy*, appendix III, and Humphries, 'First Aberdeen Philosophical Society', pp. 219–28.

82. McCosh, *The Scottish Philosophy*, appendix III, questions 6, 20, 26, and 121.

83. McCosh, *The Scottish Philosophy*, appendix III, questions 5, 10, 11, 19, 24, 29, 59, 61, 68, 71, 76, 79, 84, 96, 103, 106, 109, 113, 118, and 126.

84. McCosh, *The Scottish Philosophy*, appendix III, questions 9, 16, 41, 100, and 119; Traill's was question 9. For the preparations by the Royal Society, see Harry Woolf, *The Transits of Venus: A Study of Eighteenth-Century Science* (Princeton, 1959), p. 72.

85. AUL MSS 539/1, fol 24[r], and 2131/2/I/7, fol 1[r].

86. See Wood, 'Thomas Reid', p. 54, and the references cited there.

87. Complete texts of these discourses survive in AUL MS 480/1. For a useful guide to Skene's surviving contributions to the Wise Club, see Bernhard Fabian, 'David Skene and the Aberdeen Philosophical Society', *Bibliotheck*, 5 (1967–70), 81–99.

88. Thus George Campbell, who is not known for his scientific interests, posed a question on the theory of generation in 1758; see McCosh, *The Scottish Philosophy*, appendix III, question 10.

89. AUL MS 539/1, fol 4[r].

90. The one club which remained active in the late-eighteenth century was the Aberdeen Musical Society. University men were also extremely active in this group. For the minutes of the Society for the post-1770 period, see 'Minute Book, Aberdeen Musical Society 1770–1838', Aberdeen Public Library MS LO 780. 6 AB3. On the Society more generally, see David Johnson, *Music*

and *Society in Lowland Scotland in the Eighteenth Century* (London, 1972), pp. 14, 43–44.

91. My account of the Medical Society in what follows is based on Rodger, *Aberdeen Doctors*, pp. 54–70.

92. I owe this point to Roger Emerson.

93. For Ogilvie's involvement with the Union proposals, see Walter Robson Humphries, *William Ogilvie and the Projected Union of the Colleges, 1786–1787* (Aberdeen, 1940).

94. Copland's activities are described in John S. Reid, 'Patrick Copland 1748–1822: Connections outside the College Courtyard', *Aberdeen University Review*, 51 (1985), 226–50.

95. The seminal study of this theme is J. B. Morrell, 'Professors Robison and Playfair, and the *Theophobia Gallica*: Natural Philosophy, Religion and Politics in Edinburgh, 1789–1815', *Notes and Records of the Royal Society of London*, 26 (1971), 43–63.

96. AUL MS 3107/5/3/4, pp. 10–14 (p. 11).

97. Scott, 'Elements of General Natural History', insert before p. 16, dated 1798.

98. See especially Emerson, 'Natural Philosophy'.

4
CHEMICAL REACTIVITY AND HEAT IN THE EIGHTEENTH CENTURY

David V. Fenby

Introduction

In his 1959 Rede Lecture, C. P. Snow, commenting upon the criticism that scientists are illiterate, stated:

> Once or twice I have been provoked and have asked the company how many of them could describe the Second Law of Thermodynamics. The response was cold: it was also negative. Yet I was asking something which is about the scientific equivalent of: Have you read a work of Shakespeare's?[1]

This makes an appropriate introduction to my essay for two reasons: first, the perspective that I am going to present will be that of a physical scientist, and, secondly, I shall refer to thermodynamics.

In 1845 William Thomson (1824–1907), later Lord Kelvin, went to Paris for some postgraduate studies, having matriculated into the University of Glasgow at the age of ten and later studied at Cambridge. Paris was important in Thomson's career because it was there that his outlook was extended beyond the mathematical and theoretical, largely through his experimental work with Regnault. While in France,[2] Thomson came across a reference[3] to a work by Sadi Carnot (1796–1832), *Réflexions sur la Puissance Motrice du Feu et sur les Machines Propres à Développer cette Puissance*,[4] which had been published in 1824. He searched Paris for a copy, but without success. In 1848 Thomson was sent this book, which he later described as 'an epoch-making gift to science'.[5] During the next few years Thomson, Clausius, Joule, Helmholtz, Rankine and others established thermodynamics as we know it today. This and Clerk Maxwell's electromagnetic theory were the pinnacles of nineteenth-century physical science; they were, in that century, as revolutionary as the quantum and relativity theories of this century.

Industrialisation was the predominant social factor in nineteenth-century Europe, and in an industrialised society the important concepts are work, energy, power. This is the province of thermodynamics. Carnot's starting point was a simple but highly relevant question: what is the maximum work obtainable from a heat engine? He made use of an analogy: the maximum work obtainable from a waterfall depends on the quantity of water and the height through which it falls; the maximum work obtainable from a heat engine depends on the quantity of caloric and the temperature drop through which it falls. In his *Réflexions*, Carnot assumed that heat was a material, *caloric*, and that it was conserved.

The link between the development of thermodynamics and the heat engine is an important instance of the influence of the Scottish Enlightenment, and, in particular, of James Watt (1736–1819), on nineteenth-century physical science, but it is not one that I propose to pursue; this has been done by Cardwell.[6] In the latter part of the nineteenth century and early twentieth century came the application of thermodynamics to chemistry, with the studies of Gibbs, Nernst and others. Chemical thermodynamics enables us to make predictions about chemical reactivity and reaction yields. It can, for example, answer questions such as: can nitrogen and hydrogen react to form ammonia and, if so, what yields of ammonia can be obtained under various experimental conditions? To do so we require the heat capacities, latent heats and certain heats of reaction of each of the three chemical species (nitrogen, hydrogen, ammonia). These properties are measured using instruments called *calorimeters*. And so we have a link between chemical thermodynamics and Joseph Black (1728–99), who introduced the concepts of heat capacity and latent heat, and pioneered calorimetry. Chemical thermodynamics, and indeed thermodynamics in general, relates the properties of *bulk* matter. No underlying molecular model is assumed. Consequently, thermodynamics can predict, but it cannot explain; for example, it can tell us that nitrogen and hydrogen can react to form ammonia, but it cannot tell us why. Explanation, in terms of some assumed molecular model, is the business of another branch of physical science called statistical mechanics. This is an extension of the kinetic theory of gases, which was developed in the second half of the nineteenth century by Clerk Maxwell, Boltzmann and others. Given certain properties of the nitrogen, hydrogen and ammonia *molecules*, we can both predict chemical reactivity and understand this in terms of the molecular properties.

I have glanced at the development of thermodynamics and I have indicated two quite different approaches to questions concerning chemical reactivity: the thermodynamic approach, where one deals only with the observable properties of bulk matter, and the statistical mechanical approach, where one deals with molecular properties. In this essay, I consider theoretical approaches to chemical reactivity in the eighteenth century.

First Half of the Eighteenth Century

My starting point is the traditional one in studies of eighteenth-century science: Isaac Newton (1642–1727), and, in particular, the Queries appended to the Third Book of his *Opticks*,[7] first published in 1704. Priestley saw this collection of negative questions as evidence of Newton's 'bold and eccentric thoughts'.[8] The seventeenth century had witnessed 'The Mechanization of the World Picture';[9] as part of this, the Scholastic view of matter was replaced by mechanical models: the matter-extension equality of Descartes, the Epicurean atomism of Gassendi, the corpuscular philosophy of Boyle. Newton accepted a particulate world: 'it seems probable to me, that God in the Beginning form'd Matter in solid, massy, hard, impenetrable, moveable particles' and that changes in the material world arise from 'the various Separations and new Associations and Motions of these permanent Particles' (Query 31).[10] But to a mechanical picture centred on the sizes, shapes, configurations and motions of particles, Newton added a new variable: interparticulate forces:

> Have not the small Particles of Bodies certain Powers, Virtues, or Forces, by which they act at a distance. . .upon one another for producing a great Part of the Phaenomena of Nature? (Query 31)[11]

As well as short-range attractive forces between particles, Newton proposed longer-range repulsive forces, claiming that 'where Attraction ceases, there a repulsive Virtue ought to succeed' (Query 31).[12] Already in his *Principia*, Newton had derived Boyle's law by assuming repulsive forces between gaseous particles.

In support of his dynamic corpuscular model of matter, Newton used it to explain qualitatively a range of experimental facts: light phenomena, capillarity, vaporization, and, of particular interest in the present context, chemical changes. In Query 31[13] Newton interpreted many chemical phenomena in terms of his model: the ability of certain salt crystals to absorb moisture from the atmosphere arises from an attraction between salt and water particles; the temperature rise when water and concentrated sulphuric acid are mixed arises from a strong attraction between the unlike particles which causes them to accelerate towards one another, with some violence, this producing a motion which causes the sensation of heat: 'the sharp and pungent Tastes of Acids arise from the strong Attraction whereby the acid Particles rush upon and agitate the Particles of the Tongue' (Query 31);[14] and so on.

The problem for Newton's followers, and, indeed, the problem for many today, is that of the quantification of the dynamic corpuscular model; to derive, from the phenomena, quantitative information concerning the particles and the forces between them.[15] In the first four decades of the eighteenth century there were attempts to carry out such a programme in chemistry (by John Keill, David Gregory's student, and John Freind) and in physiology (by Archibald Pitcairne, Richard Mead, George Cheyne, John Freind and James Keill). Such exercises in Newtonian reductionism led to no quantitative successes. The underlying model, while not being rejected, was perceived as being sterile; this mode of scientific interpretation came to be seen as beyond the means then available.

In the 1717–18 edition of *Opticks*, Newton introduced eight new Queries (numbered 17–24 in reference 10) in which he speculates about an aether. Newton's aether, being extremely rare and elastic, expands through all space, including the interstices between the ultimate particles in matter. While stating that he does not know what the aether is, Newton does mention the possibility that it is made up of mutually repelling particles, which are very much smaller than those of air or even than those of light. For a particular dense body, the aether density was assumed to be least within the body and to increase with increasing distance from the body. Gravity arises from the tendency of all bodies to move from larger to smaller aether densities. Newton also used the aether to account for the reflections and refractions of light and other optical phenomena, for heat transfer, for vision and for animal motion.[16] The aetherial speculations were vague and even self-contradictory, and they were largely ignored until the 1740s.[7,15] Thereafter, they became most significant, as material causes replaced mechanical explanations in the mid and late eighteenth century. According to Newton, light can heat bodies by 'putting their parts into a vibratory motion wherein heat consists' (Query 5).[17] For Newton, as for Bacon and Boyle, heat was mechanical, arising from movements of the constituent particles.

For Herman Boerhaave (1668–1738), fire was a substance. His views are most important because of his enormous influence, exerted through both his teaching and his writing. The medical school at the University of Leyden, in which he was the outstanding luminary for many years, attracted students in large numbers from other countries: during his thirty-year tenure at Leyden, there were 659 British students in the medical school;[18] Edinburgh's medical school, founded in 1726, was modelled on that in Leyden, and the five men who initially made up the Medical Faculty had been taught by Boerhaave. (Lindeboom[19] discussed Boerhaave's influence in Great Britain.) His text on chemistry enjoyed great popularity from its first appearance, in an unauthorised edition, in 1724 until towards the end of the eighteenth century. Cullen and Black recommended it to their students, 'especialy [*sic*] on the Subject of Heat'.[20]

In a long section entitled 'Of Fire' in his chemistry text, Boerhaave attempted to uncover the nature of fire from its effects, these being heat, light, colour, expansion, burning. He concluded that fire is 'that unknown thing which has the property of penetrating all solid and fluid bodies, and dilating them so as to take up more space';[21] fire was the cause of expansion. It is 'diffused thro' all spaces and bodies, [and] is continually in motion';[22] within bodies it occupies the interstices between the ultimate particles, but it cannot penetrate these particles. Boerhaave envisaged a balance of forces in all bodies; the particles of matter attract one another, but the presence of fire introduces a repulsive force. Fire is conserved; it is 'the great changer of all things in the universe, whilst itself remains wholly unchangeable'.[23] Heat is caused by the motion of fire. An important, but puzzling and controversial aspect of Boerhaave's fire was its equal distribution in all bodies and throughout all space at the same temperature. He invoked this to account for thermal equilibrium (i.e., the fact that all bodies in the same environment attain the same temperature), and he supported his conclusion with the results of mixing experiments carried out by Fahrenheit; Black later re-interpreted the latter in terms of heat capacities. Boerhaave's fire was made up of particles very much smaller than those of ordinary matter, this accounting for the ease with which it passes through matter. (The origins of Boerhaave's conception of fire have been considered by Metzger[24] and by Love.[25] The views of Boerhaave's Dutch contemporaries, 'sGravesande and Musschenbroek, and the earlier materiality of fire proposed by Nieuwentyt have been outlined by Schofield.[26]) Boerhaave's attitude in talking about chemical change was ambivalent. In discussing general phenomena, such as effervescence or solubility, he presents a Newtonian picture of interacting particles. The chemist makes use of various 'instruments'; one of these is fire, which is able to penetrate all bodies, thereby increasing the repulsions between the constituent particles, while the fire particles themselves remain unchanged. In discussing the specifics of practical chemistry, however, Boerhaave largely abandons reference to interacting particles in favour of a taxonomic approach; classification, based on the bulk behaviour of matter, is preferred to *ad hoc* interpretations in terms of particles.

In Britain in the 1740s there occurred a major change in the basis of scientific interpretation; material causes replaced the interacting particle model. The reasons for this, analysed by Schofield,[27] include a growing disenchantment with the dynamic corpuscular approach, Dutch influences, and the impact of Linnaeus's *Systema Naturae* (1735), with its taxonomy based on observable characteristics. A revival of Newton's aether was a significant aspect of this methodological change, and in this Bryan Robinson (1680–1754), an Irish doctor and professor, was to the fore. In 1743 and 1745 he published widely influential works on Newton's aether.

For Robinson, the aether was 'a very general material Cause [and] no Doubt can be made of its Existence'.[28] Ordinary matter by itself was assumed inert, all natural phenomena arising from the presence of aether. Robinson used it to explain gravitation, capillarity, repulsion, elasticity, optical phenomena, heat, expansion, phase changes, muscular motion, sensation, cohesion, fermentation; it was indeed a universal cause. Following Newton's lead, Robinson's explanations were based on changes and differences in aether densities. '*Heat in Bodies consists in a vibrating Motion of their Parts, excited by a vibrating Motion of the* Aether *within the Bodies*',[29] and the 'Degree of Heat in a Body, is proportional to the Strength of the vibrating Motion of the *Aether* between its Parts'.[30] In a body there are two opposing forces between its particles: a cohesion, arising from aether density differences, and a repulsion, arising from heat (i.e., from aetherial vibrations). The body will be solid, liquid or gas according to the relative strengths of these opposing forces, and, in this way, heat causes phase changes. Robinson expressed his aetherial explanations in mathematical form but, as many of his variables were experimentally inaccessible, his equations were not quantitatively useful. The aether, according to Robinson, is made up of tiny particles which repel one another. What causes these repulsions? It is 'Spirit, which intercedes the Particles of Aether, and gives them a repulsive Power',[31] and, since aether pervades all space, so must 'Spirit'.

In 1747 William Cullen (1710–90) was appointed the first Lecturer in Chemistry at the University of Glasgow; in 1756 he succeeded Plummer as Professor of Medicine and Chemistry in the University of Edinburgh. His successor in both positions was his pupil, Joseph Black (1728–99).

Cullen's presentation of chemistry was that of an independent science, possessing both wide applicability and a theoretical base. His chemical investigations and doctrines have been fully discussed by Donovan.[32] In his chemistry courses, Cullen separated his discussion of chemicals and their reactions from his discussion of the *causes* of chemical change, his 'philosophical chemistry'. In the former, he was a disciple of Linnaeus using a taxonomic approach; in the latter, he rejected a dynamic corpuscular approach, and, with acknowledgement to Newton and Robinson, accepted aether as the basis of causation in his chemistry and medicine. Christie has concluded that, 'Cullen's philosophical chemistry can be described as conforming with some precision to the work of Hume and Smith'.[33]

Cullen was interested in explaining chemical reactivity and the states of matter. With the former, the problem was to account for its selective and preferential nature. In August 1718, Geoffroy presented to the Académie Royale des Sciences a table in which various classes of chemical substances were systematically arranged according to their relative reactivities.[34] This so-called *affinity table* and those that followed were important in eighteenth-century chemistry; they summarised many chemical reactions and predicted others. Such tables were empirical; the underlying assumption in presenting them was that chemical reactivity depends only on the substances involved and not on other experimental conditions. Towards the end of the eighteenth century, this assumption was shown to be incorrect, and the use of affinity tables declined. Cullen made use of Geoffroy's table in his teaching, and both he and Black introduced diagrams to depict relative reactivities.

At first, Cullen's explanations were based on the interplay of two opposing forces in matter: a cohesive force, arising from attractions between the particles of ordinary matter; and a repulsive force, arising from repulsions between the aether particles permeating matter. (The aether appears to have been identified with fire, while heat and light were produced by aetherial vibrations.) The relative magnitudes of the two forces were related to the relative densities of the ordinary and aether particles, and would depend on the material and its temperature. A substance was solid, liquid or gas according to whether the cohesive force was greater than, equal to or less than the repulsive force. The interaction between two substances depended on the relative magnitudes of the various forces involved. The problem, as always, was that of quantification. If the model was to be useful in explaining chemical reactivity, Cullen had to find some way of obtaining the aether densities in different substances. He measured the temperature changes that occur when various substances are dissolved in water and in other solvents, and compiled tables of his results.[35] These he explained[36] by proposing that two different processes can be involved when substances dissolve: 'mixture', which causes a temperature increase, and 'solution', which causes a temperature decrease. He related these to the 'state of aggregation' of the substance dissolving, and, in turn, related this to aether. The details are not relevant here; what is relevant is Cullen's attempt to use thermometric measurements to quantify his aetherial model, and in a way that centralised the importance of changes of state. Ironically, Cullen's experimental studies of solution reactions inadvertently led to the discovery of another phenomenon, one that was to pose a problem for his solution theory. Cullen described the discovery:

> one of my pupils, whom I had employed to examine the heat or cold that might be produced by the solution of certain substances in spirit of wine, observed to me: That, when a thermometer had been immersed in spirit of wine. . . ; upon taking the thermometer out of the spirit, and suspending it in the air, the mercury in the thermometer. . .always sunk two or three degrees.[37]

A series of experiments using different liquids led to the conclusion that '*the cold produced is the effect of evaporation*'. Cullen also showed that the effect is greater under vacuum, a result that his theory of solution was unable to account for.

Christie[38] has pointed out that there was later a change in Cullen's aetherial speculations. In his new model, ordinary matter was inert and discussion was centred on aether, and, in particular, variations in aether density. A substance was solid, liquid or gas according to whether the external aether density was greater than, equal to or less than the internal aether density. Cullen appears to have envisaged chemical combination as the coming into contact of the reacting particles, each with its own aether atmosphere, to produce a new particle having its own atmosphere. The approach of particles surrounded by aether posed a problem; one would expect a repulsion rather than an attraction. One solution proposed by Cullen was 'fluidity', but the details were not given and 'there was a pronounced degree of confusion'.[39] The promise of this approach, while unfulfilled, is of interest here; it suggested the possibility of quantification in the study of chemical reactivity by measuring the temperature changes accompanying chemical reactions.

Cullen's mid-century chemical studies coincided with Benjamin Franklin's (1706–90) electrical studies.[40] The influence of Franklin's theory of electricity was by no means confined to that science; of relevance here is its impact on Lavoisier and, in particular, on the caloric theory of heat. The essence of Franklin's theory is the concept of charge and its conservation. He proposed that all bodies contain an electric fluid made up of particles; these repel one another but are strongly attracted to the particles of ordinary matter, which are themselves mutually attractive. Any body contains a particular natural quantity of electric fluid, this varying from one substance to another. If more is added or some is removed, the body becomes electrified (i.e., it acquires a charge). This theory was immensely successful because of the wide range of phenomena, including the spectacular, that is explained and the new effects that it predicted. If offered mechanical explanation by coupling a material cause with a conservation principle; this was a feature of other imponderable fluid theories, including the caloric theory, that developed in the second half of the eighteenth century. While clearly drawing on the ideas of Newton, Boerhaave and others, Franklin did not identify his electric fluid with aether or fire. He viewed heat as a fluid analogous to his electric fluid; it is present in all bodies, it is conserved, it imparts a repulsive force between the particles of ordinary matter. He also noted the similarities between electrical and heat conduction, and, while not having invented the terms conductor and non-conductor, he was the first to apply them to heat.[41]

Joseph Black (1728–99)

Joseph Black placed heat at the centre of his chemistry, which he defined as the study of '*the effects produced by heat and by mixture, in all bodies, or mixtures of bodies,. . .with a view to the improvement of arts, and the knowledge of nature*',[42] adding that, 'The Study of Heat is one of the most noble and engaging in Nature [for] t'is this which Animates the whole System of Nature'.[43] In notebooks kept by Black while a student at the University of Glasgow, Robison found 'queries respecting the nature of cooling mixtures, and the cold produced by liquefaction'.[44] Clearly and not surprisingly, Black's early interest in heat derives from Cullen, his teacher. The studies of heat for which Black is renowned were carried out between 1756 and 1766 while he was the second Lecturer in Chemistry and a medical professor at the University of Glasgow. In this work, while the influence of Cullen is evident, there was a significant shift, in both approach and emphasis, from Cullen's programme.

In his courses, Black discussed the rival theories concerning the nature of heat. He was attracted to a material theory: in his 1767/8 course, for example, he claimed that this was in better agreement with the phenomena,[45] and even in Robison's edition of his *Lectures*, where Christie[46] has pointed out that the issue is obscured by editorial bias, there is reference to Cleghorn's material theory as being 'the most probable of any that I know'[47] and the expression 'matter of heat' appears.[48] Of more importance than Black's opinion regarding the cause of heat, however, is his insistence that, irrespective of what it is, heat can be studied and measured from its effects; these he listed as expansion, fluidity, vapour, ignition, combustion. In being willing to forego discussion of the cause while concentrating on observable phenomena, Black was adopting an attitude with respect to heat analogous to those of Galileo, Boyle, and Newton with respect to acceleration, the 'spring of the air', and gravitation, respectively. With Black, heat itself became central, and this was an important change in the focus of attention.

The discovery of latent heat and heat capacity has been discussed by McKie and Heathcote[49] and, more recently, by Guerlac;[50] my comments will be selective. Initially Black was interested in fluidity, this suggesting the influence of Cullen, who had attempted to relate chemical reactivity and fluidity. In discussing the conditions for chemical reaction between two substances, Black stated that 'it is in most cases necessary that one or both be fluid when they are mixed, or that they be rendered fluid, or disposed to fluidity, immediately after'.[51] Fluidity was seen as facilitating contact between reacting particles. While considerations related to chemical reactivity presumably provided Black's point of entry, his studies of heat moved in another direction; he produced a theory of change of state. When ice melts, its temperature does not change and yet it is absorbing heat. Black proposed that this heat, which he called latent heat because it is absorbed without temperature change, is the cause of the melting and that it is retained in the water produced. The water contains sensible heat, which affects a thermometer, and latent heat, which does not. The latter overcomes, to some extent, the attractions between the particles in the ice, and is combined with the particles in water; even in Robison's edition one finds, 'we can hardly avoid thinking [heat] a substance, which may be united with the particles of water, in the same manner as the particles of Glauber's salt are united with them in solution. . . But, since heat has never been observed by us in a separate state, all our notions of this union must be hypothetical'.[52] Black envisaged a specific interaction between the water particles and the latent heat, such that they are combined in some way, but without loss of identity. When water freezes, the latent heat is released. Black later extended the latent heat concept to vaporisation and to substances other than water. In so doing, he produced a theory of change of state; the liquid and vapour states of matter are caused by latent heats.

When a body absorbs heat, its temperature usually increases. Heat capacity is defined as the ratio of the heat input to the temperature rise; it is numerically equal to the heat required to increase the temperature of the body by one degree. Black pointed out that this ratio is a characteristic property of the body, varying from one substance to another. The discovery of heat capacity led Black to clearly distinguish between the intensive and extensive measures of heat, or, to use his terms, between the quality and the quantity of heat. Confusion concerning this distinction had clouded heat studies during the hundred or so years preceding Black. The intensive property is temperature, measured with a thermometer; for Black and his successors, the extensive property was the total quantity of heat in the body. Black introduced methods for measuring latent heats and heat capacities, and hence pioneered the experimental science of calorimetry. His measurements were few and, to some extent, were stimulated by Watt, who appreciated the practical significance of Black's concepts. (I have discussed calorimetry in the second half of the eighteenth century elsewhere.[53])

Unlike Cullen, Black did not attempt to apply his heat researches to a quantitative study of chemical reactivity. He pictured reactions in terms of attractions and repulsions between particles, but rejected the possibility of a quantitative approach based on such a model: 'all the mathematicians in Europe are not qualified to explain a single combination by these means'.[54] Black's approach to chemical reactivity was taxonomic: 'The only explanation to be received of a chemical phenomenon is, to shew that it is a case of a more general phenomenon already known'.[55]

William Irvine (1743–87) and his Followers

William Irvine was Lecturer in Chemistry at the University of Glasgow from 1769 until his death in 1787; he had attended Black's chemistry course and had acted as his research assistant. In the 1770s, Irvine modified Black's work on heat, producing an alternative theory based, as was Black's theory, on measurable properties. The Irvine theory centres on heat capacity, which was assumed proportional to the total quantity of heat. The thermal effects of heat transfers and temperature changes accompanying both chemical reactions and phase changes were assumed to arise entirely from heat capacity changes, and could therefore be calculated from the measured heat capacities of the substances involved; the Irvine theory was a complete thermochemical theory. In it there was no distinction between latent heat and sensible heat; what Black had called latent heat was simply the heat transfer arising from the heat capacity change accompanying the phase change. For this reason, Black, while describing it as 'an ingenious thought, and [one that] gives a very simple and intelligible view of some of the appearances',[56] rejected the Irvine theory; Black wanted latent heat as the cause of the phase change. Irvine, like Black, did not publish his work on heat. His views were edited by his son eighteen years after his death,[57] but, prior to this, others had brought the Irvine theory to the attention of the scientific world, where it had a considerable impact; with its simplicity and wide explanatory power, it was an appealing idea.

Adair Crawford (1748–95), having attended Irvine's chemistry course in 1776/7, used the Irvine theory as the basis of an explanation of animal heat and of combustion. His theory and the initial experimental evidence, obtained at Glasgow in 1777, were published two years later.[58] Criticism of the experimental work led to further measurements in London, and Crawford, while admitting that he had made 'considerable mistakes', maintained that his explanation of animal heat remained unaffected. A second edition of the book, incorporating the new work, appeared in 1788.[59] The animal heat and combustion theories of Crawford and Lavoisier, developed independently at about the same time, are similar. Both assume that oxygen gas contains a great deal of heat, some of which is released when oxygen is converted into carbon dioxide and/or water in respiration and combustion. The two theories differ primarily in the heat transfer mechanisms proposed: for Crawford, following Irvine, all heat transfers arise because of heat capacity differences; Lavoisier believed that heat was chemically involved. Crawford supported his theory with an impressive range of calorimetric measurements; the work shows considerable experimental acumen, but, in certain cases, critical conclusions were based on effects so small as to be insignificant. (The heat capacities of gases obtained in 1812 by Delaroche and Bérard showed that the Crawford theory is untenable.) The details of Crawford's theory and his experimental techniques and results are not relevant here. What is relevant is the impact of Crawford's work at the end of the eighteenth century; unlike Black and Irvine, he did publish his findings. He also had a champion in J. H. de Magellan, a scientific 'intelligencer' living in London at the time. In 1780 Magellan published an *Essai*[60] with the object of elaborating the principles on which Crawford's work was based. This lavishly praises Crawford, but also refers to Black, Irvine, Kirwan and others. Magellan used the term *chaleur spécifique*[61] for the first time, although his definition was unusual, and he published the first table of specific heats,[62] using values obtained by Kirwan and Crawford. Unlike Crawford, he assumed that heat is a substance.

In his 1779 M.D. dissertation at the University of Edinburgh,[63] William Cleghorn (1754–83) presented a particulate model of the Irvine theory. Cleghorn, an Irish student, attended Black's chemistry course in both 1777/8 and 1779/80. He pictured fire as a fluid made up of particles which repel one another but are attracted to the particles of ordinary matter, which are themselves mutually attractive. This model is the same as that proposed by Franklin for his electric fluid and as one later proposed for caloric, the matter for heat. As I have already noted, Black accorded some praise to Cleghorn's theory, but he objected that, like the Irvine theory, it does not explain changes of state in terms of latent heats.[64] Cleghorn was aware of this conflict; with respect to Black he stated, '*I shall frequently make use of his experiments and discoveries; but, with his leave, I must much against my will disagree with some of his opinions*'.[65] In the dissertation, Cleghorn qualitatively discussed many heat phenomena in terms of his model.

Before leaving the Irvine theory, it is of interest to point out that its last important exponent was John Dalton (1766–1844). In the spring of 1807 he presented lecture courses in Edinburgh and Glasgow: 'On these occasions [I] was honoured with the attention of gentlemen, universally acknowledged to be of the first respectability for their scientific attainments: most of whom were pleased to express their desire to see the publication of the doctrine in the present form, as soon as convenient'.[66] The result was the first volume of Dalton's *A New System of Chemical Philosophy* published in Manchester in 1808. Most of this work is devoted to heat, with the exposition of the celebrated atomic theory taking second place. Dalton's theory of heat combined the Irvine theory with a belief in the physical reality of caloric.

Lavoisier (1743–94)

Heat formed an integral part of Lavoisier's chemistry. His explanation of combustion and calcination centred on the chemical involvement of air and later, following the discovery of the gas, of oxygen. To account for the heat and flame familiar in combustion reactions, Lavoisier assumed that oxygen gas contains a large quantity of heat, some or all of which is released during oxidation. Manuscript evidence[67] shows that as early as 1766 Lavoisier was interested in vaporization and, in particular, in the heat absorption accompanying this process. This led him to consider water vapour, for example, as a compound made up of liquid water and matter of fire, or caloric (*calorique*), as it was later called;[68] this chemically combined caloric, unlike free caloric, did not influence temperature. This view is clearly similar to that of Black. Lavoisier went further and proposed that air is similarly a compound of some base and caloric, a view that he later incorporated into the new chemical nomenclature[69] and his table of elements[70] (e.g., oxygen gas was a compound made up of two elements: a base, called oxygen, and caloric). For Lavoisier, there was no fundamental difference between vapours and permanent gases, only a difference in boiling points, and phase changes were simply chemical reactions involving the element caloric. In 1777, Lavoisier presented his oxidation theory and his views on the chemical role of heat to the Académie Royale des Sciences, although these were not published until 1780.

A brief account of Black's work was read to the Académie in August, 1772 and published a month later.[71] This discussed only the latent heat of fusion of water, and did not refer to heat capacity. Lavoisier responded with a short paper[72] reporting his own accidental discovery of the latent heat of fusion of water. At this stage he was unaware of the extent and significance of Black's work, which he saw simply as confirmation of his own ideas. This situation changed in 1780–81, however, with the appearance in France of several publications which made reference to the contributions of Black, Irvine, Crawford, Kirwan, Wilcke, and others. Perhaps the most significant of these was the 1781 printing in France (in *Observations sur la Physique*) of Magellan's *Essai* referred to earlier; in *The Edinburgh Review* of 1806, Deluc recollected that this caused 'great agitation'[73] in Paris. This was hardly surprising. Lavoisier realised that Crawford's combustion theory was similar to his own (and that he had been anticipated in print), and, further, he became aware of an alternative hypothesis regarding the role of heat — the Irvine theory, with its promise of quantification via heat capacity measurements. Guerlac has concluded that 'There can be little doubt that it was Crawford's book, or rather Magellan's exposition of it, that launched Laplace and Lavoisier on. . .their joint work on calorimetry'.[74] In their *Mémoire sur la chaleur*, which first appeared in 1783, Crawford's name appears several times, and the work was perceived as a repetition of Crawford's investigations.

On the basis of experimental work, using their celebrated ice calorimeter, Laplace and Lavoisier decided against the Irvine theory:

a 'knowledge of the specific heats of substances and of their reaction products cannot. . .predict the heat they should develop when they combine'.[75] But there was a cautionary note: 'The precision with which it is necessary to know the specific heats of bodies makes it very difficult to test the preceding theory'.[76] Further, Laplace and Lavoisier used one aspect of the Irvine theory, the relationship between heat capacity and heat content, to explain various phenomena.

In their *Mémoire sur la chaleur*, Laplace and Lavoisier, noting that 'Scientists are divided about the nature of heat',[77] discussed the material and mechanical hypotheses. For the latter, they suggested that 'heat is the *vis viva* resulting from the imperceptible motions of the constituent particles of a body'.[78] Rather than deciding between the two hypotheses, they proceeded by accepting the principles common to both: heat is conserved, and it is reversible ('*All changes in heat. . .suffered by a [system] during a change of state recur in the opposite sense when the system returns to its original state.*'[79]). Like Black, Irvine and Crawford, Laplace and Lavoisier focused on a measurable effect of heat and not on its cause; in particular, they measured the heat evolved in various processes by weighing the quantity of ice that it melted. (In his other writings, Lavoisier was committed to a material heat, although he did concede that this view was hypothetical.)

With respect to chemical reactivity, the *Mémoire* includes an intriguing suggestion: 'The equilibrium between the heat, which tends to separate the particles of bodies, and their mutual affinities, which tend to bring them together, can furnish a very precise means of comparing these affinities with each other'.[80] The example given suggested how thermometric measurements could be used to obtain the relative affinities between various acids and water, but the implication seems to be the use of calorimetric measurements to obtain quantitative information about chemical reactivity; this was about 100 years prior to chemical thermodynamics. Perhaps this is to read too much into the statement; unfortunately a promised 'special memoir' on the topic was never published. Morris[67] has demonstrated Lavoisier's increasing use of a balance-of-forces concept after 1783, although he did not abandon his earlier chemical approach in which caloric acted as a chemical reactant; from 1783, the two modes of explanation were intertwined. Certainly Laplace pictured chemical change in terms of the interplay of interparticulate forces. Both Lavoisier and Laplace were fully aware of the difficulties attending the prediction of chemical reactivity; in their 1783 joint *Mémoire* and in subsequent writings they appear to propose a thermochemical approach. To quote Guerlac: 'If so, this is indeed prophetic, in a general way at least, of the transformation chemistry was to undergo in the nineteenth century and our own day. By means of chemical thermodynamics the physical chemist can indeed, without leaving his "cabinet", predict the course of many chemical reactions'.[74]

Conclusion

I have considered heat and its role in theories of chemical reactivity in the eighteenth century. This was a small, but significant, aspect of the chemistry of the period. It must, however, be seen in perspective. Boerhaave, Cullen, Black, Lavoisier and other chemists speculated on such matters, but they were aware of the difficulties and limitations of such a theoretical approach. When concerned, as they were for the most part, with actual chemical change in the real world, their approach was taxonomic. Lavoisier made this distinction in deciding to omit such theorectical considerations from his *Elements of Chemistry*; in the Preface he states:

> This science of affinities, or elective attractions, holds the same place with regard to the other branches of chemistry, that the higher or transcendental geometry does with respect to the simpler and elementary part; and I thought it improper to involve those simple and plain elements [of chemistry]. . .in the obscurities and difficulties which still attend that other very useful and necessary branch of chemical science.[81]

I have not mentioned phlogiston for two reasons; first, I suspect that more than enough has already been said and written on this topic, and secondly, its role in the chemistry of the Scottish Enlightenment was secondary. This is not to say that it was unimportant: it was significant in Crawford's work, the principle of inflammability appeared in Black's courses, phlogiston (identified with aether) was central in Leslie's theory of animal heat.[82]

With respect to the development of thermodynamics, there are several eighteenth-century influences:

(1) The heat engine provided not only Carnot's starting point, but the basis for much important experimental work from Watt to Regnault.

(2) Black's concepts of latent heat and heat capacity were crucial, and, as I have already indicated, they retain their importance today.

(3) Similarly, the calorimetry, pioneered by Black, was and remains important.

(4) Thermodynamics relates the properties of bulk matter. The prospect of a science of heat based on its observable properties, rather than on its underlying cause, was a recurrent theme throughout the second half of the eighteenth century. Fourier's *Analytical Theory of Heat*,[83] published in 1822, was the first triumph for such an approach; in mid-century came thermodynamics.

(5) The work of Black and other Scottish chemists contributed to the rise of the caloric theory towards the end of the eighteenth century and early in the nineteenth century.[84] This theory, and, in particular, its use by Carnot in his *Réflexions*, has often been seen as obstructing the development of thermodynamics. The problem, I believe, was a broader one: the principle of the conservation of heat. In the second half of the eighteenth century, this was both widely assumed and thought to hold irrespective of the cause of heat. Heat was considered a property of a body, and one that was conserved. In the mid-nineteenth century it was displaced from this central role by energy, and reduced to a mode of energy transfer between a body and its surroundings.

In summary, the influence of the Scottish Enlightenment and, in particular, of Watt and Black on the development of thermodynamics was both direct and considerable.

With respect to chemical reactivity, the links between the chemical thermodynamics and statistical mechanics of today and the eighteenth-century theories are more tenuous. In chemical thermodynamics we can predict chemical reactivity on the basis of calorimetric measurements carried out on the substances involved. Cullen and Lavoisier and Laplace seemed to be pointing in such a direction, but I can see no link between their vague suggestions and chemical thermodynamics, except possibly via thermodynamics itself. However, as I have already said, heat capacity, latent heat and calorimetry remain at the core of chemical thermodynamics. Similarly, it would require considerable imagination to demonstrate that the understanding, at the molecular level, of chemical reactivity that can be obtained using statistical mechanics is a direct descendant of the dynamic corpuscularity of the eighteenth century, except in so far as the interacting particle model is common to both. While not proposing any direct links, it is striking that our theoretical approaches to chemical reactivity today have their parallels in the eighteenth century.

NOTES

1. C. P. Snow, *The Two Cultures and the Scientific Revolution* (Cambridge: University Press 1962), 14.

2. S. P. Thompson, *The Life of William Thomson* (London: Macmillan 1910), 132–3.

3. E. Clapeyron, *Journal de l'Ecole Royale Polytechnique* (1834), XIV, 153–190.

4. S. Carnot, *Réflexions sur la Puissance Motrice du Feu et sur les Machines Propres à Développer cette Puissance* (Paris: Bachelier 1824).

5. S. P. Thompson, *Thomson*, 256.

6. D. S. L. Cardwell, *From Watt to Clausius: The Rise of Thermodynamics in the Early Industrial Age* (London: Heinemann 1971).

7. H. Guerlac, 'An Augustan Monument: The Opticks of Isaac Newton', in H. Guerlac (ed.), *Essays and Papers in the History of Modern Science* (Baltimore and London: The Johns Hopkins University Press 1977), 146–69.

8. J. Priestley, *Experiments and Observations on different Kinds of Air* (London: J. Johnson 1781), 3rd ed., Vol.1, 259.

9. E. J. Dijksterhuis, *The Mechanization of the World Picture* (translated by C. Dikshoorn. Oxford: Clarendon Press 1961).

10. I. Newton, *Opticks or a Treatise of the Reflections, Refractions, Inflections & Colours of Light* (based on the Fourth Edition London, 1730, New York: Dover 1952), 400.

11. *Ibid.*, 375–6.

12. *Ibid.*, 395.

13. *Ibid.*, 375–406.

14. *Ibid.*, 385.

15. R. E. Schofield, *Mechanism and Materialism: British Natural Philosophy in an Age of Reason* (Princeton: Princeton University Press 1970).

16. I. Newton, *Opticks*, 348–53.

17. *Ibid.*, 339.

18. R. E. Schofield, *Mechanism and Materialism*, 146.

19. G. A. Lindeboom, *Boerhaave and Great Britain* (Leiden: E. J. Brill 1974).

20. T. Cochrane, *Notes from Doctor Black's lectures on Chemistry 1767/8* (edited with an introduction by D. McKie. Cheshire: Imperial Chemical Industries Ltd Pharmaceuticals Division 1966), 1.

21. P. Shaw, *A New Method of Chemistry; including the History, Theory, and Practice of the Art: Translated from the original Latin of Dr. Boerhaave's* Elementa Chemiae, *as published by himself To which are added, Notes; and an Appendix, shewing the Necessity and Utility of Enlarging the Bounds of Chemistry* (London: T. and T. Longman 1753), 3rd ed., 236.

22. *Ibid.*, 246.

23. *Ibid.*, 361.

24. H. Metzger, *Newton, Stahl, Boerhaave et la Doctrine Chimique* (Paris: F. Alcan 1930).

25. R. Love, *Ambix* (1972), 19, 157–74.

26. R. E. Schofield, *Mechanism and Materialism*, 134–56.

27. *Ibid.*, 91–133.

28. B. Robinson, *A Dissertation on the Aether of Sir Isaac Newton* (London: Charles Hitch 1747), Preface.

29. *Ibid.*, 93.

30. *Ibid.*, 95.

31. *Ibid.*, 122–3.

32. A. L. Donovan, *Philosophical Chemistry in the Scottish Enlightenment: The Doctrines and Discoveries of William Cullen and Joseph Black* (Edinburgh: University Press 1975), 77–162.

33. J. R. R. Christie, *Ether and the science of chemistry: 1740–1790* in G. N. Cantor; M. J. S. Hodge, (eds.), *Conceptions of ether. Studies in the history of ether theories 1740–1900* (Cambridge: University Press 1981), 93.

34. E. Geoffroy, *Mémoires de l'Académie Royale des Sciences* (1718), 202–12.

35. J. Thomson, *An Account of the Life, Lectures, and Writings of William Cullen, M.D.* (Edinburgh and London: William Blackwood and Sons 1859), Vol. I, 52.

36. *Ibid.*, Vol. I, 580–3.

37. W. Cullen, *Essays and Observations, Physical and Literary* (1756), 2, 145–56.

38. J. R. R. Christie, *Ether*, 99.

39. *Ibid.*, 101.

40. I. B. Cohen, *Franklin and Newton* (Philadelphia: The American Philosophical Society 1956).

41. *Ibid.*, 334.

42. J. Black, *Lectures on the Elements of Chemistry* (edited by J. Robison. London: Longman and Rees, Edinburgh: William Creech 1803), Vol. I, 12.

43. T. Cochrane, *Doctor Black's lectures*, 22.

44. J. Black, *Lectures*, xxiii.

45. T. Cochrane, *Doctor Black's lectures*, 5.

46. J. R. R. Christie, *Ether*, 102–3.

47. J. Black, *Lectures*, 34.

48. *Ibid.*, 144, 277.

49. D. McKie; N. H. de V. Heathcote, *The Discovery of Specific and Latent Heats* (London: Edward Arnold 1935).

50. H. Guerlac, *Joseph Black's Work on Heat*, in A. D. C. Simpson, (ed.), *Joseph Black 1728–1799. A Commemorative Symposium* (Edinburgh: Royal Scottish Museum 1982), 13–22.

51. J. Black, *Lectures*, 271.

52. *Ibid.*, 192.

53. D. V. Fenby, *Pure and Applied Chemistry* (1987), 59, 91–100.

54. J. Black, *Lectures*, 283.

55. *Ibid.*, 284.

56. *Ibid.*, 194–5.

57. W. Irvine; W. Irvine, *Essays chiefly on Chemical Subjects* (London: Mawman 1805).

58. A. Crawford, *Experiments and Observations on Animal Heat, and the Inflammation of Combustible Bodies* (London: Murry; Sewell 1779).

59. A. Crawford, *Experiments and Observations on Animal Heat, and the Inflammation of Combustible Bodies*, 2nd ed. (London: Johnson 1788).

60. J. H. De Magellan, *Essai sur la Nouvelle Théorie du Feu Elémentaire, et de la Chaleur des Corps: avec la Description des Nouveaux Thermomètres, destinés particulièrement aux Observations sur ce Sujet*, in *Collection de Différens Traités sur des Instrumens d'Astronomie, Physique, &c.* (London: 1780), 165–92.

61. *Ibid.*, 167.

62. *Ibid.*, 177.

63. D. McKie; N. H. de V. Heathcote, *Cleghorn's* De Igne *(1779) with Translation and Annotations* (reprinted from *Annals of Science* (1958), 14, 1–82. London: Taylor & Francis 1960).

64. J. Black, *Lectures*, 195–6.

65. D. McKie; N. H. de V. Heathcote, De Igne, 11.

66. J. Dalton, *A New System of Chemical Philosophy* (Introduction by Alexander Joseph. London: Peter Owen 1965), xii.

67. R. J. Morris, *British Journal for the History of Science* (1972), 6, 1–38.

68. De Morveau, Lavoisier, Bertholet & de Fourcroy, *Méthode de Nomenclature Chimique* (Paris: Cuchet 1787), 31.

69. *Ibid.*, 32, 83.

70. A. L. Lavoisier, *Elements of Chemistry, in a New Systematic Order, containing all the Modern Discoveries* (translated by R. Kerr. 5th edition in two volumes. Edinburgh: W. Creech 1802), Vol.I, 291.

71. *Introduction aux Observations sur la Physique* (1772), 2, 428–31.

72. A. L. Lavoisier, *Introduction aux Observations sur la Physique* (1772), 2, 510–11.

73. J. A. Deluc, *The Edinburgh Review* (1806), vi, 502–15.

74. H. Guerlac, *Historical Studies in the Physical Sciences* (1976), 7, 193–276.

75. Lavoisier; de la Place, *Memoir on Heat*. Read to the Royal Academy of Sciences, 28 June 1783. (Translated with an Introduction and Notes by H. Guerlac. New York: Neale Watson Academic Publications 1982), 25.

76. *Ibid.*, 24.

77. *Ibid.*, 4.

78. *Ibid.*, 5.

79. *Ibid.*, 6.

80. *Ibid.*, 28.

81. A. L. Lavoisier, *Elements*, Vol.I, xxv.

82. P. D. Leslie, *A Philosophical Inquiry into the Cause of Animal Heat* (London: 1778).

83. J. Fourier, *The Analytical Theory of Heat* (Translated by A. Freeman. Cambridge: University Press 1878).

84. R. Fox, *The Caloric Theory of Gases from Lavoisier to Regnault* (Oxford: Clarendon Press 1971).

5

THE CHEMICAL REVOLUTION AND THE ENLIGHTENMENT — AND A PROPOSAL FOR THE STUDY OF SCIENTIFIC CHANGE

Arthur Donovan

That science occupies a position of central importance in modern culture and society is not a matter of dispute. But there is considerable dispute about the way one should study science and how it changes. Indeed, the study of science itself, as distinguished from the study of natural phenomena, is today conducted largely by specialists who use the guiding assumptions and interpretive techniques of their disciplines, most notably philosophy, history and sociology, to define science and explain its development. While this subdivision along disciplinary lines has encouraged certain types of research within science studies, it has exacerbated rather than helped solve the problem of developing a coherent picture of science and scientific change. As a result, we now have no account of science capable of rendering it intelligible to those not actively engaged in science studies. How, for instance, are we to make sense of an enterprise that at times exhibits an extraordinarily high degree of consensus, as science so often does, and which at other times is racked by disagreements so profound that they lead to revolutions? And how can we begin to weave together the various strands of influence that shape the development of science so as to present a detailed yet integrated account of the whole? Questions of this sort are seldom engaged by scholars committed to examining science, or more commonly a particular episode in science, from the perspective of a single discipline, yet they are questions that must be addressed if we are ever to understand what science is and how it works.

This essay describes two attempts to address these larger questions directly. In the first section I outline a conception of science studies that I believe meets many of the current needs of this subject, primarily by preserving what is most vital in contemporary science studies while also offering a way around the limitations imposed by an excessive attachment to discrete disciplinary approaches. The suggestion that we should conceive of science as a distinct cultural tradition and study it accordingly is hardly radical, yet I believe that it would open rewarding lines of explication and interpretation. In the second section I sketch out a research program for the study of Antoine Lavoisier's achievement as a chemist and of the Chemical Revolution that he led. In addition to exemplifying several aspects of the conception of science studies outlined in the first section, this second section will suggest how we might construct comparative studies of eighteenth-century chemistry. Those interested in comparing eighteenth-century Scottish chemistry with the French developments described below may wish to consult the currently available literature on chemistry in the Scottish Enlightenment.[1]

Science Considered as a Form of Culture

In the modern era science is a distinct mode of culture. Admittedly this observation does not take us very far, for in addition to leaving open the notoriously confused question of what is meant by culture, it does not immediately suggest how one might go about answering the hard questions in science studies. But let us try to be more specific about what kind of a cultural activity science is. If we distinguish between 'high' or formal culture and popular or customary culture, then clearly science is, in the main, part of high culture. In using these terms to distinguish broadly between two types of culture, I do not mean to imply any ranking of their intrinsic merits or their historical importance, nor do I wish to deny that there is considerable interaction between them.

High culture is marked by three characteristics:

(1) Its practitioners have through extensive and usually formal training mastered the central methods and techniques of their art;

(2) the meaning and significance of the 'goods' produced by high culture are accessible, at least in the first instance, only to initiates (in science such goods are general conceptions of nature and specific theories that order and explain natural phenomena);

(3) high culture is intensely self-conscious, in the sense that its practitioners have a highly developed sense of what constitutes exemplary work in the field, how one should go about doing good work, and what criteria should be employed in appraising one's own work and the work of others.

These characteristics suggest that we may be able to learn a good deal about science by exploring the ways in which it is analogous to other forms of high culture. Consider, for instance, the Western cultural traditions of art, architecture, music and literature. Does science resemble these enterprises and the ways they are pursued in contemporary society?

Of course obvious differences between the arts, literature and science immediately spring to mind. The products of art, architecture, music and literature appeal directly to the senses and the emotions, such as sympathy and antipathy, in ways that science, which culminates in abstract and general theories, does not. It would therefore be more exact, if less venturesome, to compare science to such other modes of intellectual culture as philosophy and political theory. And yet, while not denying the importance of the differences between science and the arts, we need not abandon entirely the original comparison. For while the *products* of science and the arts are very different in character, the *processes* by which they are produced may well be more similar than is commonly thought. As we have all learned from scholarly studies of artistic style, craft and intention, the intellectual assumptions and theories of expression and communication that guide artists and writers during the process of creation play a much greater part in the production of artistic goods than an examination of the finished products alone reveals. And in the study of science, on the other hand, it has recently been demonstrated[2] that chance, contextual considerations, tacit knowledge and instrumental skill enter into the construction of science to an extent that is also not revealed by the finished product of science, the formal paper or book.

The similarities between science and other modes of high culture, from art and architecture to philosophy and political theory, should be carefully explored with a view to investigating science as a form of culture.

What are the implications of thinking of science studies in this way? In the first place it puts the subject rather than any particular disciplinary mode of investigation and explanation at the center of attention. If the problem of how to define science can be solved — and I shall return to this serious problem shortly — then the common concerns of students of science can be defined in terms of the subject being examined rather than the theoretical or disciplinary perspective adopted. Such an approach leaves all theoretical questions open, for unlike the Positivist organization of knowledge, which also identifies areas of investigation in terms of their subject matters, the organizing principle here does not assume that a common method will be applied to all subjects studied. Students of science would be responsible for bringing to bear whatever disciplines and techniques are capable of illuminating the subject under study.

But is it possible to reach agreement on the question 'What is Science?' This question has a long history within the philosophy of science, where it is known as 'the demarcation problem'. The best-known contemporary demarcation criterion, proposed by Karl Popper, is that scientific knowledge is vulnerable to falsification by contradictory empirical evidence whereas other forms of knowledge do not submit themselves to this rigorous form of validation. As a conjecture about how science *should* work, the principle of falsification certainly has the advantage of clarity. Unfortunately, however, scientific practice is more complex than that and there is now overwhelming evidence that as a description of how science *actually does work*, falsification lacks credibility.[3]

An explication of the demarcation question is still needed, for although at any particular time there is some consensus as to what is science, if we compare the domain and internal hierarchy of science in one age to that of another, the lack of complete agreement is striking. This is also the case in other areas of culture such as art, music and literature. Perhaps we should not seek a timeless criterion for demarcating between science and non-science, but rather should ask by what process this distinction is established. We should consider introducing into science studies the venerable concept of *tradition*.

Tradition, in the sense in which I am using it here, can be thought of as a dialogue carried on by successive generations who are concerned with understanding their shared assumptions, beliefs and practices. Cultural traditions are sustained by self-examination and they articulate for both practitioners and critics alike the nature and meaning of the cultural activity in question. Traditions of this sort are specific to different cultural enterprises, although they are also shaped by their interactions with other aspects of society and culture. Many have died out or have been destroyed in the rough and tumble of history, but so long as they last, they define a context of interpretation and a sense of continuity for those engaged in cultural activities.[4]

What work will the concept of tradition do for science studies? Consider the problem of continuity and change in science. Thomas Kuhn, in his attempt to reconcile the high degree of consensus characteristic of what he calls 'normal science' and the conceptual ruptures associated with scientific revolutions, was finally driven to locating the continuity of science in enduring communities.[5] But this sociological move, while perhaps justified in particular cases, evades the general problem of explaining how scientists who find their fundamental beliefs called into question during periods of revolution none the less continue to think of themselves as scientists. But is their situation so very different from that of painters or musicians whose stylistic conventions are suddenly called into question? In all cultural activities there are periods of rapid and extreme destruction and reconstruction, and it is the function of tradition to find ways of connecting past and present so as to sustain the continuity and collective identity of the enterprise. Scientists may not think of themselves and what they do in these terms, but the student of culture can see that this is in fact what is happening when old methods and beliefs are displaced by newer ones.

Traditions of interpretation also perform a function that offers a solution to the demarcation problem. One of the responsibilities associated with sustaining a tradition is defining the canon of works considered central to the cultural tradition in question. In political theory one is not obliged to treat as equally important every scribbler who wrote on politics, yet one is expected to be able to give reasons for denying any particular writer a prominent place in this tradition. To put the point another way, cultural traditions are unavoidably normative in determining what is and what is not to be treated as exemplary work, but the decisions they render are neither arbitrary nor absolute. The canon of works considered central to the enterprise is always open to revision, but it is only in fact revised when new standards of taste or truth force their way to the fore and new modes of interpretation are being articulated. The situation is very much the same in science. To solve the problem of what is to be considered part of science at any particular time, we need to determine what the leading 'keepers of the scientific tradition' included within science. But with the advantage of hindsight we can also identify developments that, while lying outside the scientific tradition of the time, shaped the subsequent direction of scientific advance. It is this ability to range beyond and revalue the perceptions of the leading figures of the past that enables us to construct a tradition in science studies that is more than a restatement of the self-understanding of previous 'keepers of the scientific tradition'.

There are two main advantages associated with conceiving science as a cultural activity and science studies as a tradition of critical and interpretive commentary. The first advantage is that we can agree on the central problems of science studies, the problems that give it distinctiveness, continuity and coherence, while at the same time we are freed from *a priori* commitments to particular modes of interpretation and explanation. There is considerable evidence that in science 'the age of disciplines' is coming to an end and that contemporary scientists are quite prepared to bring intellectual resources of all sorts, whatever their origins, to the task of solving problems encountered in the study of nature. It would be atavistic, as well as counterproductive, for students of the history of science to bind themselves to the assumptions and methods of the established disciplines at precisely the moment the practitioners of the subject they study are throwing off those very bonds. The second advantage speaks to the need to establish a community of scholars committed to science studies and to define their purpose within the larger world of cultural studies. The beginnings of such a community already exist, but it is astonishing how little has been done to promote the study of science and its place in contemporary culture and society. There is therefore good reason to think that were a more compelling case made for such studies, more support would be forthcoming.

The 'works' of science are concepts, methods and theories, the 'things' with which scientists describe, order and explain natural phenomena. It is therefore the knowledge claims of science, or what is commonly called its cognitive content, that ought to constitute the defining concern of science studies. Critics and interpreters of art and architecture study paintings, sculpture and buildings; critics and interpreters of science study the cognitive content of science. In all these cases the distinctive cultural 'product' is the central concern of the enterprise. What does it (a poem, a painting, a theory) mean? How did it come into being and become accepted as part of the canon of the enterprise? How did it alter other beliefs? As these question indicate, keeping the cognitive content of science at the centre of attention does not impoverish the range of investigations open to students of science. On the contrary: such attention is essential and studies of scientific institutions, for instance, which discuss their social influence to the exclusion of their detailed scientific beliefs would not, in my view, satisfy this criterion, however excellent they may be as sociology or history. To construct a distinctive, coherent and enduring tradition of science studies, we ought to insist that engagement with the cognitive content of science is a *sine qua non*.

The need to create a distinctive community of scholars committed to science studies directs attention to several interesting problems. The intellectual purpose of such a community can fairly readily be defined in terms of the desirability of fostering an enduring tradition of criticism and interpretation focused on the cognitive content of science. But when one looks closely at the current state of affairs, one discovers a vast difference between what is wanted and what exists. Consider, for instance, the analogs mentioned above. Critical and interpretive studies of art, music and literature have long since been separated from general philosophy, general history and general sociology and are pursued within institutional units, such as research institutes and university departments, that support broadly conceived research programs ranging from textual analysis and theoretical studies of criticism and aesthetics to historical investigation and social analysis. At the focus of these various approaches are the relevant cultural artifacts; the methods employed are those that the investigators find fruitful. An analogous scheme would be appropriate for science studies, although so far as I know no one has ever tried to organize a science studies unit along these lines.

The failure to articulate and organize institutional arrangements that foster science studies is closely related to the isolation of science studies from the enterprise of science itself. Again, consider the situation in analogous cultural activities. In practically all forms of high culture those who create significant artifacts have been extensively schooled in the styles, techniques and traditions of their art. There are of course 'natural' and untutored writers, painters and musicians, but the overwhelming number of those who have made a mark in the formal traditions of these fields were intensely aware of working within a cultural tradition with which they were intimately familiar. The gap that separates creators of cultural artifacts from the authors of critical scholarship is, of course, a real one, but in almost all areas of cultural life a dialogue is maintained between these two groups, especially in the formal training of future practitioners. Yet in science this is not the case. The understanding of science that most scientists carry around is compounded out of textbook introductions on method, unsystematic reflection on personal experience, and randomly collected snippets of popularized philosophy of science. And since science students are not expected to give serious attention to the understanding of science made available by contemporary students of science, this ill-informed and unreflective mindlessness about science is reproduced in each succeeding generation. Whether this state of affairs is helpful or harmful to science remains an open question, and whether exposing science students to science studies in its current state would enlighten them is yet another question altogether.[6] But it can hardly be denied that given the importance of science in contemporary culture, and given the well-demonstrated inadequacies of the positivist conception of science that informs most scientists' understanding of what they do, it is hardly an enlightened policy to allow science and science studies to remain apart.

The most promising starting point for constructing a coherent program of science studies is to be found in the theories of scientific change proposed by philosophers and historians of science such as Thomas Kuhn, Imre Lakatos and Larry Laudan. Because these theories concentrate on the cognitive content of science and treat history and philosophy as equally important, at least in principle, they provide a suitable point of departure for the kind of science studies described above. But there are also severe inadequacies and areas of conflict within and between these theories and they will have to be radically revised and supplemented if they are to be employed as a basis for a comprehensive program of science studies.[7]

The Origins of Lavoisier's Program for the Transformation of Chemistry

The Chemical Revolution, one of the great revolutions in the history of science and the only one to have occurred in the eighteenth century, certainly qualifies as one of the canonical events in the history of science. If, as recommended above, investigations of such an event should begin and end by focusing on the cognitive content in question, then we need to direct our attention at the outset to the new chemical concepts and theories developed by Antoine Lavoisier, the leading figure in this event. A memoir he drafted in 1792 provides a convenient text for this purpose. Harried by the turmoil of the political revolution and desperate to defend his position as France's leading chemist, Lavoisier hastily summarized what he considered to be his major contributions to the new chemistry: 'No one, I hope, will seek to deny me credit for the theory of oxidation and combustion, the analysis and the decomposition of air by the use of metals and combustible bodies, the theory of acidification, determining the exact nature of a great number of acids — especially the vegetable acids, original ideas on the composition of vegetable and animal substances, [and] the theory of respiration'.[8]

This list provides a useful corrective to two popular misconceptions about Lavoisier's achievement. The first is that the discovery of new gases was at the heart of the Chemical Revolution and that the theories developed to explain how these gases interact with other chemical substances were of secondary importance. Clearly this was not Lavoisier's view, for he emphasized the originality and importance of his *theoretical* contributions to the new chemistry. The second misconception is that the one great theoretical innovation in the Chemical Revolution was the recognition that oxygen is simply phlogiston turned on its head. Lavoisier obviously thought otherwise, for he listed the theory of oxidation as only one among a comprehensive and ambitious set of theories he developed. And as he argued elsewhere, the theories he proposed differed from the older phlogiston theory in many ways, the most important being that they were confirmed by analytic and synthetic experimental evidence. The myth that the new chemistry emerged from a simple Gestalt switch in which the old theory was perceived in a new way must therefore be abandoned.[9]

Having identified the cognitive content central to this episode, we may now explore its origins, meanings and consequences in whatever ways the available evidence will support. We are fortunate in Lavoisier's case in having evidence that illuminates the nature of the research program he had in mind when he began systematically to investigate chemical phenomena. In a well-known private memorandum jotted down on the opening pages of a laboratory notebook he began using in February, 1773, Lavoisier said that the research plan he proposed to follow 'seemed to me destined to bring about a revolution in physics and chemistry'.[10] This statement, first published nearly a century ago, has long fascinated historians of science, for it indicates that at the very beginning of his career as a chemist Lavoisier was convinced he was in a position to effect a scientific revolution. Yet there was no evident reason to think that the subject of his first research program, the role of air in the calcination of metals, was intrinsically revolutionary, and at the time he made his astonishing prediction he had no experimental results or theoretical insights that could possibly justify such confidence. And yet in the end he did what he said he would do, though it took him many years to bring all the components of his new chemistry into alignment. This programmatic statement therefore opens up an intriguing and potentially revealing line of investigation into the origins of Lavoisier's new theories of chemistry. How, we must wonder, could he have been so sure of himself and of the consequences of his research at such an early stage?

Before exploring possible answers to this question, we must ask what we mean, and what Lavoisier meant, by the term 'revolution'. Today the term is usually used to describe periods of profound and rapid conceptual change within established scientific disciplines. This is certainly the way Thomas Kuhn uses the term in his famous account of *The Structure of Scientific Revolution*,[11] and it has become commonplace to speak of such events as 'the plate-tectonic revolution in geology'. And yet there are reasons to believe that Lavoisier did not think of the revolution he led as occurring entirely within chemistry as that subject was defined in the middle of the eighteenth century. As his statement indicates, he set out to make a revolution 'in chemistry and physics', rather than in chemistry alone. I therefore agree with those historians who argue that Lavoisier saw the Chemical Revolution as a reconstruction of chemistry that transformed it *into* a science, rather than as a revolution that occurred entirely *within* a well-established and autonomous discipline of chemistry.[12]

Even before beginning his career as a chemist Lavoisier had found a model outside chemistry that defined for him what kind of a science chemistry might become. His conviction that he could transform chemistry into a true science was based not on the discovery of new chemical facts or the availability of novel instrumental techniques, but rather on what he perceived to be the powerful new methods utilized in his model science. We know by his own report that Lavoisier studied physics and chemistry in conjunction, and we also know that he believed that the revolution he set out to make could only be realized through careful experimentation. And indeed it was, I suggest, the methods of mid-eighteenth-century experimental physics that Lavoisier believed would enable him to transform the chemistry of his day into a theoretical science.[13] It was the model of experimental physics that inspired him in 1773 and he still had experimental physics in mind, I believe, when a decade later he wrote that

> It is time to recall chemistry to a more rigorous manner of reasoning, to separate the facts with which this science is enriched every day from those which speculation and prejudice add to it, to distinguish between facts and observations and systems and hypotheses, and finally, to indicate what sort of goal chemical knowledge should be directed towards . . ..[14]

Is it possible to go one step further and connect Lavoisier's great faith in the model of experimental physics and his activities as an administrative reformer? Lavoisier was intensely involved in administrative reform during the final decades of the Old Regime. A Parisian by birth, a descendant of prominent lawyers and himself trained in law, a man of considerable private means, Lavoisier in fact pursued two careers, one in science and one in state administration. He was by all accounts, including his own, an ambitious and purposeful man; as he recalled in the historical memoir quoted above, in 1772 'I was young, I had just entered on my career in science, I was hungry for glory'.[15] It is therefore not unreasonable to look for some link between Lavoisier's intense commitment to reform of the royal administration, which was an entirely appropriate commitment for someone of his background and talents, and his equally intense if somewhat more unexpected commitment to reform the practical art of chemistry. And if we are correct in concluding that his program for the reform of chemistry was grounded in the methods of experimental physics, can we also wonder whether that subject in some way influenced his efforts in administrative reform?

This chain of suppositions will appear less hypothetical if we recall that one of the commonplaces of the Enlightenment in France was the belief that reform consists of conforming to nature. Acquiring more extensive and reliable knowledge about the relations between natural phenomena was therefore an essential precondition of individual, social and administrative reform. It is this connection, I believe, that reveals how experimental physics informed both of Lavoisier's programs of reform. Like Turgot, Condorcet and the Physiocrats, with whom he was associated as friend, colleague and collaborator, Lavoisier assumed that a well-founded understanding of nature provides a reliable and entirely appropriate basis for social and political action. He knew, of course, that hard conceptual and empirical work was required to gain an understanding of nature adequate to the needs of social and political reform, but he believed such knowledge could be attained. He was, in short, a true *philosophe* who placed great faith in the power of reason and method and founded his hopes on the belief that beneficial effects would flow from an improved knowledge of nature.[16]

This brief attempt to identify the origins of Lavoisier's program for the reform of chemistry has led us far beyond the realm of science and into the broader cultural concerns of the Enlightenment.[17] This is neither surprising nor unusual, for while the appearance of such discrete cultural developments as the Chemical Revolution is more than a mere manifestation of historical tendencies, cultural artifacts of this sort do draw on and in turn influence the more general social and cultural belief systems of which they are a part. Major events in cultural history frequently mark major transformations in cultural traditions, and such was the case with the Chemical Revolution. It was, as I argued above, a revolution that transformed a well-established art into a science that met the standards of a new conception of science then being articulated, and its success was instrumental in making this new conception of science central to the self-understanding of the scientific tradition as a whole. To put the point more directly and rather baldly, the Chemical Revolution was the first great triumph of Positivism. It embodied and made central to the concept of science the central non-historical elements of the philosophy of science that August Comte forged into a system in the 1830s: the sciences are to be distinguished in terms of the phenomena they study; the sciences share a common method; scientists should not address because they cannot resolve questions about the real nature of matter; the truth of scientific claims is guaranteed by agreement with experimental evidence, which is the bedrock of all positive knowledge.

Of course Positivism has a history of its own and I do not mean to imply that everything Comte asserted can be found in Lavoisier's reconstruction of chemistry. But the common elements and links are there and the connection is both historical and natural. I call it 'natural' because new philosophies of science do not spring fully-formed from the minds of philosophers, they emerge rather from attempts to understand new developments in science. Science and the critical interpretation of science are locked in an inescapable mutual dependence, however much either party may wish to deny the relationship. Perhaps in time scientists and students of science will come to accept this fact, as the devotees of other forms of high culture have, and learn to dance rather than to struggle. Were they to do so, the public comportment of both parties might improve and they might even collaborate in developing a civilized and sophisticated understanding of the nature of science and its place in contemporary society and culture.

NOTES

I am especially grateful to Roger Emerson and Nicholas Fisher for written comments on an earlier version of this essay. The research on which it is based was supported in part by the University of Edinburgh Institute for Advanced Studies in the Humanities, by the National Science Foundation, and by the National Endowment for the Humanities.

1. See, for example, A.L. Donovan, *Philosophical Chemistry in the Scottish Enlightenment* (Edinburgh: Edinburgh University Press, 1975); Arthur L. Donovan, 'William Cullen and the Research Tradition of Eighteenth-Century Scottish Chemistry', in *The Origins and Nature of the Scottish Enlightenment*, eds. R.H. Campbell and Andrew S. Skinner (Edinburgh: John Donald, 1982), pp.98–114; and R.G.W. Anderson, 'Joseph Black', in David Daiches, Peter Jones and Jean Jones, *A Hotbed of Genius: The Scottish Enlightenment, 1730–1790* (Edinburgh: Edinburgh University Press, 1986), pp.93–114.

2. For an introductory discussion of science as culture, see Maurice N. Richter, Jr., *Science as a Cultural Process* (Cambridge, Mass: Schenkman Publishing Company, 1972). The works of E.H. Gombrich provide an accessible and learned introduction to the role of theories in the creation and interpretation of art; see especially his 'Art History and the Social Sciences', in his *Meditations on a Hobby Horse and Other Essays on the Theory of Art* (Chicago: University of Chicago Press, 1963). A contemporary classic in the ethnography of science is Bruno Latour and Steve Woolgar, *Laboratory Life: The Social Construction of Scientific Facts* (Beverly Hills, Calif: Sage, 1979). For a detailed reconstruction of Antoine Lavoisier's research activities in chemistry, with particular emphasis on the role of creativity in science, see Frederic Lawrence Holmes, *Lavoisier and the Chemistry of Life* (Madison: University of Wisconsin Press, 1985).

3. For a brief history of the demarcation problem and a critique, see Larry Laudan, 'The Demise of Demarcation', in R.S. Cohen and L. Laudan, eds., *Physics, Philosophy and Psychiatry* (Dordrecht: Reidel, 1982), pp.111–128.

4. The importance of tradition in modern cultural life has been most forcefully emphasized by students of Christian, and especially Catholic, doctrine; see, e.g., John Henry Newman, *An Essay on the Development of Christian Doctrine*, C.F. Harrold, ed. (New York: Longmans, Green, 1949); Yves M.-J. Congar,

Tradition and Traditions - An Historical and a Theological Essay (New York: Macmillan, 1967); Jaroslav Pelikan, *The Vindication of Tradition* (New Haven: Yale University Press, 1984). For philosophical and sociological perspectives on tradition, see George Boas, 'La Tradition', *Diogène*, no.31 (Juillet-Septembre 1960), pp.75–88; and Edward Shils, *Tradition* (Chicago: University of Chicago Press, 1981). For recent uses of the concept of tradition in examinations of science and political thought, see M.D. King, 'Reason, Tradition, and the Progressiveness of Science', *History and Theory*, 1971, *10*:3–32; and Peter L. Janson, 'Political Thought as Traditionary Action: The Critical Response to Skinner and Pocock', *History and Theory*, 1985, *24*:115–146.

Anthropologists study the role of traditions in terms of the reproduction and transformation of social and cultural systems. Recent theoretical discussions that address historical aspects of traditionary behaviour include Richard Handler and Jocelyn Linnekin, 'Tradition, Genuine or Spurious', *Journal of American Folklore*, 1984, 97:273–290; Marshall Sahlins, *Historical Metaphors and Mythical Realities* (Ann Arbor: University of Michigan Press, 1981); Sherry B. Ortner, 'Theory in Anthropology since the Sixties', *Comparative Studies in Society and History*, 1984, *26*:126–166; and George E. Marcus and Michael M.J. Fischer, *Anthropology as Cultural Critique* (Chicago: University of Chicago Press, 1986). I am grateful to my colleague Gary Downey for introducing me to this anthropological literature.

5. 'A scientific community consists . . . of the practitioners of a scientific specialty . . . . Communities of this sort are the units that this book has presented as the producers and validators of scientific knowledge. Paradigms are something shared by the members of such groups.' Thomas Kuhn, *The Structure of Scientific Revolutions*, 2nd. ed. (Chicago: University of Chicago Press, 1970), pp.177–78.

6. See the classic article by Stephen G. Brush, 'Should the History of Science Be Rated X?', *Science*, 22 March 1974, *183*:1164–1172.

7. For a recent attempt to initiate a critical re-examination of the theories of Kuhn, Lakatos, Laudan, Feyerabend and others, see Larry Laudan, Arthur Donovan, *et al*, 'Scientific Change: Philosophical Models and Historical Research', *Synthèse*, 1986, vol.69, no.2, pp.141–223; and Arthur Donovan, Larry Laudan, and Rachel Laudan, eds., *Scrutinizing Science: Empirical Studies of Scientific Change* 1988 (Dordrecht: D. Reidel).

8. 'Détails historiques sur la cause de l'augumentation de poids qu'acquièrent les substances métalliques, lorsqu'on les chauffe pendant leur exposition à l'air', in A. Lavoisier, *Oeuvres de Lavoisier*, 6 vols., vols.1–4 ed. J.-B. Dumas, vols.5-6 ed. Edouard Grimaux (Paris: Imprimerie Impériale, 1862–1893), reprinted (New York: Johnson Reprint, 1965), II:99–104.

9. The reduction of the Chemical Revolution to the overthrow of the phlogiston theory is one of the commonplaces of modern history of science; see, for example, James Bryant Conant, ed., 'The Overthrow of the Phlogiston Theory: The Chemical Revolution of 1775–1789', in James Bryant Conant, ed., *Harvard Case Histories in Experimental Science*, 2 vols. (Cambridge, Mass: Harvard University Press, 1957), 1:76–90; Kuhn, *Structure of Scientific Revolutions*, pp.53–56, 70–76, 100, 118, 159 and *passim*; Alan Musgrave, 'Why did Oxygen supplant Phlogiston? Research Programmes

in the Chemical Revolution', in Colin Howson, ed., *Method and Appraisal in the Physical Sciences* (Cambridge: Cambridge U.P., 1976), pp.181–209; and H. Gilman McCann, *Chemistry Transformed: The Paradigmatic Shift from Oxygen to Phlogiston* (Norwood, N.J.:Ablex, 1978). The inadequacy of this interpretation of Lavoisier's achievement has most recently been demonstrated in Holmes, *Lavoisier and the Chemistry of Life, passim*, and in Frederic L. Holmes, 'Lavoisier's Conceptual Passage', in Arthur Donovan, ed., *The Chemical Revolution — Essays in Reinterpretation*, vol.4 of *Osiris*, new series (Philadelphia: History of Science Society, 1988), pp.82–92.

10. First published in Marcellin Berthelot, *La révolution chimique - Lavoisier* (Paris, 1890), pp.46–49; reprinted in Henry Guerlac, *Lavoisier — The Crucial Year: The Background and Origin of His First Experiments on Combustion in 1772* (Ithaca: Cornell University Press, 1961), pp.228–230; English translation in Andrew Norman Meldrum, *The Eighteenth Century Revolution in Science - The First Phase* (Calcutta: Longmans, Green, n.d.[1930]), pp.8–10. On the dating of this memorandum, see Henry Guerlac, 'The Chemical Revolution: A Word from Monsieur Fourcroy', *Ambix*, 1976, 23:1–4, n.2.

11. '. . . scientific revolutions are here taken to be those non-cumulative developmental episodes in which an older paradigm is replaced in whole or in part by an incompatible new one', Kuhn, *Structure of Scientific Revolutions*, p.92. Cf. n.5 above for Kuhn's identification of paradigms and communities of specialists. For additional evidence that Kuhn sees the 'internal' history of science as a history of disciplines, see his article 'The History of Science', first published in the *International Encyclopedia of the Social Sciences*, vol.14, reprinted in Thomas S. Kuhn, *The Essential Tension* (Chicago: University of Chicago Press, 1977), pp.105–26, especially pp.110–12.

12. Cf. Henry Guerlac — 'As August Comte long ago observed, it is perhaps the outstanding feature of Lavoisier's Chemical Revolution that chemistry emerged as an autonomous discipline, a body of theoretical knowledge at last worthy of standing beside such older sciences as astronomy and physics', in his 'French Antecedents of the Chemical Revolution', originally published in *Chymia*, 1959, 5:73–112, reprinted in Henry Guerlac, *Essays and Papers in the History of Modern Science* (Baltimore: The Johns Hopkins University Press, 1977), pp.340–374, which is the version cited here; p.363. More recently Thomas Hankins has stated that 'In fact, the Chemical Revolution was more the creation of a new science than a change in an existing one. Before 1750, chemistry could not be regarded as an independent discipline. It had long antecedents, but they were ancillary to other fields', in his *Science and the Enlightenment* (Cambridge: Cambridge University Press, 1985), p. 85.

13. On the development of experimental physics in the eighteenth century, see R.W. Home, 'The Notion of Experimental Physics in Early Eighteenth-Century France', in Joseph C. Pitt, ed., *Change and Progress in Modern Science* (Dordrecht: D. Reidel, 1985), pp.107–131; Jean Torlais, 'La Physique Expérimentale', in René Taton, *Enseignement et diffusion des sciences en France au XVIII-siècle* (Paris: Hermann, 1964), pp.619–645; J.L. Heilbron, *Electricity in the 17th & 18th Centuries* (Berkeley: University of California Press, 1979); and Hankins, *Science and the Enlightenment*, Ch.3.

14. A. Lavoisier, 'Réflexions sur le phlogistique', *Oeuvres*, II:640.

15. Lavoisier, *Oeuvres*, II:102.

16. For a brief discussion of Turgot's scientific interests, see the article by Rhoda Rappaport in the *Dictionary of Scientific Biography*, Charles C. Gillispie, ed. (New York: Scribner's), vols.13-14, pp.494-497; On Condorcet, see Keith Baker, *Condorcet* (Chicago: University of Chicago Press, 1975); on Lavoisier and the Physiocrates, see G. Schelle and E. Grimaux, eds., *Lavoisier - statistiques agricole et projets de réformes* (Paris: Guillaumin, n.d.). For other accounts of Lavoisier as a *philosophe*, see Douglas McKie, *Antoine Lavoisier* (New York: Schuman, 1952); Henry Guerlac, *Antoine-Laurent Lavoisier* (New York: Scribner's, 1975); and Charles Coulston Gillispie, *Science and Polity in France at the End of the Old Regime* (Princeton: Princeton University Press, 1980).

17. For a more detailed but still preliminary account of the interpretation summarized in the second part of this essay, see my 'Lavoisier and the Origins of Modern Chemistry', in Donovan, ed., *The Chemical Revolution*, pp.214-231.

6

IMPROVEMENT AND ENLIGHTENMENT: AGRICULTURE AND NATURAL HISTORY IN THE WORK OF THE REV. DR. JOHN WALKER (1731–1803)

Charles W.J. Withers

Introduction

The Rev. Dr. John Walker, natural historian, university professor, and known to his parishioners as 'the mad minister of Moffat', is a somewhat curious individual upon whom to focus in the context of the Scottish Enlightenment. He was the first person in an English-speaking university to give lectures on agriculture, and professor of natural history in Edinburgh University from 1779 until 1803. His friends and correspondents included Linnaeus, Henry Home (Lord Kames), James Hutton, John Hope, John Playfair, Joseph Black, and William Cullen. Hutton noted of Walker that he was '. . . very intelligent both in Zoology and Mineralogy'. John Hope, professor of botany in Edinburgh from 1761 to 1786, considered Walker 'a very clever man' in botanical research.[1]

Yet despite half a century of writings on natural history, a wide correspondence on scientific matters, and despite being a founder member of the Royal Society of Edinburgh, Walker is not as well known to us now as he was highly regarded by his contemporaries. Walker was, and is, however, an interesting and important figure. His work as a natural historian, his classificatory studies in the earth sciences, his role as professor and lecturer mark Walker as representative of that involvement with natural philosophy, cultural knowledge as a civilising pursuit, and utilitarian practice that characterised Scotland's eighteenth-century enlightenment. In several ways, his work is more than representative. One botanical author considered him 'the best of all authorities', and others have argued that his work in botany has not received its deserved attention.[2] Linnaeus, several of whose classifications Walker anticipated and refined, respected him highly.[3] Ritchie claims that Walker's lectures on natural history set a standard upon which much later teaching was based.[4] Taylor has drawn further attention to Walker's importance in the history of botany, and Porter has considered Walker's role as natural philosopher and utilitarian scientist within 'the

Scottish earth science tradition'.[5] Scott claims Walker to be 'the father of geological teaching'.[6] Shapin has outlined Walker's involvement in the foundation of the Royal Society of Edinburgh.[7] An edition has been produced of his geology lectures,[8] and of his Highland tours,[9] and some attempt has been made to examine Walker's agricultural writings.[10]

These endeavours in various fields suggest that Walker's life and work as an enlightenment scientist merit closer examination. What follows examines Walker's work as a natural historian in relation to eighteenth-century Scottish concerns with philosophical investigation and practical improvement. For Walker, natural history was an empirically-derived practice rather more than a subject area in the modern sense. It involved, too, philosophical speculation on the orders and structures of the natural world. It was, additionally, a means to material improvement. Agriculture was central to his interests in all three senses: as a practical pursuit; as an area of theory or discourse within his natural history lectures; and as a leading element of economic advance. Of particular interest here are the links between his natural history lectures within which he discussed agricultural topics, and contemporary concern in Scotland with agricultural advance. Several themes are considered in investigating these relationships: his agricultural writings including his correspondence on agrarian topics; his public lectures on agriculture and the audience for those lectures including his involvement with the institutional bases to improvement through the Edinburgh Agricultural Society; and his writings on the Scottish Highlands in which region many ideas on improvement were implemented in the eighteenth century.

Improvement and Enlightenment: the role of agriculture

The beginnings of interest in agricultural improvement may be traced to the late 1600s.[11] More rapid improvement of the agricultural basis of Scottish life is a particularly eighteenth-century phenomenon. Several principal components may be identified: new ways of managing and working land; new leasing structures; and enclosure — all occurred alongside shifts in Scottish rural society including the passing of the 'fermtoun' and the move from single to multiple tenancies. These changes were paralleled by the active involvement of a cultural and scientific 'audience' for agricultural theory and practice, and by the establishment of agricultural 'improvement' societies. Interest in agriculture was reflected, too, in a growth of literature upon agriculture and in lectures upon agricultural subjects.[12]

The audience for agricultural improvement in part concerned itself with discussing then established methods but was more concerned to deride traditional procedures and propose new practices founded on better principles. For Donaldson (1795), agrarian advance as a means of economic improvement was central to the interests of both individual and nation: 'The industrious husbandman not only enriches himself, but also advances the general prosperity of the community'.[13] The association of agricultural advance with the cultural and civic activity of social improvement was apparent in the involvement of many eighteenth-century Scottish scientists with what one author has termed the 'utilitarian impulse', an impulse itself part of the development of a Scottish 'earth science tradition' embracing geology, chemistry, mineral discovery, and natural history.[14] The universities figured centrally in the move to improvement. Outside the universities were numerous cultural and scientific institutions, through which new knowledge and new techniques were mediated through groups made up of practising scientists and landowning gentry, and disseminated into principles and practice for the benefit, first, of an audience of like-minded individuals, and, second, the nation as a whole.[15] The demand for knowledge and the importance attached to practical ends was reflected in what Shapin has described as an 'institutionalized alliance between agricultural improvement, powerfully urged by the august landed audience, and the rationalizing impulse of scientific intellectuals'.[16] It may be suggested that the notion of improvement intrinsic to this alliance operated at three levels simultaneously: the *cultural* in the sense of the institutional pursuit of natural knowledge as a means of maintaining that social order and particular rank of which constituent members were part; the *individual* in regard to personal status within any given community of interest; and the *economic*, both in the sense of the betterment of any one estate and the advancement of the country as a whole. As an active member of several improvement institutions, as university professor and public lecturer on agriculture to this improving audience, Walker holds a position of special interest.

The Rev. Dr. John Walker: enlightenment scientist

Walker was born in Edinburgh in 1731 and died there on 31 December 1803. From 1758 to 1762 he was minister at Glencorse in Midlothian and from 1762 to 1783 minister at Moffat. During this period he undertook extensive tours in the Scottish Highlands. From

1783 until his death, he was minister at Colinton near Edinburgh. From 1779, he was Regius Professor of Natural History and Keeper of the Museum in the University of Edinburgh. In addition to his university lectures on agricultural topics, he gave public 'Georgical lectures' in 1789 and 1790. Walker was, however, an unsuccessful candidate for the Chair of Agriculture in Edinburgh in 1790. He was a principal agent behind the 1783 foundation of the Royal Society of Edinburgh, which in its original intention considered agricultural improvement part of its plans 'for extending useful knowledge', and he maintained an extensive correspondence with improving landowners and farmers throughout Scotland. Prominent among his patrons was Henry Home, Lord Kames, who, in his capacity as a commissioner to the Forfeited Annexed Estates and member of the Board of Trustees, directed Walker to tour the Highlands.

Assessment of Walker's importance and involvement in agricultural theory and practice and in the development of natural history in Scotland rests upon examination of his university lectures in natural history within which he included discussion of agricultural topics and agriculture's place in national improvement, upon his public lectures in agriculture, and his work on the Scottish Highlands. What is also apparent from assessment of Walker's work is that whilst he actively promoted discourse on agriculture in the *general* interests of improvement, he was strongly defensive of what he regarded as his *individual* interests – the practice of natural history including agriculture and georgics – within scientific and public circles of the Enlightenment. This is particularly evident in the matter of the Chair of Agriculture and in his dealings with Andrew Coventry, the first incumbent.

Agriculture and Improvement in Walker's 'Natural History'

Walker never completed his intended 'Natural History of Scotland', and an understanding of what he understood by the subject has to be gleaned from the printing of his 1788 public lecture 'On the utility and progress of Natural History and manner of philosophizing'[17] and from comments in his university lectures, many of which survive as students' notes. In his university lectures Walker defines natural history as 'The arrangement, description and history of the works of creation contained in the terraqueous globe':

To avoid being bewildered amongst such variety, it is necessary to proceed with all the precision we are able and first to mark all the different branches of the science. It consists of six following:

1 Meteorology	⎱	Contain the natural
2 Hydrography	⎰	history of the globe in
3 Geology		general as marked by
		Hippocrates.
4 Mineralogy	⎱	Contain the natural
5 Botany	⎰	history of the fossil,
6 Zoology		vegetable and animal kingdom.[18]

Walker's agricultural material falls principally within 'botany' in the 'Vegetable Kingdom'. Underlying all of this work is the utilitarian philosophy of the eighteenth-century improver expressed not only in a concern with the application of natural knowledge as the basis of national *economic* utility, but also in a concern to provide useful knowledge for the *cultural* advancement of his audience of landed gentry and Edinburgh gentlemen:

> During the survey of natural history I have had in reflection I am surprised that so many branches of useful and ornamental knowledge should in this place never have been the subject of public instruction. Among men of education scarcely a day passes in which some part of the natural history does not occur in conversation, and yet few know any thing of it but what they have reap'd from books, or the conversation of other.
>
> I look upon natural history as necessary to form an accomplished Gentleman tho' too much neglected in their education, and I likewise esteem it necessary to form an accomplished Physician.[19]

Walker was well advantaged by his own long interest in natural science and his detailed knowledge of Scotland's natural productions. He laid great emphasis on field collection and on the sensory observation and examination of nature. His empirical bent was evident early in his life:

> I began to collect Fossils in the Year 1746, when attending the Natural Philosophy Class, and was first led to it, by the Perusal of Mr. Boyle's Works, and especially his Treatise on Gems. In this Pursuit I was accompanied by two of my most intimate Companions at the Time, Edward Wright, and Alexander Wight. We often traversed the Kings Park, the Sea Shores between Cramond & Musselburgh, and visited the Quaries & Coalleries near Edinburgh, but had no Book at the Time, to

direct us concerning the Species of Fossils, but Woodwards Catalogues. After studying the Works of Boyle, Becker, Stahl, Boerhaave, & some others, I attended Dr. Plummers Course of Chymistry in the Year 1749, and became still fonder of Mineralogy.[20]

In 1750, he toured Lothian and Tweeddale. In 1751, he visited Moffat and Annandale, and from 1753 he spent four years in Galloway and Kirkcudbrightshire at which time he gathered together a collection of marls and prepared a prizewinning essay on the subject.[21] It was at this period that Walker met William Cullen, after attending Cullen's chemistry lectures, and in 1758 and again in 1764 Cullen and Walker toured parts of Highland Perthshire together, both men engaged in their 'favourite pursuit' of mineralogy.[22]

This excursion into Walker's past is not without relevance to our more general concern. It highlights Walker's own practical basis to natural history, the social context within which much scientific work was undertaken and the empirical nature of his work. Whilst in his classifications of natural phenomena, Walker was a systematiser, an organiser of natural knowledge, in his lectures and writings his principal importance lies more in his inductive empiricism and utilitarian pursuit of improvement. In his lectures he notes, for example, how 'It is the task of a Botanist to discover unknown plants with a view to their future usefulness . . . It is the business of a *naturalist* to discover useful quantities in those that are already known'.[23] Most forceful is the following:

My leading idea in Natural History is to render it subservient to the Purposes of Life; to which great End, it is indeed eminently adapted. With this View, when I first drew out the general Plan, I was to follow in teaching; I engrossed in it three favourite Subjects; Agriculture, Plantation, and Gardening . . . I had Experimented and written to a considerable Extent, upon these Subjects and wished greatly to teach them . . . I have for sometime proposed; to give a course of Georgical Lectures upon Agriculture . . . I expected, that among the Gentlemen of the Parliament House, the Landed Gentlemen residing in Edinburgh, their Sons pursuing a general Education, and among the Intelligent Farmers in this Neighbourhood, I might find an Audience that would reward my Labour.[24]

Walker's decision to give public lectures on agriculture in 1789 and 1790 thus arose not only out of the successful prosecution of agricultural topics within his university natural history lectures but was also a conscious decision to meet the demands of a public audience pursuing improvement that was at once cultural and economic, individual and national.

Walker's Public Lectures on Agriculture

The material covered by Walker in these public lectures is outlined most clearly in his 'Syllabus of a Course of Lectures on Rural Oeconomy',[25] drawn up about 1790 in relation to the then advertised chair of agriculture under the patronage of Sir William Pulteney. The detailed content of the 'Syllabus' and of the lectures for which it formed the basis has been discussed elsewhere.[26] Important to consider in this context is the emphasis placed throughout upon economic improvement, and the lectures' impact and reception within that enlightenment audience engaged in agricultural advancement.

Walker was selective of the topics within his 'Syllabus' given the range of subjects to be considered, yet he was at all times aware of the importance of a utilitarian purpose: 'But those certainly are entitled to the fullest Illustration, which are most material to the Interest of the Country'.[27] Elsewhere he notes:

> As a course of lectures of this kind should be of public as well as private utility every opportunity should be embraced that can in any way be applied to the advantage and improvement of the useful arts – and such an opportunity occurs here.[28]

Walker's agricultural lectures usually make reference to general perspectives upon given subjects and to particular detailed instances and then to illustration of both general and particular through Scottish examples. We find him thus treating, for example, 'of the nature of soils in general & of those in Scotland in particular, with their particular properties and names and distinguishing marks, & the particular plants each of them is fitted to rear'; 'of the discovery of some grounds & other plants not now in use, but which are fitt to be tried as Green or Dry forage. Of the reclaiming of wild land, & to these we shall add a review of those obstacles which obstruct the improvement of Agriculture in Scotland'.[29]

These public lectures were well received and in consequence of the interest they aroused amongst Edinburgh's social and scientific circles 'an Agricultural Society was projected, which under his patronage and direction, may prove essential service to the practical farmer, and tend to the general diffusion of Georgical science over the country'.[30] The Edinburgh Agricultural Society was established in 1790.

Walker, the Edinburgh Agricultural Society and the 'Diffusion of Georgical Science'

It was principally through his involvement with the Edinburgh Agricultural Society that Walker corresponded on matters of agrarian improvement with a large number of Scottish farmers and landowners and other improving institutions. In January 1792, for example, the Jedburgh Farmers' Society asked Walker's advice on those topics that ought 'to be taken under consideration by a Society of Country Farmers who meet here Monthly to Communicate to one another such Observations as Cast up to them in the Course of their practice'.[31] To a request for advice from the Presbytery of Shetland in May 1790 on behalf of farmers there concerning the prevalence and treatment of sheepscab, Walker replied in two letters: the first a series of questions enquiring about the extent and nature of the disease in the northern isles and the remedies currently practised, the second a recommendation to smear the sheep with butter and tar. Such a practice was, according to Walker, then unknown in Shetland: 'But I well know from long observation, that in the South Country, its chief if not sole use is to preserve the sheep from Diseases, & especially from the Scab'.[32] Walker's correspondence also contains letters on the draining and management of moor lands, the most efficient method of weeding, and the rotation of crops. On this last topic, Walker communicated with several farmers and improvers. One lengthy letter from Thomas Scott, a Midlothian farmer, documents the way Scott experimented in the planting of crops to increase the yield. He writes to Walker of how the yields of potatoes or wheat increased, then, despite rotation, declined dramatically when the land was insufficiently dunged or kept in one crop too long: 'Thus [writes Scott] I found that what will appear very promising in Theory, may turn out Very Differently in practice'.[33]

George Henderson of Craigtoun near Kirkliston in Midlothian wrote to Walker in April 1791 concerning his son, Peter, attending Walker's lectures in the following year: 'Your fame for Knowledge in Natural History, One of the more usefull and Entertaining Studies, Draws on you this Trouble'. And for Capt. Charles Williamson, who had been corresponding with Walker on the relative merits of reaping with sickle or scythe, Walker's advice and comments are likewise highly regarded: 'The scheme you mention for advancing the knowledge of agriculture [his lecture course and the Edinburgh Agricultural Society] is certainly the best that can be adopted'.[34]

Not only was he a source and imparter of agricultural information: Walker was, importantly, a collector of it, gathering much from correspondence with those farmers and others scattered throughout Scotland who were engaged, like Scott, in practical experiments on more advanced farming methods. Simultaneously, he was discussing these and other ideas on agricultural improvements with the 'improving' gentlemen of urban Scotland through his own lecture courses and his own knowledge of Scotland's agriculture and natural resources. This complex relationship between agriculture and natural history and, in a wider context, between the pursuit of natural knowledge and social and material improvement is evident, too, in Walker's work on the Scottish Highlands.

Walker and the Improvement of the Highlands

Walker made six major Highland trips between 1764 and 1786. At least one was on behalf of the General Assembly of the Church of Scotland and the Society in Scotland for Propagating Christian Knowledge, which bodies, given their expressed interest in educating the Highlander and in providing for the spiritual improvement of the population of the region, asked Walker to examine and review the 'religious condition' of the Highlands.[35] The principal purpose of most of his visits, however, was to assess 'the Oeconomical improvements' of the Highlands and Islands with a view to their potential development. In one report to the Commissioners of the Annexed Estates, Walker recommended the introduction of various manufactures as principal 'Heads of Improvement'. Included were such things as the making of ropes; plans to instruct natives in quarrying, the need to create harbours to promote fishing; instructions to Highlanders on the collection of various 'natural productions' – green jasper and marble, for example – and Walker argued for the advantages likely to accrue 'if the Gentlemen would form themselves into Oeconomical Societies in the three great counties of *Argyll, Inverness, and Ross*'.[36] Elsewhere Walker writes at length about the economic benefits of kelp-making and peat.[37]

Agricultural methods and the means for their advance formed a major part of Walker's interest in Highland improvement and natural productions. His principal published works, both of which appeared posthumously, include much on Highland rural economy, usually with a view to its betterment, and Walker's emphasis on 'Oeconomical Societies' illustrates the importance he attached to the institutional means of improvement. His unpublished 'Queries concerning the North of Scotland', for example, record thirty-eight questions on the agriculture of the Highlands,[38] including 'the present manner of tillage and the succession of crops', the advantages arising from the use of the spade or *cas chrom* in the Highlands as opposed to the plough, the rents of different kinds of land, and what parts of the country might be improved by draining. Enclosure and artificial grasses were seen as particularly important agricultural agencies in that more general social and economic cultivation of the Highlands taking place in the 1700s:

> These are the two leading steps of improvement, in the uncultivated parts of Scotland, & yet are unknown in many places, where they might be beneficially practis'd. They are introductory to every sort of polishd Culture, & urge the Farmer to inclose; not only from Interest, but through Necessity.[39]

Elsewhere in his commentaries on the Highlands, we find him discussing the different types of economic interest embraced by the term 'improvement':

> In the improvement here recommended, there are four separate interests to be regarded. The interest of the landlord, of the farmer, of the inferior people, and of the public at large . . . These four interests, though separate, are by no means incompatible, or placed at irreconcilable variance with one another. They are in most cases capable of being justly advanced by the same means. In rural economy that measure will always be the best which unites and promotes these several interests.[40]

In his work on the Highlands, Walker was doing no more than he was for other parts of Scotland: observing and documenting agricultural improvements and natural productions as the basis of a more structured understanding of the classes of natural knowledge and thus promoting at the same time the means to national material and intellectual improvement.

Walker and the Edinburgh Chair of Agriculture

Whilst he used agriculture and natural history to promote such material interests, Walker was quite prepared to defend his own cultural and scientific interests particularly when he considered them threatened as in the case of Andrew Coventry's election to the chair of Agriculture, established under the patronage of Sir William Pulteney in 1790. For reasons that remain unclear, Walker was an unsuccessful candidate despite having drawn to Pulteney's attention his 'Syllabus' and his agricultural lectures, all of which, noted Walker, 'depend entirely on the Principles of Natural History'.

Coventry was appointed to teach and research upon a subject area which Walker had, in effect, been teaching as part of his Natural History for ten years and to a public audience for two years:

> . . . a set of Instructions or Lectures on the Subject of Agriculture respecting the Nature of Soils and Manures the Modes of Cultivation the Succession of crops the Construction of Implements of Husbandry the best and most successful known practices the manner of instituting Experiments to ascertain the Effect of any proposed practice in any Soil or climate and the best manner of introducing or training Skilful Labourers and Country artificers where these may be wanting.

Walker represented to the University Senate that, since he had been appointed to the natural history chair,

> . . . he thereby considers himself entitled to teach that Science in its full extent, as he hath hitherto done, with its application to the different useful Arts, and especially to all the different Branches of Rural Oeconomy, which are well known to depend entirely on the principles of Natural History.[41]

Walker continued that although he did not regard Coventry's appointment 'as an Interference; . . . as every such appointment must tend to the advancement of useful knowledge, and the good of the Public', he hoped that neither he nor his successors would be excluded 'from teaching any Branch of Natural History, though it may be taught by others'.[42] Reading between the lines, we may infer that Walker *did* object to this more formal presentation of agricultural topics partly because it would detract from their treatment within *his* domain of natural history, but chiefly, one senses, out of a feeling of being personally snubbed: Walker had not been elected to the chair of a subject he had long been teaching to that enlightenment audience for whom agricultural knowledge was of both polite and practical benefit.

Conclusion

Walker was not, of course, the sole source of practical and polite knowledge on agriculture in eighteenth-century Scotland and was far from being the only person engaged in the philosophical investigation and utilitarian pursuit of natural history. Little can be said in detail here in comparison of Walker's agricultural writings, particularly his *Syllabus*, with those of contemporary Scottish agricultural writers and theorists: for example, Francis Home's *The Principles of Agriculture and Vegetation* (1757), Adam Dickson's *A Treatise on Agriculture* (1762), Maxwell's *The Practical Husbandman* (1757), Kames' *The Gentleman Farmer* (1776), Wight's *Present State of Husbandry in Scotland*, published in six volumes from 1778 to 1784, or James Donaldson's *Modern Agriculture* of 1795. And this is to say nothing of English and continental texts upon agriculture, many of which Walker possessed in his personal library. Yet even without direct comparison, Walker's public lectures on agriculture, his consideration of 'georgical subjects' within his natural history course and his extensive correspondence and field-based researches suggest he was a central figure in the context of informed agricultural improvement during the Scottish enlightenment.

He was important in the context of those persons actively developing the rural economy for whom improvement was a marketable commodity and had exchange value in the form of yields and profits, and important, too, within that group made up of his university students and public audience for whom improvement was useful knowledge, use value, in the polite culture of Enlightenment Scotland. Walker derived his prestige then and his significance to research now both from his intellectual abilities, his philosophical enquiries and empirically-grounded research background, and from the social groups and cultural context of which he was part. The fact that he was, on the one hand, teaching natural history as a university professor and imparting agricultural knowledge and the benefits of natural science to some individuals whilst, on the other, himself enquiring on agrarian topics and gathering advice from practising farmers is important. Such an involvement by Walker and the fact, too, that these farmers and other members of the 'audience' for improvement were keen enough and 'scientific' enough to record and make known their experiences in practical improvement points to a considerable complexity in the relationships between natural history and agriculture, between enlightenment and improvement, in eighteenth-century Scotland.

NOTES

The research on which this essay is based was funded by a grant from the British Academy. For comments I am grateful to John Christie,

Roger Emerson, Charles Waterston, Rudiger Schreyer, Nick Fisher, and Peter Jones.

1. Hutton's reference to Walker is in a letter from Hutton to John Strange of London, c.1770; see V.A. Eyles and J.M. Eyles, 'Some Geological Correspondence of James Hutton', *Annals of Science*, 1951, 7, 316–399: the reference by Hope is in a letter of Hope to David Skene, 25 August 1763: Aberdeen Univ. Lib., MS 38, f.119.

2. G. Johnston, *A Flora of Berwick-upon-Tweed* (Edinburgh, 1831), II, p.322; S. Macvicar, in *Annals Scott. Nat. Hist.*, 1895 (Part 16), p.257; *idem* in *Trans. Proc. Bot. Soc. Edin.*, 1901, 22, p.20.

3. On Walker's zoological classifications, see R.K. Greville, *Algae Britannicae* (Edinburgh, 1830), p.iii; G. Johnston, *A History of the British Zoophytes* (Edinburgh, 1828), p.252; on correspondence between Linnaeus and Walker, see Edinburgh University Library (hereinafter EUL), La. III. 352/1, 22 Feb. 1762; 12 Oct. 1762; 20 June 1763; and W.M. Smallwood, in *The Scientific Monthly*, 1939, XLIX, 65–70.

4. J. Ritchie, 'Natural History and the Emergency of Geology in the Scottish Universities', *Trans. Edin. Geol. Soc.*, 1952, XV, 297–316.

5. G. Taylor, 'John Walker, D.D., F.R.S.E., 1731–1802: a notable Scottish naturalist', *Trans. Proc. Bot. Soc. Edin.*, 1959, XXXVIII, 180–203; R. Porter, *The Making of Geology: Earth Science in Britain, 1660–1815* (Cambridge, 1977), pp.147–156.

6. H. Scott (ed.), John Walker: *Lectures on geology, including hydrography, mineralogy and meteorology* (Chicago and London, 1966), p.xliv.

7. S. Shapin, 'Property, Patronage, and the politics of science: the founding of the Royal Society of Edinburgh', *Brit. Jour. Hist. Sci.*, 1974, 25, p.25; see also N. Campbell and R. Martin S. Smellie, *The Royal Society of Edinburgh, 1783–1983* (Edinburgh, 1983), pp.41, 103, 113, 116, 118.

8. Scott (ed.), *op. cit.*

9. M. McKay (ed.), *The Rev. Dr. John Walker's Report on the Hebrides of 1764 and 1771* (Edinburgh, 1980).

10. H. Scott, 'John Walker's lectures in agriculture (1790) at the University of Edinburgh', *Agric. Hist.*, 1969, xliii, 439–445; Charles W.J. Withers, 'A Neglected Scottish Agriculturalist: the Georgical Lectures, and agricultural writings of the Rev. Dr. John Walker (1731–1803)', *Agric. Hist. Rev.*, 1985, 33(II), 132–146.

11. I. Whyte, *Agriculture and Society in Seventeenth Century Scotland* (Edinburgh, 1979); R.A. Dodgshon, *Land and Society in Early Modern Scotland* (Oxford, 1982); see also T.C. Smout and A. Fenton, 'Scottish Agriculture before the Improvers – an exploration', *Agric. Hist. Rev.* 1965, XIII, 83–93; J.A.S. Watson and G.D. Amery, 'Early Scottish Agricultural Writers (1697–1900)', *Trans. High. Agric. Soc.*, 1931, XLIII, 60–85.

12. A number of works cover these general aspects of agricultural improvement in Scotland: J.E. Handley, *Scottish Farming in the Eighteenth Century* (Oxford, 1953); M.L. Parry and T.R. Slater (eds.), *The Making of the Scottish Countryside* (London, 1980); D. Turnock, *The Historical Geography of Scotland since 1707* (Cambridge, 1982); G.W. Whittington and I. Whyte (eds.),

An Historical Geography of Scotland (London, 1983); see also T.B. Franklin, *A History of Scottish Farming* (Edinburgh, 1952).

13. J. Donaldson, *Modern Agriculture; or the present State of Husbandry in Great Britain* (Edinburgh, 1795), p.4.

14. Porter (1977), *Op. cit.*, pp.149–165.

15. These relationships have been detailed elsewhere: see particularly R.L. Emerson, 'The social composition of enlightened Scotland: the select society of Edinburgh, 1754–1764', *Studies on Voltaire and the Eighteenth Century*, 1973, CXIV, 291–329; *idem*, 'The Philosophical Society of Edinburgh, 1737–1747', *British Journal for the History of Science*, 1979, 12, 165–209; *idem*, 'The Philosophical Society of Edinburgh, 1848–1768', *British Journal for the History of Science*, 1981, 14, 133–176; *idem*, 'Natural Philosophy and the problem of the Scottish Enlightenment', *Studies on Voltaire and the Eighteenth Century*, 1986, CCXLII, 243–291; S. Shapin, 'The audience for science in eighteenth-century Edinburgh', *History of Science*, 1974, 12, 95–121; *idem*, 'Property, Patronage, and the Politics of Science: the founding of the Royal Society of Edinburgh', *British Journal for the History of Science*, 1974, 7(25), 1–41: Shapin in this latter article shows how agriculture was considered part of the RSE's original remit; Emerson shows for the Philosophical Society that only 5 per cent of known topics discussed were on agriculture and improvement.

16. Shapin (1974), 'The audience . . .', p.102.

17. In his *Essays on Natural History and Rural Economy* (Edinburgh, 1808). That work and his *An Economical History of the Hebrides and the Highlands of Scotland* (Edinburgh, 1812) were published posthumously.

18. EUL, *Institutes of Natural History containing the Head of the Lectures in Natural History* (Edinburgh, 1792), ff.1–2.

19. Quoted in Scott (ed.), *op. cit.*, p.2.

20. Glasgow University Library (hereafter GUL), MS Gen 1061, f.3.

21. This essay formed the basis of Chapter VI of his *Essays on Natural History and Rural Economy* though the material was researched by Walker between 1753 and 1757; GUL, MS Gen 1061, ff.2–3.

22. GUL, MS Gen 1061, f.4, f.6.

23. EUL, MS Dc. 10.33.

24. EUL, MS La.III. 352/3.

25. Aberdeen University Library, MS 56.

26. Withers (1985), *op. cit.*

27. EUL, MS La.III. 352/3.

28. EUL, MS Dc. 10.33.

29. Ibid.

30. *Caledonian Mercury*, 3 April 1790.

31. EUL, MS La.III. 352/3, 4 January 1792.

32. Ibid., 12 May 1790.

33. Ibid., letters of 2 April 1789; 26 April, 5 & 9 May, 7 July, 3 November 1790; 2 March 1791; 25 February 1792.

34. Ibid., letter from Henderson, 11 April 1791; letter from Williamson, 12 June 1790.

35. Scottish Record Office, CH8/212/1; CH8/212/2; CH1/1/113; EUL, La. MS 484, f.24; *Scots Magazine* (1766), XXVIII, 680–689; (1772), XXXIV, 288–293. .

36. National Library of Scotland, MS 5007, f.20, ff.106–107, f.137.

37. In H. Mackenzie (ed.), *Prize Essays and Transactions of the Highland Society of Scotland*, I, 1–31 (An Essay on Kelp); II, 1–137 (An Essay on Peat); 164–203 (On the Cattle and Corn of the Highlands); 270–304 (On the herring); 346–376 (On the natural history of the salmon).

38. EUL, MS Dc. 2. 36, ff.13–45.

39. Ibid., f.19.

40. J. Walker, *An Economical History of the Hebrides and Highlands of Scotland* (Edinburgh, 1812), I, p.14.

41. EUL, MS Minute Book of the Senatus Academicus, Volume 2 (1790–1811), f.11; see also S. Richards, 'Agricultural Science in Higher Education: problems of identity in Britain's first chair of agriculture, Edinburgh 1790–c.1831', *Agric. Hist. Rev.* 1985, 33(I), 59–65.

42. EUL, MS, ibid., ff.13–41, 22 November 1790.

7
SIR JAMES STEUART:
ECONOMIC THEORY AND POLICY

Andrew S. Skinner

I

System

One of the most important features of Sir James Steuart's career was his extensive knowledge of the Continent. The Foreign Tour (1735–40) and exile as a result of his association with the Jacobites (1745–63) meant that by the end of the Seven Years' War Sir James has spent almost half of his life in Europe. In this time he mastered four languages (French, German, Spanish and Italian); facts which may help to explain Joseph Schumpeter's judgement that 'there is something un-English (which is not merely Scottish) about his views and his mode of presentation' (1954, p. 176n).

In the course of his travels Steuart visited a remarkable number of places which included Antwerp, Avignon, Brussels, Cadiz, Frankfurt, Leyden, Liège, Madrid, Paris, Rome, Rotterdam, Tübingen, Utrecht, Venice and Verona. He seems, moreover, consistently to have pursued experiences which were out of the common way. For example, when he settled at Angoulême not long after his exile began, he took advantage of his situation to visit Lyons and the surrounding country. During his residence in Tübingen, he undertook a tour of the schools in the Duchy of Württemberg. Earlier he had spent no less than fifteen months in Spain where he was much struck by the irrigation schemes in Valencia, Mercia, and Granada; the mosque in Cordoba, and the consequences of the famine in Andalousia in the Spring of 1737.[1] In fact very little seems to have been lost and it is remarkable how often specific impressions found their way into the main body of the *Principles*. In his major book Steuart noted the economic consequences of the Seven Years' War in Germany, the state of agriculture in Picardy, the arrangement of the kitchen gardens round Padua, and the problem of depopulation in the cities of the Austrian Netherlands[2] – not as

117

isolated examples, but as a part of the broader fabric of the argument as a whole.

The critical point to note is that a broad fabric of argument *is* present, reflecting Steuart's attempt to produce a single great conceptual system, linking the most interesting branches of modern policy, such as '*population, agriculture, trade, industry, money, coin, interest, circulation, banks, exchange, public credit,* and *taxes*' (p. 7). As Paul Chamley has pointed out, Steuart's attempt to produce a systematic treatise shows that he sought to include economics in the body of organised science, and that as such it conforms to the design of the *Encyclopédie* as described by D'Alembert (1965, p. 50).

Steuart's desire to produce a *scientific* system whose parts are linked by common principles shows a certain similarity, as to *motive*, with that later articulated by Adam Smith – and the parallel extends to the former's attempt to *organise* his discourse by 'contriving a chain of ideas, which may be directed towards every part of the plan, and which, at the same time, may be made to arise methodically from one another' (p. 28). The intention is therefore clear. It was rather the execution of the plan which presented Steuart with his initial difficulties; difficulties which were compounded by the sheer mass of material which was available to him and by the lack of a single clear model on which to base his account.[3]

Indeed Steuart himself, in the Preface to the *Principles*, explicitly drew attention to the difficulties under which he laboured precisely because he thought they would be of interest to the reader at the time of writing (pp. 5–6):

> I have attempted to draw information from every one with whom I have been acquainted: this however I found to be very difficult until I had attained to some previous knowledge of my subject. Such difficulties confirmed to me the justness of Lord Bacon's remark, that he who can draw information by forming proper questions, must be already possessed of half the science (pp. 5–6).

In approaching the problems involved, Steuart chose to adopt the broadly historical perspective associated with his friend David Hume whose essays he had read closely. Steuart too had taken a hint from what the late revolutions in the politics of Europe had pointed out to be the regular progress of mankind, from great simplicity to complicated refinement (p. 28).[4]

The approach was to find expression in a number of areas which include sociology, politics and economics. The outcome was distinctive, not least as a result of Steuart's sensitivity to the issue of scientific method (Skinner, 1966, p. lx). He was also acutely aware of the diversity of conditions in the countries which he had visited, and of the problems of economic development.

II

Historical Analysis

Steuart made use of a theory of stages, now recognised as a piece of apparatus which was central to the historical work notably of the Scottish School.[5] He cites, for example, the Tartars and Indians as relatively primitive socio-economic types of organisation (p. 56) while concentrating primarily on the third and fourth stages – the stages of agriculture and commerce. In the former case, Steuart observed that those who lacked the means of subsistence could acquire it only through becoming dependent on those who owned it; in the latter, he noted that the situation was radically different in that all goods and services command a price. He concluded, in passages of quite striking clarity:

> I deduce the origin of the great subordination under the feudal government, from the necessary dependence of the lower classes for their subsistence. They consumed the produce of the land, as the price of their subordination, not as the reward of their industry in making it produce (p. 208).

He continued: 'I deduce modern liberty from the independence of the same classes, by the introduction of industry, and circulation of an adequate equivalent for every service' (p. 209).

Steuart was also aware of the political aspect of these changes, and its effect upon the state:

> From feudal and military, it is become free and commercial. I oppose freedom in government to the feudal system, to mark only that there is not found now that chain of subordination among the subjects, which made the essential part of the feudal form.

He continued:

> I oppose commercial to military; because the military governments now are made to subsist from the consequences and effects of commerce only;

that is, from the revenue of the state, proceeding from taxes. Formerly, everything was brought about by numbers; now numbers of men cannot be kept together without money (p. 24).

Steuart noted that the gradual emergence of the stage of commerce had generated new sources of wealth which had affected the position of Princes:

> The pre-rogative of Princes, in former times, was measured by the power they could constitutionally exercise over the *persons* of their subjects; that of modern princes, by the power they have over the *purse* (p. 290).[6]

Perhaps with the fate of his former Jacobite associates in mind, Steuart also observed that 'an opulent, bold, and spirited people, having the fund of the Prince's wealth in their own hands, have it also in their power, when it becomes strongly their inclination, to shake off his authority' (p. 216).

The change in the distribution of power which was reflected in the changing balance between proprietor and merchant led Steuart to the conclusion that 'industry must give wealth and wealth *will* give power' (p. 213). As an earnest of this position, he drew attention (in his Notes on Hume's *History*) to the reduced position of the Crown at the end of the reign of Elizabeth: a revolution which appears 'quite natural when we set before us the causes which occasioned it. Wealth must give power; and industry, in a country of luxury, will throw it into the hands of the commons' (p. 213n).[7]

There is a further side to the analysis in that Steuart was concerned not only to contrast and compare the feudal and exchange economies, but also to consider the process of transition between them. In doing so, he started from a position where property was mainly in land, where the relationship between landlord and vassal or tenant was primarily based on service and where rents were chiefly paid in kind. To these institutions he added small towns, mainly located around the great seats, and composed of the few tradesmen and manufacturers who were necessary. Cities were represented as ecclesiastical centres which, significantly, had gradually 'formed themselves by degrees into small republics' (p. 60).

More rapid change came with trade, especially to the Americas and the East Indies, providing a stimulus to manufacturing and commerce on the model of the Hanstowns. While there is something of a parallel with Smith (*Wealth of Nations*, Book III), it is equally important to note that Steuart's analysis provides a link between economy, community, and state.

III

The Theory of Population

The analysis of the emergence of the exchange economy is not untypical of the period and intrinsically interesting even if Steuart did consider that it was more properly the province of the science of politics than that of political economy strictly defined. But he also argued that the subjects reviewed above were not 'altogether foreign to this' science, i.e. to economics (p. 208), illustrating the truth of the remark by deploying the 'stadial' thesis in a purely economic context. The technique finds illustration in a number of fields, and generally involves the use of the stages of society treated as *models* which gradually increase in complexity. As Steuart put it, in constructing any body of theoretical knowledge:

> Every branch of it must, in setting out, be treated with simplicity, and all combinations not absolutely necessary, must be banished from the theory. When this theory again comes to be applied to examples, combinations will crowd in, and every one of these must be attended to (p. 227).

The first analytical problem to which Steuart addressed himself was that of population where his stated purpose was 'not to inquire what numbers of people were found upon the earth at a certain time, but to examine the natural and rational causes of multiplication' (p. 31). In so doing he stated that the 'fundamental principle' is 'generation; the next is food' (*Ibid.*), from which it follows that where men live by gathering the spontaneous fruits of the soil (the North American Indian model), population levels must be determined by their extent:

> From what has been said, we may conclude, that the numbers of mankind must depend upon the quality of food produced by the earth for their nourishment; from which, as a corollary may be drawn.
> That mankind have been, as to numbers, and must ever be, in proportion to the food produced; and that the food produced will be in compound proportion to the fertility of the climate, and the industry of the inhabitants (pp. 36–7).

Where some effort is applied to the cultivation of the soil (the agrarian stage), Steuart recognised that the output of food and therefore the level of population would grow. But here again he drew a distinction between cultivation for subsistence, which was typical of the feudal stage, and the application of industry to the soil as found in the modern situation where goods and services command a price, and where the potential for economic growth (and therefore population) is greatly enhanced.[8]

Perhaps two major points arising from this argument deserve further notice.

To begin with, attention should be drawn to the emphasis which Steuart gives to the interdependent state of the sectors in his model of the exchange economy, recognising as he did that '*Agriculture among a free people will augment population, in proportion only as the necessitous are put in a situation to purchase subsistence with their labour*' (p. 40). Secondly, Steuart gave a good deal of attention to the point that the whole process depended on 'reciprocal' wants and that there are cases where the limited extent of the latter will constrain economic development and population growth:

> Experience everywhere shows the possible existence of such a case, since no country in Europe is cultivated to the utmost: and that there are many still where cultivation, and consequently multiplication, is at a stop. These nations I consider as being in a *moral incapacity* of multiplying: the incapacity would be *physical*, if there was any actual impossibility of their procuring an augmentation of food by any means whatsoever (p. 42).

Although we cannot review the theory in any detail here, it can be said that in Book I we confront a single major theme, the theory of population; a theory which while owing a great deal to David Hume (and possibly to Cantillon) nonetheless represents one of Steuart's most distinguished contributions and one of the best examples of his capacity for the systematic deployment of different levels of abstraction. But equally characteristic of his mode of argument is the fact that the theory is built up in such a way as to permit him to provide an account of the modern or exchange economy (the last of the 'models' used above), thus gradually widening the scope of the inquiry while still preserving a coherent 'chain of ideas'.

IV

The Exchange Economy

In dealing with the *nature* of the exchange economy, it is significant that Steuart made little use of the division of labour in the Smithian sense of the term (although he does cite the example of the pin at page 158). On the other hand, he gave great emphasis to the *social* division of labour in using the basic sectoral division to be found in Cantillon, Hume, Mirabeau, and Quesnai's *Encyclopédie* articles:

> we find the people distributed into two classes. The first is that of the farmers who produce the subsistence, and who are necessarily employed in this branch of business; the other I shall call *free hands*; because their occupation being to procure themselves subsistence out of the superfluity of the farmers, and by a labour adapted to the wants of the society, may vary according to these wants, and these again according to the spirit of the times (p. 43).

In both cases productive activity involves what Steuart defines as *industry*, namely, '*the application to ingenious labour in a free man, in order to procure, by means of trade, an equivalent, fit for supplying every want*'. *Trade*, on the other hand, is defined as '*an operation by which the wealth, or work, either of individuals, or of societies, may, by a set of men called merchants, be exchanged, for an equivalent, proper for supplying every want, without any interruption to industry, or any check upon consumption*' (p. 146). The whole pattern is carried on through the use of *money*, also defined, with characteristic care as '*any commodity, which purely in itself is of no material use to man . . . but which acquires such an estimation from his opinion of it, as to become the universal measure of what is called value, and an adequate equivalent for anything alienable*' (p. 44).

For Steuart the modern system was clearly an exchange economy characterised by a high degree of dependence between forms of activity and the individuals who carried them on, so that the idea or ideal of a free society emerges as involving '*a general tacit contract, from which reciprocal and proportional services result universally between all those who compose it*' (p. 88). Later Steuart was to state an hypothesis of obvious relevance to the situation under review in remarking that 'the principle of self-interest will serve as a general key to this inquiry; and it may, in one sense, be considered as the ruling principle of my subject, and may therefore be traced throughout the whole. This is the main spring . . .' (p. 142).

But the main underlying theme remains that of the interdependence of economic phenomena; a theme which brought Steuart quite logically to the treatment of price and allocation.

As far as the supply price of commodities is concerned, Steuart noted two elements: 'to wit, the real value of the commodity, and the profit upon alienation'. Real value was defined in such a way as to include three elements:

The first thing to be known of any manufacture when it comes to be sold, is how much of it a person can perform in a day, a week, a month, according to the nature of the work.

The second thing to be known, is the value of the workman's subsistence and necessary expence, both for supplying his personal wants, and providing the instruments belonging to his profession, which must be taken upon an average as above . . .

The third and last thing to be known, is the value of the materials, that is the first matter employed by the workman. . . . These three articles being known, the price of the manufacture is determined. It cannot be lower than the amount of all three, that is, than the real value; whatever it is higher, is the manufacturer's profit (pp. 160–61).

He went on to note that in a position of *equilibrium*, prices are found in the adequate proportion of the real expence of making the goods, with a small addition for profit to the manufacturer and merchant (p. 189).

As far as the *process* of price determination was concerned, Steuart contended that the outcome of the 'contract' would be determined by competition between and among buyers and sellers:

Double competition is, when, in a certain degree, it takes place on both sides of the contract at once, or vibrates alternately from one to the other. This is what restrains prices to the adequate value of the merchandize (p. 172).

Thus, for example, if there is a relative shortage of some commodity, there may be competition between buyers in order to procure limited supplies, causing prices to rise. In the event of an excess supply, for example of a perishable commodity such as fish, there will be competition between sellers to rid themselves of excess stocks, thus causing prices to fall below their equilibrium values. Both cases present examples of what Steuart called 'simple competition' prevailing in effect in one side of the 'contract' only.

Two points follow from this argument: first, that a 'balance' between demand and supply does not of itself indicate a position of equilibrium; and, second, that the process of bargaining will normally affect both parties to the exchange.

Steuart was thus able to offer a definition of *equilibrium* but also a statement of a *stability* condition in noting that:

In proportion therefore as the rising of prices can stop demand, or the sinking of prices can increase it, in the same proportion will competition prevent either the rise or the fall from being carried beyond a certain length (p. 177).

Finally, it should be noted that Steuart was aware, in general terms, of the allocative functions of the market. As he put it:

> Trade produces many excellent advantages; it marks out to the manufacturers when their branch is under or overstocked with hands. If it be understocked, they will find more demand than they can answer; if it be overstocked, the sale will be slow (p. 158).

Arguments such as these are obviously broadly 'static' in character but in fact are to be found in a setting which illustrates that preoccupation with long-run dynamics which characterised the argument of the first Book, thus presenting the reader with yet another change of focus.

V

Economic Trends: The Closed Economy

Adam Smith would have had little difficulty in appreciating the broadly optimistic assessment which Steuart offered with regard to economic growth. It is readily apparent that Steuart saw no reason to doubt the potential for economic development in the context of the *exchange* economy. Here, and for the first time in an *institutional* sense:

> Wealth becomes *equably distributed*; . . . by *equably distributed* I do not mean, that every individual comes to have an *equal* share, but an equal chance, I may say a certainty, of becoming rich in proportion to his industry (*Works*, 1805, ii. 156).

Steuart also argued that the potential for economic growth was almost without limit or certain boundary in the current 'situation of every country in Europe' – and especially France, 'at present in her infancy as to improvement, although the advances she has made within a century excite the admiration of the world' (p. 137). An equally dramatic confirmation of the general theme is to be found in the chapter on machines, which he considered to be 'of the greatest utility' in 'augmenting the produce or assisting the labour and ingenuity of man' (p. 125).[9]

Again in the manner of Smith (and indeed Adam Ferguson), it was Steuart's contention that the modern economy had opened up new forms of demand and new incentives to industry. In a passage reminiscent of Smith's *Moral Sentiments* (which he may have read), Steuart drew attention to man's love of ingenuity and to the fact that the satisfaction of one level of perceived wants tends to open up others by virtue of a kind of 'demonstration' effect (p. 157).[10]

The general point at issue is best caught by Steuart's earlier (but recurring) contrast between the feudal and modern systems:

> *Men were then forced to labour because they were slaves to others; men are now forced to labour because they are slaves to their own wants* (p. 51).

But Steuart was to offer a further application of the thesis just considered which was to have a significant effect on his policy recommendations.

It will be recalled that Steuart's definition of equilibrium required that the balance between supply and demand be such that 'prices are found in the adequate proportion of the real expence of making the goods, with a small addition for profit to the manufacturer or merchant'. It was Steuart's view that this definition, originally applied to particular commodities, must also apply to *all* goods, thus suggesting, as in the case of Smith's *Lectures*, an intuitive grasp of the general interdependence of economic phenomena. Indeed this perspective seems to dominate Steuart's treatment of the long run, where he argues in effect that the balance of work and demand, *taking the economy as a whole*, is likely to change over time with consequent effects on the components of real value and on the relationship between real value and price (as described above).

Some causes of change were easily explained. Steuart recognised that taxes, for example, could affect the prices of commodities. He also drew attention to a tendency for the prices of primary products (subsistence and materials) to rise over time, especially as the result of 'the increase of population, which may imply a more expensive improvement of the soil' (p. 198). But the most significant problem, for Steuart, was located on the demand side.

It was in this connection that he drew attention to two problems of particular importance. First, he suggested that the long-run trend would be for the balance of demand to preponderate (i.e. over supply), thus suggesting a tendency for prices to rise over time and to generate higher levels of profit. In this connection he suggested that higher profits 'subsisting for a long time . . . insensibly become *consolidated* or, as it were, transformed into the intrinsic value of goods' in such a way as to become 'in a manner necessary' to their existence (p. 193). Secondly, and related to the above, Steuart distinguished between *physical* and *political* necessities, where the former is defined almost in biological terms as '*ample subsistence where no degree of superfluity is implied*' (p. 269). He added:

> The nature of man furnished him with some desires relative to his wants, which do not proceed from his animal oeconomy, but which are entirely similar to them in their effects. These proceed from the affections of his mind, are formed by habit and education, and when once *regularly established*, create another kind of necessary which, for the sake of distinction, I shall call *political* (p. 270).

Steuart went on from this point to suggest that the political necessary was 'determined by birth, education or habit' and 'rank' in society, clearly recognising that it is 'determined by general opinion only, and therefore can never be justly ascertained' (p. 271). But he was clear in respect of one point; namely, that there will be a tendency for the accepted definition of political necessary to rise over time, with consequent effects on the supply prices of commodities. The importance of this argument was to emerge in the next stage of the exposition: the treatment of international trade.

VI

Aspects of International Trade

In the second book Steuart dropped the assumption of the closed economy and proceeded to examine the issue of international trade. Characteristically, he traced the interrelationship between developed and undeveloped nations in terms of the distinction between active and passive trade, which had already been established by Malachy Postlethwayt.[11] Here the purpose was to examine the positive impact of foreign demand on a backward economy in terms of an argument which would not have disgraced one of Adam Smith's most notable disciples, the French economist, J.B. Say,[12] who in effect elaborated on an argument which is implicit in Smith's Book III.

Equally striking is the fact that Steuart treated different *states* as competitive firms:

> The trading nations of Europe represent a fleet of ships, every one striving who shall get first to a certain port. The statesman of each is the master. The same wind blows upon all; and this wind is the principle of self-interest, which engages every consumer to seek the cheapest and the

best market. No trade wind can be more general, or more constant than this (p. 203).

Steuart's treatment of international trade take as its basic premiss the proposition that economic conditions and performance will differ even in the context of relatively developed nations whose trade he described as 'active'.

He was clearly aware of variations caused by 'natural advantages' such as access to materials, transport and the nature of the climate (p. 238), as befits a close student and admirer of 'the great Montesquieu' (p. 121). To these he added the form of government in arguing that 'trade and industry have been found to flourish best under the republican form, and under those which have come nearest to it' (p. 211).[13] But equally important for Steuart were the spirit of a people and 'the greater degree of force' with which 'a taste for refinement and luxury in the rich, an ambition to become so, and an application to labour and ingenuity in the lower classes of men' manifested themselves in different societies at any one point in time and over time.

He also believed that there are likely to be variations in the extent to which the definition of 'political necessary' changes through time and the rate and extent to which the 'balance' of demand tends to preponderate in different countries. Steuart was acutely conscious of the sheer variety of economic conditions and indeed noted early in the book that:

> If one considers the variety which is found in different countries, in the distribution of property, subordination of classes, genius of people, proceeding from the variety of forms of government, laws, climate, and manners, one may include, that the political oeconomy of each must necessarily be different (p. 17).

The number of possible 'combinations' opened up by the proposition that growth rates and other characteristics will vary is virtually endless. In recognition of this point Steuart employed three broad classifications, all of which may derive from Mirabeau's *Friend of Man* (1756): the stages of infant, foreign, and inland trade.[14]

Infant Trade represents that situation 'known in all ages, and in all countries, in a less or a greater degree' and which is antecedent to supplying the wants of others. Here the ruling principle

> is to encourage the manufacturing of every branch of natural produc-
> tions, by extending the home-consumption of them; by excluding all
> competition with strangers; by permitting the rise of profits, so far as
> to promote dexterity and emulation in invention and improvement; by

relieving the industrious of their work, as often as demand for it falls short; and, until it can be exported to advantage, it may be exported with loss, at the expense of the public (p. 263).

At the same time Steuart suggested that the statesman must control profit levels so that when the real value of commodities indicates that they are competitive in the international context, trade may begin. In the same vein he argued that while protection is essential if industry is to be established (p. 262), 'the scaffolding must be taken away when the fabric is completed' (*Works*, ii. 235).

In the case of *foreign trade*, taken as representing the attainment of a competitive stage, the policies recommended are simply designed to retain the capability: here the ruling principles are 'to banish luxury; to encourage frugality; to fix the lowest standard of prices possible; and to watch, with the greatest attention, over the vibrations of the balance between work and demand. While this is preserved, no internal vice can affect the prosperity of it' (p. 263).

Inland Trade, on the other hand, represents a situation where a developed nation has lost its competitive edge. Here the basic preoccupation must be the maintenance of the level of employment. He also recognised the importance of the balance of payments in advocating a restrictive monetary policy, and concluded:

> I will not therefore say, that in every case which can be supposed, certain restrictions upon the exportation of bullion or coin are contrary to good policy. This proposition I confine to the flourishing nations of our own time (p. 581).

In the state of inland trade, the basic problem was to keep domestic price levels as low as possible with a view to taking advantage of the difficulties of others. With the possible exception of Holland, it was Steuart's contention that because all nations would suffer the same long-run trends, but at different rates, it followed that:

> as industry and idleness, luxury and frugality, are constantly changing their balance throughout the nations of Europe, able merchants make it their business to inform themselves of these fluctuations, and able statesmen profit of the discovery for the re-establishment of their own commerce (p. 296).[15]

Finally, it may be noted that although Steuart presents the three stages as being representative of various states of an economy, he also made the point that industries or regions within any *given* economy

might manifest characteristics of all of them at any particular point
in time:

> I shall only add, that we are not to suppose the commerce of any nation
> confined to any one of the three species. I have considered them separately,
> according to custom, in order to point out their different principles. It is
> the business of statesmen to compound them according to circumstances
> (p. 265).

VII

Economic Policy

The duties of the statesman in the economic sphere are clear: having
defined the essence of the exchange economy as involving a 'general tacit
contract', Steuart went on to note that 'Whenever . . . anyone is found,
upon whom nobody depends, and who depends on everyone, as is the
case with him who is willing to work for his bread, but who can find
no employment, there is a breach of contract and an abuse' (p. 88). In
Steuart's view, the true purpose of the science of political economy

> is to secure a certain fund of subsistence for all the inhabitants, to obviate
> every circumstance which may render it precarious, to provide every thing
> necessary for supplying the wants of the society, and to employ the inhab-
> itants (supposing them to be freemen) in such a manner as naturally to
> create reciprocal relations and dependencies between them (p. 17).

As in the case of Smith, the justification for intervention is market
failure although Steuart's position with respect to the functions of the
state in fact arises directly from the areas of analysis and policy with
which he was primarily concerned.[16]

Looking back over the arguments which we have reviewed, it is
appropriate firstly to recall Steuart's interest in *pre*-modern societies and
in the *emergence* of the exchange economy. Steuart's concern with society
in a process of transition is reflected in his attempt to formulate policies
designed to deal with the problems generated by *historical* developments;
developments which had caused cities to expand, and feudal retainers
to be dismissed. It is in this context that the statesman is invited to
consider the employment of redundant nobles and of the 'multitudes
of poor' together with the all-important issue of the means of
communication (such as good roads). Steuart suggested that the
historical and contemporary record would also provide an invaluable

guide to the problems which would confront a statesman who adopted a self-conscious policy of economic *and therefore* of social development. It was Steuart's contention that in many cases the transition from a state of 'trifling industry' and subsistence farming (which could be described as the primitive version of the stage of commerce) could not occur without the interposition of the sovereign (p. 108). In a striking passage, which reminds the reader of his remarkable range of experience, Steuart observed that:

> Pipers, blue bonnets, and oat meal, are known in Swabia, Auvergne, Limousin, and Catalonia, as well as in Lochaber: numbers of idle, poor, useless hands, multitudes of children, whom I have found to be fed, nobody, knows how, doing almost nothing at the age of fourteen . . . If you ask why they are not employed, their parents will tell you because commerce is not in the country: they talk of commerce as if it was a man, who comes to reside in some countries in order to feed the inhabitants. The truth is it is not the fault of these poor people, but of those whose business it is to find out employment for them (*ibid.*).

Steuart's general interest in regional issues is a marked feature of the *Principles* and was to find further expression in his *Considerations of the Interest of the County of Lanark in Scotland*, which was first published in 1769 under the name of Robert Frame. This short work was explicitly designed to illustrate general principles by reference to a particular case; namely that of a backward county in which Steuart resided and which supplied corn to the neighbouring city of Glasgow. Steuart was concerned to demonstrate the impact of the city's demand for agricultural products on an undeveloped region (*Works*, v., p. 321). He also drew attention to the fact that economic development had enhanced local demand, and thus temporarily reduced the supply of food available for sale outwith the region.

From the point of view of the city, the fact that local supply was fitful had lent support to the proposed Forth and Clyde Canal which was intended to link the two coasts and further to improve the market for grain. Steuart clearly welcomed this development, while warning his contemporaries that its *short-run* effect would be to *ruin* local agriculture *unless* steps were taken to further the cause of agricultural improvement and of the local infrastructure.[17] In particular he contended that the infant industry argument which merchants had applied to the textiles of Paisley should be extended to agriculture (*Works*, v, p. 308). He also advocated high and stable prices for agricultural products, while calling for a granary scheme which would in effect secure supplies and stabilise incomes at a level which was consistent with improvement.[18]

As we have seen, Steuart also gave a great deal of attention to policy with respect to international trade, in emphasising the need for protection in *particular* cases: to employment policy, and to monetary restrictions especially in the context of the stages of 'infant' and 'inland' trade. Yet it should be recalled that he also defended more liberal policies for nations which were able to compete (the stage of foreign trade) and that intervention was justified only in cases of necessity:

> Were industry and frugality found to prevail equally in every part of these great political bodies, or were luxury and superfluous consumption everywhere carried to the same height, trade might, without any hurt, be thrown entirely open. It would then cease to be an object of a statesman's care and concern (p. 296).

But there is a certain realism in Steuart's general conclusion:

> Nothing, I imagine, but an universal monarchy, governed by the same laws, and administered according to one plan, well concerted, can be compatible with an universally open trade. While there are different states, there must be separate interests; and when no one statesman is found at the head of these interests, there can be no such thing as a common good; and where there is no common good, every interest must be considered separately (p. 365).[19]

VIII

Government and Constraint

In view of the emphasis which Steuart placed on the statesman it is important to bear in mind that he was not speaking of 'ministers of state, and even such as are eminent for their knowledge in state affairs' (p. 16n), nor yet of a particular type of government. As he put it, within the context of the *Principles* the *statesman* is taken to be a 'general term to signify the legislature and supreme power, according to the form of government' (p. 16). Steuart spoke

> of governments only which are conducted systematically, constitutionally, and by general laws; and when I mention princes, I mean their councils. The principles I am enquiring into, regard the cool administration of their government; it belongs to another branch of politics, to contrive bulwarks against their passions, vices and weaknesses, as men (p. 217).

In a political sense the statesman is an essentially abstract concept, which reminds us once more that Steuart differentiated more clearly than most between economics, politics, and ethics:

> Did I propose a plan of execution, this supposition, I confess, would be absurd; but as I mean nothing further than the investigation of principles, it is no more so, than to suppose a point, a straight line, or an infinite, in treating of geometry. (16, n.3).

Yet the discussion is not wholly abstract.

Steuart gave a great deal of emphasis to the constraints confronting the statesman, in drawing attention, much as Smith had done, to the importance of the 'spirit' of a people as 'formed upon a set of received opinions relative to three objects: morals, government, and manners' (p. 22) – opinions of such significance 'that many examples may be found, of a people's rejecting the most beneficial institutions, and even the greatest favours, merely because some circumstances had shocked their established customs' (p. 27). Linked to the above, but separate from it, was Steuart's concern with the subject's imperfect knowledge of the purposes of particular policies – indeed he pointed out in the Preface that although the work may 'seem addressed to a statesman, the real object of the inquiry is to influence the spirit of those whom he governs'. He went on to note that 'A people taught to expect from a statesman the execution of plans, big with impossibility and contradiction, will remain discontented under the government of the best of kings' (pp. 12–13).

To such constraints must be added those of a broadly constitutional kind in that the major instruments of modern policy (for example public debt and taxes) have to be sensitively applied if they are not to be counterproductive. Steuart also noted that the advent of the modern economy had led to a shift in the balance of political power as noted above (cf. Winch, 1978).

But perhaps the most important element in what A.O. Hirschman (1977) has recently called Steuart's 'deterrence model' of government is the emphasis given to the role of purely economic laws. For Steuart, the statesman 'is neither master to establish what oeconomy he pleases, nor, in the exercise of his sublime authority, to overturn at will the established laws of it, let him be the most despotic monarch upon earth' (p. 16). Later he wrote:

> When once a state begins to subsist by the consequences of industry, there is less danger to be apprehended from the power of the sovereign.

> The mechanism of his administration becomes more complex, and . . . he finds himself so bound up by the laws of his political oeconomy, that every transgression of them runs him into new difficulties (p. 217).

This point did not go unnoticed.

When the *Principles* was reviewed in 1767, it was in the main criticised for the role ascribed to the statesman. The point was repeated in the reviews of Steuart's *Works* (1805) when the *Monthly* complained that the author had committed a 'capital and injurious mistake' when insisting on the 'statesman's constant superintendence over trade'.[20] Yet the same reviewer perceptively remarked that:

> a reader of the present day will most prize, in these volumes, their illustration of the influence of political economy on civil government; which places in the strongest light the mischiefs of arbitrary rule, and which exhibit it as not less prejudicial to its depositaries than to their subjects. This very momentous question, is no where, to our knowledge, so satisfactory treated.

The reviewer of the Playfair edition of the *Wealth of Nations* in the same journal, noted that:

> Wide as have been the excursions of Dr Smith into politics and statistics, he never discussed the influence of the true principles of political economy over civil government. This fine subject, however, has been treated by Sir James Steuart with considerable success.[21]

IX

Conclusion: Steuart and Smith

The lives of Steuart and Smith, like their careers, scarcely touched. Steuart was called to the bar in 1735 two years before Smith became a student in Glasgow. Having embarked on the Foreign Tour in the same year, Sir James returned to Scotland at the very time that Adam Smith went to Oxford as the Snell Exhibitioner (1740). By the time Smith left Oxford in 1746, Steuart was already in exile, and when in 1764 the Professor left for France as tutor to Buccleuch, Steuart had just returned to Scotland. At this time he was busily engaged in completing a work which was published within a year of Smith's return from France. In their later years, the two men lived on opposite sides of the country: Smith as a government official based in Edinburgh, and Steuart as a country gentleman living in Lanarkshire, having abandoned all hopes of further official recognition.[22]

Smith's position with regard to the *Principles* has not emerged with any clarity.[23] While it is known that he owned a copy of the book, he made no mention of it even in respect of areas where Steuart had provided relevant information – notably with regard to the Bank of Amsterdam where Smith claimed in the advertisement to the fourth edition of the *Wealth of Nations* that 'no printed account had ever appeared to me satisfactory, or even intelligible'. Steuart's interesting account of Law's Bank suffered the same fate, as did his careful analysis of the Scottish Banks (Book IV, Part 2).[24]

On the other hand, it is reported that Smith had 'been heard to observe that he understood Sir James's system better from his conversation than from his volumes' (Rae, 1895, p. 63). It is also known that Smith wrote to William Pulteney on September 4th, 1772, to the effect that:

> I have the same opinion of Sir James Stewart's book that you have. Without once mentioning it, I flatter myself, that every false principle in it, will meet with a clear and distinct confutation in mine (*Correspondence*, Letter 132).

Yet such a statement does not preclude recognition of the fact that there were principles in the book which were not incorrect. Reading the work in 1767, the author of the essay on 'Astronomy' could hardly fail to appreciate Steuart's scientific purpose; his concern with the emergence of the 'present establishments in Europe', the successful deployment of the 'theory of stages' which Smith himself had used in his *Lectures*, or the interest shown by a *trained lawyer* in the relationship between the mode of subsistence and the patterns of authority and subordination. There is a similar emphasis on the importance of 'natural wants' as a stimulus to economic activity, and the same broadly sociological dimension to a discussion which features so strongly in Smith's ethics.

In terms of economic analysis Smith would have confronted a sophisticated theory of population, an advanced theory of the determination of prices, and the same clear grasp of the interdependence of economic phenomena that marked his own early work in the *Lectures on Jurisprudence*. Other and more general parallels are to be observed in Steuart's awareness of the enormous potential for economic growth and in his appreciation of the contributions made by international trade to the process (p. 119).

If this is hardly surprising in view of the influence exerted by David Hume[25] on both his friends, it might also be claimed that the *Principles* outstrips the economic sections of the *Lectures* in terms of technical sophistication.

But the *Wealth of Nations* differs from the *Principles* analytically; especially in respect of Smith's clear distinction between factors of production (land, labour, capital), and categories of return (rent, wages, profit), and in Smith's use of a macro-economic model of the circular flow which was informed throughout by physiocratic teaching. It can plausibly be argued that Smith's visit to Paris in 1766 transformed the analytical structure envisaged in the *Lectures* quite fundamentally: a transformation effected by Smith's knowledge of economic models of which Steuart was unaware in the late 1750s, when Books I and II were completed.[26]

There is a further contrast. In the case of Smith there is a clear presumption against interference by government – although that is not to be taken to mean that Smith saw a limited role for the state.[27] But in Steuart's work, 'the science of domestic policy' is consistently directed to the 'statesman'. His government is 'continually in action'. As he noted: 'In treating every question of political oeconomy I constantly suppose a statesman at the head of government, systematically conducting every part of it' (p. 122).

Economists have long been troubled by a contrast which makes it all too easy to conclude that Smith was in some sense 'enlightened' whereas Steuart was not. Without wishing further to comment on the issue by way of direct comparison, it may be helpful to recall the distinction between the principle which justifies intervention (such as market failure) and the specific agenda which is presented. The point is of course that while the basic principle may claim wide validity, the agenda actually presented will depend on the author's perception of the problems to be addressed.

In Steuart's case there may be a genuine difference, as compared to Smith, in respect of the confidence with which he believed governments could identify just when and where markets have failed (cf. Skinner, 1986). But there are other, perhaps more fundamental, differences in approach which are easier to assess.

The *Wealth of Nations* succeeded in supplying a great conceptual system whose component parts had a perceived relevance in an industrial age which Smith did not see, and which continued to meet the needs of the modern science of economics long after his death.[28] Steuart, in contrast, sought immediate relevance in an institutional sense, and thus gives the reader some inkling of the problems of economic and social policy actually to be confronted at the time of writing.[29] It is perhaps in this respect that Steuart has been somewhat neglected by economists – and by students of the Scottish Enlightenment. A number of areas commend themselves to our attention.

To begin with, it should be emphasised that while Smith and others gathered information about remote peoples, Steuart exploited a unique if unwanted opportunity with respect to *contemporary Europe*. In the course of his travels he visited, as we have seen, a number of places which would be remarkable even by modern standards and which is astonishing given the problems of communication at the time. It is scarcely surprising that Dugald Stewart, that most perceptive of commentators on Adam Smith, should have recommended his students to *begin* their study of political economy with the *Wealth of Nations* and *then* proceed to the *Principles* as a work which contained 'a great mass of accurate details' gleaned by 'personal observation during a long residence on the Continent' (1857, ix. 458). Dugald Stewart may also have intended his students to appreciate a very different perspective, in that Sir James's stance is European rather than English in orientation.

Secondly, attention should be drawn to Steuart's interest in 'that spirit of liberty, which reigns more and more every day, throughout all the polite and flourishing nations of Europe' (p. 18). He was acutely aware of a current 'revolution' in the affairs of Europe: '*Trade* and *Industry* are in vogue: and their establishment is occasioning a wonderful fermentation with the remaining fierceness of the feudal constitution' (p. 215).

In fact, Steuart, notably in Book I of the *Principles*, directly addressed a problem, which is implicit in the analysis of the third book of the *Wealth of Nations*, but which was not *explicitly* considered by Smith: namely, the *economics* of the process which finally resulted in the emergence of the fourth stage of commerce in its *advanced* form. *Steuart's* model is that of 'primitive accumulation' in *contrast* to Smith where 'the process of primitive accumulation has now been completed' (Kobayashi, 1967, p. 19).[30] The same point has been made by Michael Perelman in noting that Steuart *directly* addressed the problems of a *primitive* version of the stage of commerce (1983, p. 454) in a way which led Marx to appreciate his sensitivity to historical differences in modes of production (*op. cit.*, p. 468).[31]

It is a striking fact that although Smith uses primitive and advanced versions of the stages of pasture and agriculture (*Wealth of Nations*, Book III), he does *not* consider the primitive case of the stage of commerce.

It should be noted that although Steuart was to introduce a great number of changes to his text between 1767 and 1780 (the year of his death), he did *not* introduce materials which reflect a reading of the *Wealth of Nations*, or of physiocratic writing. The reason is not analytical deficiency; rather Steuart believed the model of primitive accumulation to have intrinsic merit and *continuing relevance*: as indeed it does to this day where the economic and social conditions which he *actually* confronted are duplicated.

The model, and the use made of it, constitutes a uniquely valuable contribution to our understanding of the 'stadial' thesis. This was, in fact, matched by Steuart's analysis, primarily in Book II, of the 'rich country, poor country' relationship recently noticed by Istvan Hont (1983). As Dr. Hont has reminded us, this major debate began with the publication of Hume's *Political Discourses* and ended in one version (for variation in economic performance is still a major problem), with Lauderdale's *Inquiry into the Nature and Origin of Public Wealth* (*op. cit.*, Ch. 11).[32]

It may be also suggested that more attention should be given to Steuart's appreciation of the wider, historical, significance of his own preoccupation with policy. The whole object of the exercise, as we have seen, was to obviate the effects of *relatively* short-run problems; of what Steuart called 'sudden revolutions'. At the same time, the purpose of policy is, for example, to protect employment levels and to encourage or induce economic growth and the social changes associated with it. Even in the more purely political sphere Steuart observed the effects of intervention: 'in our days, we have seen those who have best comprehended the true principles of the new plan of politics, arbitrarily limiting the power of the higher classes, and thereby applying their authority towards the extension of public liberty' (p. 216).

The point is made with greater clarity in the course of a critique of the 'principles of M. de Montesquieu, who deduced the origin of many laws, customs, and even religions, from the influence of climate':

> This great man reasoned from fact and from experience, and from the power and tendency of natural causes, to produce certain effects, when they are not checked by other circumstances; but in my method of treating this subject, I do not suppose that these causes are ever to be allowed to produce their natural and immediate effects, when such effects would be followed by a political inconvenience: but I constantly suppose a statesman at the head of government, who makes every circumstance concur in promoting the execution of the plan he has laid down (p. 238).

Policy itself was recognised to be an instrument of *change*, thus suggesting that while the emergence of the 'present establishments' in Europe could be adequately explained in terms of the eighteenth-century vision of a 'science' of history, the future course of events could be affected by contemporary interpretation of its meaning and direction. This is a point of some importance, and not least for our understanding of Smith's own work in the field.

Finally, it should not be forgotten that Steuart can be regarded as an *economist* who had an acute grasp of the methodology to be applied and who did much to differentiate this particular branch of the social sciences from others. In recent years it has been fashionable to refer to 'available languages' – for example, of natural jurisprudence or of civic humanism. Steuart uses the language of economics in a way which is recognisably modern but which also reminds us of those links which exist between the *Principles* and an older, seventeenth-century tradition dating back at least to the works of Sir William Petty (see Roncaglia, 1986).

Surely there is enough here to suggest that Steuart was also a worthy contributor to an 'Augustan Age' (p. 6), and that assessment of his contribution can only effectively be made once the *commentator* has freed himself from Smith's long shadow?

Yet the task, important though it may be, will not be easy. Even the urbane Donald Winch has recently remarked of Steuart's *Principles* that 'the difficulties in making this part of Smith's context are well-known. To put it bluntly, one has to take on board a Jacobite traitor tainted with Continental notions, and an author whose work was largely ignored by his Scottish contemporaries' (1983, p. 268).[33]

'A traitor tainted with Continental notions . . .'. The point echoes comments made in the reviews of 1767 which accused Steuart of *imbibing prejudices abroad, 'by no means consistent with the present state of England, and the genius of Englishmen'* (p. 4). Steuart replied that his work 'will not, in general, correspond to the meridian of nation opinions anywhere' (*Ibid.*). He went on: 'Can it be supposed, that during an absence of near twenty years, I should in my studies have all the while been modelling my speculation upon the standard of English notions?' 'If from this work I have any merit at all, it is by divesting myself of English notions, so far as to be able to expose in a fair light, the sentiments and policy of foreign nations, relatively to their own situation' (pp. 4–5). Could Smith, so pre-eminent a citizen of the world, have disagreed with so praiseworthy a *sentiment*?

NOTES

This essay partially 'conflates' the arguments of Skinner (1981) and (1985). I am indebted to the editors of the journals concerned for permission to reproduce a number of passages.

References to Steuart's *Principles* (1767) are given in parenthesis and are to the Skinner edition (1966). Biographical details are drawn from the latter work, together with P. Chamley (1963, 1965). There is an interesting chapter on Steuart in a forthcoming study by J.E. King (Lancaster).

1. Steuart wrote two interesting letters from Spain, dated 5th and 17th March, 1737, addressed to Thomas Calderwood, his brother-in-law, and Charles Mackie. Laing MS, Edinburgh University. The former is reprinted in Chamley (1965), pp. 127–29.

2. Steuart's treatment of land-use theory was the subject of the presidential address to the Regional Science Association of the USA in 1980, by Martin J. Beckman (1981); cf. W.J. Stull (1986).

3. Steuart was familiar with the works of Sir William Petty, Hume's *Essays* (in French translation) and with Mirabeau's *Friend of Man* (1756). The edition used was that published prior to Mirabeau's meeting with Quesnai, but would have made him familiar with the substance of Cantillon's teaching. For a list of authorities cited by Steuart, see Skinner (1966), p. 739.

4. He added: 'I am far from being of the opinion that this is the only road to happiness, security and ease: though from the general taste of the times I live in, it be the system I am principally employed to examine' (p. 214). It is in this light that we are to read the following chapter (Book II, ch. 14) on Lycurgus Plan, entitled, 'Security, Ease, and Happiness, no Inseparable Concomitants of Trade and Industry'.

5. See R.L. Meek (1976). Steuart's analysis of the relationship between the mode of subsistence and the patterns of authority and dependence are mainly located in Book II, ch. 12 – where, like Smith, he appears as a critic of the contract theory of government.

6. Steuart continued: 'I know of no Christian monarchy (except, perhaps, Russia) where either the consent of states, or the approbation and concurrence of some political body within the state, has not been requisite to make the imposition of taxes constitutional' (p. 290).

7. Steuart's manuscript writings are detailed in Skinner (1966), pp. 741–43.

8. Cf. Hume, 'Of the Populousness of Ancient Nations', in Rotwein (1955), where a similar argument is advanced. M.A. Akhar has drawn attention to the presence of a *model* in Steuart's work (1978), (1979).

9. See especially, Book I Ch. 19.

10. Steuart went on: 'Let any man make an experiment of this nature upon himself, by entering into the first shop. He will nowhere so quickly discover his wants as there. Everything he sees appears either necessary, or at least highly convenient; and he begins to wonder (especially if he be rich) how he could have been so long without that which the ingenuity of the workman alone had invented, in order that from the novelty it might excite his desire; for when it is bought, he will never once think of it, perhaps, nor ever apply it to

the use for which it first appeared so necessary' (p. 157). Cf. Smith, *Theory of Moral Sentiments*, Part IV, Ch. 1, 'Of the Effect of utility upon the Sentiment of Approbation'. See also Loasby (1986), p. 17.

11. The point is made by Johnson (1937), p. 225.

12. Cf. J.B. Say (1821), Book I, Ch. 15. For further comment on the regional dimension in Say's formulation of 'his' famous 'law', see Skinner (1967).

13. The argument is elaborated in Book II, Ch. 13.

14. See Chamley, *op. cit.*, pp. 77–82.

15. Steuart's use of the thesis of 'growth and decay' is to be interpreted in the light of this statement; *op. cit.*, p. 195, cf., p. 196n.

16. Steuart's emphasis was not on planning *ad hoc*, but on the 'corporate state'. See the paper with this title given by Walter Eltis for the British Association, in R.D.C. Black (1986).

17. Steuart's thesis was that with the development of local roads and of agriculture, the proposed Canal would improve the operation of the market and further stimulate agriculture in Lanark. He addressed the problem of good roads in pamphlets published in 1766 and 1770. Cf. the arguments of his son, General Sir James Steuart (1805).

18. See Steuart's *Memorial on the Corn Laws*, dated 10th October, 1777, reprinted in Chamley, *op. cit.*, pp. 140–42 and Skinner (1966), pp. 737–38; see also Skinner, *op. cit.*, pp. lii–iv, for an analysis of the debate for and against free trade in corn.
See also Steuart's *Dissertation on the Policy of Grain* (1759), *Works*, vol. 5. Eltis has argued that Steuart's position anticipated that of the modern EEC (*op. cit.*, p. 44).

19. Steuart added: 'But as this scheme of laying trade quite open, is not a thing likely to happen, we may save ourselves the trouble of enquiring more particularly into what might be its consequences' (p. 365).

20. The main commentaries appeared in the *Monthly* and *Critical* Reviews for 1767. Assessments of the *Works* were published in the *Annual* (1805) and *Monthly Review* (1806). James Mill contributed a critical piece to the *Literary Journal* (1806).

21. *Monthly Review*, vol. 50 (1806), pp. 115 and 123.

22. In 1772, Steuart was invited by the East India Company to advise on currency problems in Bengal. The Report was published as the *Principles of Money Applied to the State of the Coin in Bengal* (*Works*, vol. 5). See especially S.R. Sen (1957), Ch. 10. Smith's name may also have been mentioned to the Company, see Rae (1895), pp. 253–54.

23. Cf. Chamley, *op. cit.*, pp. 67–69.

24. There is also an interesting (and hitherto largely un-noticed) treatment of unproductive labour in Book II, Ch. 26.

25. Hume may have assisted Steuart when the latter was preparing for publication. See Skinner (1966), p. xiv. In a letter dated Coltness, 10th November 1767, Steuart refers to the 'many proofs you have given me of your friendship' (Burton, 1849, p. 174). Hume's patience was somewhat strained in the course of a jocular debate about Mary Queen of Scots; see Skinner (1966), p. 742.

26. Steuart left France just before the outbreak of war with England and finished the first two books of the *Principles* in Germany, during the course of 1759. Chamley, *op. cit.*, pp. 130–37; 138–39. For the present writer's views as to Smith's debt to Physiocracy, see Skinner (1979), Ch. 5. A comprehensive analysis of physiocratic work, which includes both commentary and translations, is to be found in Meek (1962).

27. See Skinner (1986).

28. See especially Caton (1985) and cf. Kindleberger (1976).

29. A rather similar contrast is drawn by A.L. Macfie when comparing Smith's position with that adopted by his pupil John Millar, where the latter is shown to have been interested in *reform*, while the 'truest final image of Adam Smith seems to me to be the system weaver, his mind ever moving on to further logical consequences' (1961), p. 203. See also Raschid (1982) and (1986) for an extremely interesting assessment of the reception accorded to the two works at the time of writing, and cf. Anderson and Tollison (1984).

30. Kobayashi has also suggested that Steuart's emphasis on primitive accumulation may explain the popularity of the work in contemporary Ireland and Germany. See also Chamley, *op. cit.*, pp. 88–89.

31. The relationship between Steuart and Hegel has also been noted, especially by Paul Chamley (1963) and (1965).

32. Steuart's analysis of the relationship between relatively developed and undeveloped economies is a feature of his critique of Hume's doctrine of the 'specie flow' (Book II, Ch. 28, 29). Later in the book the argument is extended to include a clear distinction between the balance of trade and the balance of payments (pp. 489, 494). Steuart also argued that the flow of specie from a relatively undeveloped country (for example Scotland) could be irreversible (p. 500), arguing that banks should borrow abroad to fund current deficits while continuing to support domestic credit in the interests of development (pp. 505–520). See also Walter Eltis, *op. cit.*

33. There is an interesting letter written by Elizabeth Mure of Caldwell and addressed to Steuart's sister, Mrs. Calderwood, which touches on her brother's politics (Chamley, 1965, pp. 115–117). Elizabeth Mure wrote:

> Were we by the fireside alone, no doubt I could give you more information than most people now alive, but those incidents are improper for a publication.

> Our friend's notion of government would ill suit the rage for freedom (I may call it) that now reigns in this country, and is fast running on to licentiousness. His ambition was to have an active share in a government that he approved of, and was a Jacobite on some whig principles, but not the whole of them . . . had that revolution taken place which he wished, he would have been the first man in the state.

Elizabeth Mure's affectionate remembrance was dated 20th December, 1787 – a little more than *seven* years after Steuart's death.

REFERENCES

M.A. Akhar, 'Steuart on Growth', *Scottish Journal of Political Economy*, vol. 25, 1978.

M.A. Akhar, 'An Analytical Outline of Sir James Steuart's Macro-economic Model', *Oxford Economic papers*, vol. 31, 1979.

G.M. Anderson, and R.D. Tollison, 'Sir James Steuart as the Apotheosis of Mercantilism and his Relation to Adam Smith', *Southern Economic Journal*, vol. 51, 1984.

J. Beckmann, 'Land-use theory then and now: a tribute to Sir James Steuart', in *Papers Regional Science Association*, vol. 48, 1981.

R.D.C. Black, (ed.), *Ideas in Economics* (London, 1986).

J.H. Burton, *Letters of Eminent Persons Addressed to David Hume* (Edinburgh, 1849).

H. Caton, 'The Pre-Industrial Economics of Adam Smith', *Journal of Economic History*, vol. 45, 1985.

P. Chamley, *Economie Politique et Philosophie chez Steuart et Hegel* (Paris, 1963).

P. Chamley, *Documents Relatifs à Sir James Steuart* (Paris, 1965).

W. Eltis, 'Sir James Steuart's Corporate State', in R.D.C. Black (ed.) (1986).

A.O.Hirschman, *The Passions and the Interests, Political Arguments for Capitalism before its Triumph* (Princeton, 1977).

I. Hont, 'The Rich Country – Poor Country debate in Scottish Classical Political Economy', in Hont and Ignatieff (ed.), *Wealth and Virtue: The Shaping of Political Economy in the Scottish Enlightenment* (Cambridge, 1983).

E.A.G. Johnson, *Predecessors of Adam Smith* (New York, (1937) 1960).

C. Kindleberger, 'The Historical Background: Adam Smith and the Industrial Revolution', in T. Wilson and A.S. Skinner, (eds.), *The Market and the State: Essays in Honour of Adam Smith*, (Oxford, 1976).

N. Kobayashi, *Sir James Steuart, Adam Smith and Friedrich List* (Toyko, 1967).

B. Loasby, 'Marshall's Economics of Progress', in *Journal of Economic Studies*, vol. 13, 1986.

A.L. Macfie, 'John Millar', *Scottish Journal of Political Economy*, vol. 8, 1961.

R.L. Meek, *The Economics of Physiocracy* (London, 1962).

R.L. Meek, 'The Rehabilitation of Sir James Steuart', in *Economics and Ideology and Other Essays: Studies in the Development of Economic Thought* (London, 1967).

R.L. Meek, *Social Science and the Ignoble Savage* (Cambridge, 1976).

M. Perelman, 'Classical Political Economy and Primitive Accumulation', *History of Political Economy*, vol. 15, 1983.

John Rae, *Life of Adam Smith* (London, 1895).

S. Raschid, 'The Policy of Laisser Faire during Scarcities', *Economic Journal*, 90, 1980.

S. Raschid, 'Adam Smith's Rise to Fame: A Re-examination', *The Eighteenth Century, Theory and Interpretation*, vol. 23, 1982.

S. Raschid, 'Smith, Steuart and Mercantilism', *Southern Economic Journal*, vol. 52, 1986.

A. Roncaglia, *Sir William Petty: The Origins of Political Economy* (New York, 1985).

E. Rotwein, *David Hume: Writings on Economics* (Edinburgh, 1955).

J.B. Say, *A Treatise on Political Economy*, transl. C.R. Prinsep (London, 1821).

J.A. Schumpeter, *History of Economic Analysis* (London, 1954).

S.R. Sen, *The Economics of Sir James Steuart* (London, 1957).

A.S. Skinner, *Sir James Steuart: Principles of Political Oeconomy* (ed.) (Edinburgh and Chicago, 1966).

A.S. Skinner, 'Say's Law: Origins and Content', *Economica*, vol. 34, 1967.

A.S. Skinner, *A System of Social Science: Papers Relating to Adam Smith* (Oxford, 1979).

A.S. Skinner, 'Sir James Steuart: Author of a System', *Scottish Journal of Political Economy*, vol. 28, 1981.

A.S. Skinner, 'Sir James Steuart, A Perspective on Economic Policy and Development', *Quaderni di storia dell' economia politica*, vol. 3, 1985.

A.S. Skinner, 'Adam Smith, Then and Now', in Black (1986).

Adam Smith, *The Theory of Moral Sentiments* (1959), ed. A.L. Macfie and D.D. Raphael (Oxford, 1976).

Adam Smith, *An Inquiry into the Nature and Causes of the Wealth of Nations* (1776), ed. R.D. Campbell, A.S. Skinner and W.B. Todd (Oxford, 1976).

Sir James Steuart, *A Dissertation on the Policy of Grain, with a view to a Plan for preventing scarcity or exorbitant prices, in the Common Markets of England* (1759) (*Works*, vol. 5).

Sir James Steuart, *Observations on the Advantages arising to the Public from Good Roads, particularly of the Utility of a short and easy Communication between the Firths of Forth and Clyde; with Remarks on the Present Roads Leading to Glasgow* (Glasgow, 1766).

Sir James Steuart, *Principles of Political Oeconomy: being an Essay on the Science of Domestic Policy in Free Nations* (1767), ed. A.S. Skinner (Edinburgh and Chicago, 1966).

Sir James Steuart, *Considerations on the Interest of the County of Lanark in Scotland; which (in several respects) may be applied to that of Great Britain* (1769) (*Works*, vol. 5).

Sir James Steuart, *Sketch of a Plan for Executing a Set of Roads over the County of Lanark* (Glasgow, 1770).

Sir James Steuart, *Works, Political, Metaphysical and Chronological*, 6 vols., (London, 1805).

General Sir James Steuart, *Remarks on the proposed Bill for the Improvement of the Roads in the County of Lanark, by Statute Labour* (Glasgow, 1805).

D. Stewart, *Works*, ed. Sir William Hamilton, 10 vols. (Edinburgh, 1854–60).

W.J. Stull, 'The Urban Economics of Adam Smith', *Journal of Urban Economics*, vol. 20, 1986.

K.P. Tribe, 'Cameralism and the Science of Government', *Journal of Modern History*, vol. 56, 1984.

D. Winch, *Adam Smith's Politics: An Essay in Historiographic Revision* (Cambridge, 1978).

D. Winch, 'Adam Smith's enduring particular result', in Hont and Ignatieff (1983).

8

APES AND RACES IN THE SCOTTISH ENLIGHTENMENT: MONBODDO AND KAMES ON THE NATURE OF MAN

Robert Wokler

I

When Hutcheson remarked, 'I am called 'New Light' here',[1] he spoke not only for himself, but for his age. The intellectual movement which he with his contemporaries and followers lit up the North of Europe glowed more brightly than Scotland had ever shone before, and even when the light grew pale at home it remained as a beacon which abroad has illuminated the history of philosophy and of the social sciences to the present day. Of course that beacon did not gleam all at once, nor even always in the same direction. But from Hutcheson's own conception of the moral sense to Reid's idea of common sense, from Hume's philosophical scepticism to Smith's political economy — most strikingly, perhaps, in a widely conjectured theory of the progress of society — the New Light from Scotland brought a fresh brightness to the world. Participants at a colloquium on the Scottish Enlightenment need not be reminded of this spectacle. They may, however, have cause to wonder why in such an illustrious cast the obscure and indistinct figures of Monboddo and Kames should still be worthy of credit.

While Monboddo's pre-eminent contemporaries believed society had advanced from barbarism to civilisation, he, by contrast, was convinced it had declined. His six-volume *Origin and Progress of Language* was one of the few eighteenth-century Scottish works to contain the word 'progress' in its title, but readers could form a better judgment of his doctrine from the title of his second major book of equal length: *Antient Metaphysics*. So far as common sense was concerned, this was a faculty which many commentators were convinced had been denied to him by Nature. 'Other people have strange notions, but they conceal them', Dr. Johnson observed about his claim that men are often born with tails. Monboddo was nevertheless 'as jealous of his tail as a squirrel'.[2] Nor was his grasp of political economy especially impressive. About the greatest masterpiece produced by a fellow countryman, and perhaps of

145

the whole century, Monboddo could only remark, 'I see that [Smith] has produced a book upon trade, from the style of which one would think he had never read any of the writers of Greece and Rome'.[3] It was for such writers, and particularly those of Greece, that he felt his deepest affection. There, in unworldly contemplation of Platonic forms and Aristotelian categories, was his true abode.[4]

Whereas Monboddo thus really belonged in the Temple of Parnassus, Kames, for his part, seems rather to have been a figure of the Middle Kingdom. It is true that he was closer to both Smith and especially Hume than Monboddo had ever been or could be, but he nevertheless recoiled from scepticism and conceived his *Essays on Natural Religion* largely to refute Hume's work. If, in the minds of his enlightened associates, God's Almighty purposes had been largely supplanted by the frailties of human design, Kames's profound faith in Providence stood him apart. While other political commentators forcefully encouraged the development of a commercial society in Scotland, he, equivocally, came also to regret the loss of a more benign and gentle, but most archaic and indeed fanciful, Scottish past. Where other jurisprudential writers sought to retrace the establishment and development of our legal institutions, Kames instead focused much of his attention upon the links between philosophical history in general, and the laws of his native country in particular.[5] No wonder Hume was bemused by what he termed Kames's 'agreeable composition' of 'Metaphysics and Scotch Law'.[6]

Of course it would be a mistake to exaggerate these differences, or to suggest that either Monboddo or Kames was a remote Highland thinker whom the great Enlightenment of the eighteenth century passed by. In his own day, Kames was celebrated as a leading philosophical jurist, and as one of Scotland's most distinguished writers, while Monboddo was a renowned scholar, almost without equal, even in England. Each kept closely abreast of Continental thought and literature in the period, and if as judges they were rooted to their bench while their professorial colleagues were at their lecterns, they nevertheless addressed themselves to many of the same subjects and questions as their apparently more progressive contemporaries. In particular, each conceived, in his own fashion, that most characteristic of all Scottish Enlightenment inventions — I mean, a theory of human nature. I believe that Kames's and Monboddo's theories together, on a familiar theme but in each case from an unusual perspective, are among the more engaging and compelling contributions to the period, just because they lie askance from its mainstream. They stand apart from prevailing Scottish doctrines of man's nature, and, to my mind, they have remained largely unexplored by commentators because of this.[7] For reasons which I trust will become apparent from my remarks here, I am convinced that this scholarly neglect should be remedied and overcome.

II

The *Origin and Progress of Language* was conceived along lines which are characteristic of much Enlightenment speculation about the nature of man. Following Locke's *Essay on Human Understanding*, and in a manner similar to Condillac's work on the same subject (with which he had a second-hand acquaintance), Monboddo regarded the development of language as the principal manifestation of the advancement of the human mind, and he believed the improvement of our linguistic skills to be the measure of our intellectual progress in general. But in his account of the operations of the mind he took issue with earlier thinkers for their failure to recognise that the very faculty which made the formation of our ideas possible was an acquired trait, which could only be brought to fruition through human industry and endeavour. It was a habit of mind which men formed for themselves, not a gift bestowed upon them by Nature. The elaboration of these themes, largely by way of commentaries on Plato and Locke, occupies much of the first book of *The Origin and Progress of Language*, where Monboddo attributes a similar notion to Harris, the author of *Hermes*, and acknowledges his debt.[8]

If our ideas were not naturally conceived but acquired, so too, Monboddo next maintained, their articulation or expression in speech had to be learned. The one was the form of language, the other its matter, and both could only be developed slowly through experience and observation, and cultivated in use and exercise. It was thus manifestly clear, according to Monboddo, that for language to have been invented, it was first necessary that society should be established — a proposition which might have been inspired by Smith, or Ferguson, or any number of his Scottish contemporaries, but which, as a matter of fact, he drew mainly from Rousseau. Just as Rousseau had supposed, Monboddo thought that a proper treatment of this question required a meditation upon the whole history of mankind, and in his own investigation of human origins he was to follow Rousseau's theory more closely than that of any other author.[9] But he did not entirely agree with Rousseau, and indeed actually conceived his work, in some measure, as a solution to a dilemma which Rousseau had posed. For in a passage of the *Discours sur l'inégalité* which Monboddo cites, Rousseau had claimed that the use of language was itself as much a prerequisite of the creation of society as was society for the formation of language, so that it was impossible to determine which had come first.[10] Monboddo judged that this contention was false, since the construction of language and the formation of society could and must be disengaged, as witnessed by the fact that the most primitive societies — that is, of men herded together out of fear or for sustenance — would have had no language other than the most inarticulate cries. Indeed, in the animal world, he argued, whole societies were known to exist, and beavers, for instance, had even formed political states, without the use of language. Rousseau had introduced an unnecessary confusion in his hypothesis, Monboddo concluded, since society quite plainly came first, and language second.[11] But the proposition that society was a prerequisite of language seemed to him unassailable, and in drawing that thesis from Rousseau he pursued it in several stages to a conclusion which he had also found in the *Discours sur l'inégalité*, in effect, that orang-utans are really human and thus members of our species. Monboddo's defence of this proposition, which differs in important respects from that of Rousseau,[12] took roughly the following lines, which I abstract from the second rather than the first edition of the *Origin and Progress of Language* for reasons I shall explain presently.

His first point is that savages who show no command of language are still human. This proposition struck him as self-evident, since we did not regard the inability of infants to speak at birth, or of mutes to speak at all, as sufficient grounds for excluding them from membership of our species. In contending, furthermore, that none of the solitary savages who had been caught in Europe 'had the use of speech', he pointed particularly to the widely documented case of Peter from the forest of Hanover, who lived for a long time in society after his capture without ever really learning to speak, with Monboddo thus recognising — as Linnaeus and some other naturalists had failed to do — that the unfortunate creature still remained 'a man in mind as well as body'.[13] All of these observations are of course informed by his premise that language is an acquired skill, and not an attribute of human nature.

Monboddo's second point is that the fundamental marks of human intelligence are rendered in behaviour rather than speech. To construe human nature, in effect, we must perceive that actions speak louder than words. This claim appears to draw its strength from another premise of Monboddo discussed already — that language is a verbal skill which can only be learned in society — and he was in no doubt that experience and reflection confirmed it. A person who lived alone, Monboddo wrote, even if he might in time acquire the habit of forming ideas, could never invent a method of communicating them for which he had no occasion.[14] It was absurd for philosophers to regard the actual *use* of words by individuals as a necessary constituent of the definition of our species, since this would imply that men whose organs of speech have been damaged thereby pass into a different species from the rest of us, or even that persons who choose to refrain from speaking, when, for instance, they play chess or dine alone, are sometimes human and sometimes not. It appears to me surprising, he reflected, that philosophers should be unsatisfied by the expression of human intelligence in *actions* and should require instead those signs of arbitrary institution which we call words, before they will allow an animal to deserve the name of man.[15] Parrots, however articulate, clearly are not human.

Monboddo's third and perhaps most crucial point is that creatures which partake of our own physical characteristics, including our organs of speech, must as a consequence be deemed members of our species. On the evidence of comparative anatomy set forth by Tyson at the end of the seventeenth century and by Buffon in his own day, orang-utans, he claimed, are exactly of the human form. They have bodies which in their constitution are in all essential respects the same as our own, and they are endowed with a brain, larynx, pharynx and tongue which are identical. According to these naturalists, however, the very fact that orang-utans possessed vocal organs just like our own proved that material and bodily structures alone were incapable of producing either thought or speech, which must instead be animated by a higher principle. Orang-utans, it had been supposed, lacked the nobler faculties of the mind which gave effect to our organs and enabled us alone in the natural world to make use of them and thus to speak.[16] For Monboddo, this contention was surely false. Why should orang-utans have been encumbered with organs which they could not use, he wondered, just to enable naturalists to regard such animals as qualitatively different from themselves? Was Nature so lacking in economy of purpose as to engage in redundant design? It was in fact contrary to Nature, he claimed, to suppose that creatures which resembled one another were actually members of disparate species. Everywhere throughout the world an animal which had the outward form and internal organs of a lion or tiger or bear, he insisted, must be deemed to have the same disposition, too, and was therefore incontrovertibly just another lion, or tiger, or bear. So why should Nature have shaped the members of one species alone — that is, the human race — with a body that was just like that of another species, while still intending that there should be an unbridgeable gulf between them? That gulf had been manufactured not by Nature but in the wayward minds of naturalists such as Tyson and Buffon.[17]

Fourthly, Monboddo maintaind that in their behaviour, as reported by travellers to Batavia, Java, Angola, and elsewhere, orang-utans showed that they were perfectly rational creatures who possessed the fundamental attributes of humanity, albeit not yet in any verbal form. 'I believe it will be . . . impossible', he observed, 'for a man who is accustomed to divide things according to specific marks, not individual differences, to draw the line betwixt the Orang Outang and the dumb persons among us. They have both their organs of pronunciation, and both shew signs of intelligence by their actions, with this difference, no doubt, that our dumb persons, having been educated among civilised men, have more intelligence. But how is it possible, from this difference only of greater or less, and which can be so well accounted for, to conceive them to be of different species?'[18] The marks of humanity borne by orang-utans were incontestible, and among these traits Monboddo listed the facts that orang-utans walk erect, that 'they live in society', that 'they use sticks for weapons', that 'they carry on . . . undertakings' and 'carry off negro girls', and that they 'attack elephants'. It had been established, moreover, that orang-utan males possess a sense of justice and honour in their disputes with one another, and that orang-utan females display a sense of modesty when caught naked and unawares by men who are clothed. While it was true that no orang-utan had ever been known to utter a single word, the creatures were nevertheless known to play the harp, with both skill and grace, so that even if they could not yet communicate their ideas in speech, they could at least express their thoughts in music.[19]

Having surveyed these matters at length elsewhere,[20] I shall pass no comment on them here, except perhaps to note that Monboddo's misconstrual of both the nature and appearance of orang-utans is entirely second-hand. None of these animals had yet been seen alive in Europe at the time he drafted his remarks, and his credulous descriptions of their behaviour are scarcely more fanciful than those accepted and reported by leading naturalists of the period, including Linnaeus, and above all, Buffon, who was his principal source, at least on matters of comparative anatomy. The term 'orang-utan', which is a Malay expression meaning 'man of the woods', was employed as a generic description of a whole host of creatures — great apes and fabulous animals alike — throughout this period and even beyond the mid-nineteenth century European discovery of the African gorilla, but above all, it pertained to the chimpanzee, whose cadaver had been dissected by Tyson. Not until the past twenty years or so have we had any reliable reports of the behaviour in the wild of this endangered species native only to Southeast Asia,[21] and Monboddo's misrepresentations of the animal's conduct, although extensive, were not particularly unusual, nor even his own. Against this, however, it has to be acknowledged that his (actually mistaken) supposition that orang-utans live in society[22] ill accords with his claim that they are mute for the same reasons which account for the silence of solitary or unsociable men.

Monboddo's fifth point, as I read him, is that a proper definition of humanity can be formulated only in terms of our capacities, and not of our attainments. Like Rousseau, once more, he believed that we were distinguished from animals by virtue of our more flexible nature rather than our superior constitution, and he adopted Rousseau's neologism, the term *perfectibility*, to identify that capacity which had enabled some members of our species to master the subtle art of communication through verbal signs. If man had been endowed with language at the moment of his creation, then he must in the beginning already have perfected those qualities of mind and character which in fact he could only have come to acquire and devise for himself, in his relations with other men, in the course of a long history. It is a wonder that some men invented languages at all, he declared, for even our non-linguistic cries and exclamations do not spring so spontaneously from our lips as sight from our eyes and hearing from our ears.[23]

His last point, and one which some of his unwitting scientific disciples have put to fruitless test over recent years, is his claim that orang-utans might indeed, and in time, be taught to exercise their vocal organs, or, as he put it, 'come the length of language'. Of course this would depend upon their being instructed in such a way, which he allowed was difficult, as to overcome their indolence and excite their desire for learning. But if only a few of the creatures could be tutored, for instance, at Dr. Braidwood's classes for the deaf in Edinburgh, there was still hope for their future development.[24] La Mettrie had put forward a similar claim in his *L'Homme machine* when he suggested that through hard work and good will apes might be transformed into *parfaits hommes de ville*, that is, perfect little men about town.[25] What human accomplishments would be beyond their grasp then? Yet neither La Mettrie nor Monboddo foresaw just what could befall orang-utans if they were absorbed into human society. 'Parle, et je te baptise', confides the Cardinal de Polignac to the orang-utan in the glass cage, according to Diderot in one of his works.[26] Such a prospect might make any sensible creature pause. As Rousseau remarks, in a letter to Hume, it's no wonder that these animals *pretend* to be mute.[27]

III

So much, then, for the main lines of Monboddo's anthropology. I turn next to Kames, whose grasp of human nature was in many respects more subtle and perceptive, although perhaps lacking some of the force and coherence of Monboddo's approach. For reasons which I trust will soon be apparent, Kames showed scant interest in the humanity of orang-utans, and he did not have so much to contribute, either, on the origins of language. His conception of mankind was addressed to other problems and was developed in a different idiom. To my mind, it revolved around four main themes which I shall consider briefly in turn, albeit — for the sake of my own presentation here — in almost reverse order from that in which they appear in his *Sketches of the History of Man*. The first of these themes is his account of the Caledonian ancestors of the people of Scotland; the second is his view of the characteristics of native Americans; the third, his observations on the influence of climate; and the fourth, his reflections on the different races of mankind.

Now Kames's remarks about the ancient Caledonians must be set against the conjectural history of our passage from barbarous to civilised society, which is such a central feature of Scottish, and indeed French, Enlightenment thought in this period. By and large, Kames agreed with Smith, Ferguson and others that humanity advanced through four main stages of development, culminating in commercial society, and he acknowledged that as our modes of social life and economic activity progressed, so too did our moral sense improve and our manners become more cultivated and refined. But he also believed that men in all circumstances act out of mixed motives in diverse proportions, or, as he put it, 'a compound of principles and passions, some social, some dissocial'.[28] A tendency towards corruption, with the desire for property in conflict with the impulse of benevolence, was characteristic even of the most advanced states, while, by contrast, the inhabitants of certain savage societies could display qualities of mind and character more virtuous and polite than our own. Thus it was that the ancient Caledonians, an otherwise primitive people, had been endowed with traits of compassion and benevolence, and, in general, with 'manners so pure and refined', he wrote, 'as scarce to be equalled in the most cultivated nations'.[29] Unlike the ancient Greeks, who were crude in their diet and cruel in battle, the Celtic forebears of the Scottish people were restrained, gentle, and courteous, above all towards women. Time and again in his *Sketches* Kames contrasted the evidence of the Homeric epics with the Ossianic legends, always to the moral advantage of the Caledonians over the Greeks. He could not bring himself to doubt the authenticity of the poems of Ossian, and, to my mind, his reliance upon them constitutes the principal source of confusion between primitivism and progress in his theory of history. Of course his veneration of a Scottish past convinced precious few of his readers, even if they might have lacked the inclination to agree instead with Dr. Johnson that 'the noblest prospect which a Scotchman ever sees is the high road that leads him to England'. Kames's protrayal of the Ossianic Scots, by contrast, is perhaps the clearest example of the idea of the 'noble savage' in late-eighteenth century thought, a myth so often, and so wrongly, associated with Rousseau.[30]

If his judgment of the Caledonian Scots was perhaps too high, Kames's assessment of the natives of America seems rather too low. The whole continent of America, he believed, was populated by a race of men which had essentially failed to progress from the hunting and fishing, to the pastoral, stage of civilisation. The natives of Guiana were indolent, he argued, the Iroquois were cowardly, and, most important of all, perhaps, the savage inhabitants of America had generally been retarded in their development because their organs of generation were feeble, with the males in consequence displaying insufficient ardour for the female sex, so that matings were infrequent and children scarce, which in turn kept the population low, so that these peoples had not been subjected to the pressures of numbers which had forced the hunting savages of the Old World to find more ample sustenance first through livestock and then agriculture, thereby ensuring the advance of European culture and society.[31] Kames allowed that this was not universally true of Americans, since some tribes appear to have established agriculture without ever before having tended sheep, thus passing over a whole stage of their development much as Marx would later suppose to be possible for the Russian peasantry in its advance directly from feudalism to communism. But, in the main, it was the backwardness and lack of progress of Americans which Kames found most striking, and whose explanation this most genteel of Scots traces principally to their diminutive sexual organs and appetites. That argument, on Kames's own testimony, was drawn directly from the portrait of the Americans which he found in Buffon's *Histoire naturelle*, where the same observations figure in the context of a general discussion of the shortcomings of all creatures in the New World, by comparison with their counterparts in the Old.

F

Buffon had shown that no major animal species was common to both worlds, and that in every case of apparent similarity — the llama with the camel, for instance, or the puma with the tiger, the New World species were inferior in stature to those of the Old.[32] In his *Sketches*, Kames accepted and incorporated this testimony, but he was unconvinced by Buffon's explanations for it, and in fact objected to the theory of the development of the human race which Buffon had proffered in the light of his own evidence.[33] Kames's critique of Buffon reads just as if it were a cross-examination of France's leading naturalist by Scotland's pre-eminent judge, and it led to the two most original conclusions of his anthropological theory.

The first of these, and my third of his themes here, is that climate does not determine race. Buffon had argued that the white inhabitants of Europe, the black men of Africa, the yellow peoples of Asia, and the red men of America were all of the same species of humanity, tinged only with the colours of climate. And yet the Abyssinians, who are tall and of olive complexion, contend with much the same torrid climate as the short black men of Guinea, while however dark Europeans become in their exposure to the midday tropical sun, their children will nevertheless be born with white complexions. Those who ascribe *all* to the Sun, wrote Kames, ought to consider how little probable it is that the colour, if impressed in the parents, should be communicated to their infant children. Above all, he concludes, Buffon had been totally silent with regard to one fact which alone overturns his whole theory of the influence of climate, in effect, that Americans are without exception of a copper colour, despite there being every variety of climate in that vast continent.[34] Three years after the appearance of the *Sketches*, Robertson, in his *History of America*, largely adopted Buffon's theory of climatic influence and found a certain continental consistency in the New World which had perhaps escaped Buffon's notice — to wit, that America is predominantly cold, gripped by frosts where Europe is temperate, and by fog even in the tropics. Kames, however, was more discriminating, and his reliance upon Buffon more critical.

With regard to the impact of climate, moreover, he also took issue with those commentators, including Ferguson and most notably Montesquieu, who supposed that our qualities of *mind* were shaped by it. Montesquieu had argued that the physiological effect of climate was to make people timid when it was hot, and courageous when cold, but this claim about our inward dispositions Kames found no more cogent than Buffon's thesis about the colour of our skin.[35] Together with Hume and many other contemporaries who remarked on the subject, Kames believed that custom, education, and even chance were more important determinants of national character than any physical causes, a point of view which led him to conclude that Negroes were not intellectually inferior to whites, but rather had a defective faculty of understanding on account of their social conditions in both the Old World and the New. Who can say, he exclaimed, how their understanding might improve if they had occasion to exercise their powers in a state of freedom? At any rate, he found no opposition in human affairs between heat and courage, and, referring once more to the evidence of natural history he pointed to the fact that the most enterprising and courageous animals — lions and tigers, for instance — thrived in hot climates.[36] If climate did not shape animal behaviour, how much less still could it be counted the main determinant of human conduct?

Buffon's reflections on American savages, and on New World animal species, seemed to Kames, finally, to provide the most telling evidence of all against the theory of mankind's origins which they were intended to support. For if it were true that all native Americans were physically distinct from Europeans, and equally that all New World animals were of distinct species from those of the Old, then why should Buffon not allow that American humans, like American animals, were also of a different species from other humans, and, in effect, that there were different races of men in the world? Kames acknowledged that Buffon's basic definition of a species — that the offspring of copulations between its members should be fecund as well — appeared to exclude this hypothesis, since Americans and Europeans, unlike horses and asses, for instance, could procreate, and their progeny likewise, indefinitely. But having described Americans, with their copper colour and lack of body hair, as a wholly different variety of mankind from Europeans, how could Buffon account for their origins? 'No problem has more embarrassed the learned',[37] he remarked, than this. The climate of the American continent, as we have seen, does not explain the uniform colour of the American race, nor its difference from other races in similar latitudes. Neither can it be supposed that Americans are descended from any people in the north of Asia or Europe, Kames continued. No land passage from the Old World to the New has been discovered, and even if there had been such a passage once, say, through Kamskatka (that is, the tip of modern Siberia), the population of the continent would have thinned around the equator as the southerly migrations dispersed, rather than been clustered, as it was when discovered by the Spaniards, around Mexico and Peru. When we consider their physical features and complexion we must regard Americans as distinct from all other races no less than New World animal species are from the Old, so that, concluded Kames, 'we have herein Monsieur Buffon's authority against himself'. Until positive evidence be brought to the contrary, our presumption should be that differences between races subsisting at present have always subsisted.[38]

Well how, then, could *Kames* explain the origin of Americans? In this way. If we concurred with Buffon once more that the continent of the New World had emerged from the sea later than any other part of the globe, we had only to suppose that the American race might have been planted there by God later than in the days of Moses. Holy Scripture would not be contravened by this hypothesis, since Adam and Eve might still have been the first parents of mankind, that is, of all humanity who existed at the time of the emergence of the New World, without being the first parents of the Americans.[39] This theory of the local and separate creation of the American race forms Kames's principal contribution to eighteenth-century anthropological thought.[40] Unlike any other Scottish thinkers of the period, so far as I know, Kames formed the view that the diverse races of men comprised distinct species. In the next century, that doctrine came to be termed the theory of polygenesis.

IV

Now *why* Monboddo and Kames adopted these divergent ideas about the nature and origins of man is a profoundly important question, which I gladly leave to others — perhaps psychoanalysts or social historians — to answer. I turn next instead to some considerations as to *how* they came to put forward their views, in the light of the textual evidence which has survived. The propositions I have ascribed to Monboddo are drawn, as I have said, from the second rather than the first edition of *The Origin and Progress of Language*, indeed, only from the second edition of the first volume, which was published in December 1774, more than eighteen months after its initial appearance. The difference between the two editions is striking, particularly with regard to the material on orang-utans, which is far more extensive in the revised text. In the first edition, Monboddo had commented briefly upon Rousseau, Buffon, and the humanity of orang-utans, but not at all in the same way, or to the same purpose, as in his later version. The first contains no reference to the contrast between the orang-utan and man which forms the cornerstone of Buffon's treatment, and although Monboddo must have consulted the essay on the subject which had appeared in 1766 in the *Histoire naturelle*, he had clearly failed to notice the main thrust of

Buffon's argument about orang-utans, which was that these creatures could not be human. Buffon believed that Rousseau's speculations on the subject were false, as Tyson had already established from the evidence of comparative anatomy in his exhaustive work, entitled *Orang-Outang*, published in 1699. Tyson had shown in the most minute detail that the creature's body was in all its parts and their relations exactly like that of a man, though its organs evidently were not animated by the higher faculty with which mankind alone is endowed. There could be no greater proof of the spiritual origins of speech and thought, Tyson had concluded, than the fact that an animal which possessed the same brain and larynx as man was unable to put these organs to use. The organisation of matter alone, in effect, produces neither thought nor speech.[41]

Tyson himself had been inspired to adopt this Cartesian perspective upon the nature of animals through his reading of the supplement to Perrault's *Histoire des animaux*, which dates from 1676, and Buffon had come in all essentials to much the same conclusion in adopting Tyson as his source. Indeed, this doctrine had been well assimilated by most scientific thinkers of the Enlightenment, and throughout the greater part of the eighteenth century it was the principal thesis cited by naturalists and theologians alike when pointing to the discontinuity between the orang-utan and man. Although at the time he drafted his *Discours sur l'inégalité* Rousseau could not yet have consulted Buffon's commentary, he appears to have been independently familiar with Tyson's work.[42] But when Monboddo drafted the first edition of his *Origin and Progress of Language*, he was blissfully unaware of these facts. He had not read Rousseau with sufficient care, nor had the slightest grasp of Buffon's meaning. He knew nothing of Tyson, or Perrault, and seems to have imagined that any reference to orang-utans which he uncovered simply lent weight to his own view, and to Rousseau's claim, that orang-utans are really men. So the absence of any mention of Tyson in the first edition of the *Origin and Progress of Language* is explained quite simply by Monboddo's initial ignorance, which he later admitted and sought to remedy. His ignorance may itself be explained, moreover, at least in part, by the fact that the Library of the Faculty of Advocates in Edinburgh, where he completed nearly all of his research, and, which, indeed, he helped to expand by judicious purchases over a number of years, did not in his own lifetime contain a copy of Tyson's text. It would appear that every other work among the hundreds on natural history and on ancient and modern civilisations which are cited in the *Origin and Progress of Language* could be found in the Advocates'

Library, but not Tyson's *Orang-Outang*.[43] Of course, if Monboddo had only discussed his views with others before submitting them to print, he might have been spared his embarrassment.

At any rate, his omission of Tyson and his mistakes about Buffon were to be promptly rectified, as soon as Monboddo's friends alerted his attention after his work appeared. Two correspondents in particular, Sir John Pringle, then President of the Royal Society, and Lord Lyttelton, the celebrated student of divinity, commented at length in several letters upon his treatment of the orang-utan and in each case referred to Tyson's work.[44] Both Pringle and Lyttelton disagreed with Monboddo, but from their detailed observations he became acquainted with the prevailing scientific treatments of orang-utans which had escaped his notice before. He turned to Tyson, he reread Buffon, he identified the main point of contention between these authors and Rousseau, and he reflected afresh on the whole subject in a long essay entitled 'Of the Orang-Outang, and whether he be of the Human species', which he drafted mainly in the winter of 1773-74.[45] It was this material which was to figure in the second edition of his *Origin and Progress of Language*, published with a prefatory tribute to Lyttelton, who had just died, and a grateful acknowledgement, as he put it, of 'the many useful hints I have got from several, who have done me the favour to correspond with me upon occasion of the publication of the first edition'.[46]

While Monboddo was engaged in covering his embarrassment, Kames, for his part, might well have hoped to increase it through the publication of his *Sketches of the History of Man*. This text, as it happens, was printed in 1774, in the period just between the first and second editions of Monboddo's work. In a certain sense, at least, the *Sketches* may be regarded as Kames's retort to Monboddo, with its levelling portrait of the coarse vulgarities of a Homeric world which Monboddo had regarded as sublime. Here was Fingal's vengeance, wreaked upon Achilles, the venerable Athens of the North putting the lie to the Southern pretender. Yet orang-utans, by contrast, were not much to Kames's taste, and the creature which took central stage in the only volume of the *Origin and Progress of Language* which had yet appeared is relegated by Kames to an insignificant footnote,[47] a postscript which he may well have added after reading Monboddo, or, more likely still, after he observed the fuss which Monboddo's first volume had caused. It would of course have been surprising, even for Kames, if he had managed to produce the one thousand pages of his work in a matter of months, and it is in fact clear from some exchanges of 1772 with his publisher, William Creech, that he had been engaged in assembling material for his own, and quite independent, history of mankind, over many, perhaps thirty, years before that.[48] But there is a certain disorder and haste apparent in the final preparation of Kames's work, for which Monboddo may have been partly responsible. Somewhat like Darwin, who was to be pressed into print too quickly by Wallace, Kames seems to have been anxious that his thunder might be stolen just as the lightning was about the strike. The *Origin and Progress of Language* is nowhere mentioned, still less challenged, in the *Sketches*, but its appearance in 1773 may well help to explain some of the imperfections and lack of coherence of Kames's work.

If the paths of Monboddo and Kames could scarcely cross in their respective texts, however, they appear to have intersected at a point of departure common to both. In a notable letter of 1772 addressed to the physician James Lind, who had been invited to circumnavigate the world with Captain Cook, Kames confided several ideas which comprise the central themes of his anthropological theory in the *Sketches*. It is 'a deep speculation', he reflected, to determine 'what is the scheme of providence for peopling the earth with the human race. Abstracting from Revelation it is natural to conjecture, that as there are many different climates, there were formed originally different races of men fit for these climates, in which only they flourish and degenerate in every other climate'. Every experiment, he concluded, seems to confirm this conjecture, that each race of man flourishes in only one climate and degenerates in every other. How else could we account for the fact that the colony of South Carolina, especially around Charleston, was so unkind to Europeans that 'there is not a single descendant of the first settlers remaining'?[49]

Kames's interest in the degenerative effects upon humanity of climate in general and the American climate in particular had been stirred by an extraordinary work to which he refers in his correspondence with Creech,[50] the *Recherches philosophiques sur les américains* of the abbé Cornelius De Pauw, originally published in 1768-69. This remarkable book, which caused great offence to many readers and prompted dozens of replies in several languages, is essentially a diatribe against the whole American continent, whose species of flora and fauna De Pauw regarded as degenerate forms of their counterparts in the Old World. The human inhabitants of America, moreover, were assailed by De Pauw for their utterly stupid, brutish, weak, depraved, debauched, and sexually aberrant behaviour. Native Americans, in short, he concluded, were a race of men scarcely above the level of that miserable animal, the orang-utan.[51]

What Monboddo might have made of such a slur against the noble creature he portrayed is a matter for conjecture, but we should not be surprised to learn that the marquis de Sade relished De Pauw's work almost above all others to which he had access in the period of his confinement at the Bastille. Kames undoubtedly read it differently, for he recognised its author as a disciple and follower of Buffon who had merely extended Buffon's thesis about the inferiority of animal species in the New World to embrace mankind. American savages formed a degenerate race of men for the same reason that the llama was shorter than the camel and the puma more squat than the tiger. De Pauw, that is, excited Kames's interest in the fundamental inconsistency in Buffon's theory around which his *Sketches* would be drawn. Of course he did not agree with De Pauw about the degenerate nature of Americans. It was only Europeans who degenerated in America, he thought, particularly if they ended up near Charleston. But he differed over this point only because he found both De Pauw and Buffon mistaken in their supposition that human nature was determined and altered by climate. So long as it was recognised that Providence had shaped every species of animal so that it might flourish in a particular climate, then the conclusion that this thesis applied equally to the different races of man must hold too. Buffon had failed to take stock of the implications of his own theory, and De Pauw's invective against America appears to have directed Kames's attention to the inconsistency of the French naturalist's doctrine around which the opening chapters of the *Sketches of the History of Man* were to be formed.

If these observations on the genesis of Monboddo's and Kames's anthropological theories are correct, then I hope they may be thought to lend some weight to a proposition about the treatment of the history of ideas which those who practise it too often forget, in my view, to the detriment of their subject. And this is, that original thinkers generally march into battle backwards. To understand such thinkers' true meaning it seems to me that we do better to consider the antecedent philosophies they deliberately set out to refute, rather than those they somehow manage to reflect. With the disparate ideas of both Kames and Monboddo which are at issue here, we find a common point of departure — a point of embarkation in each case for a very distant journey — in Buffon's speculations on the nature of man.

V

I conclude with a few remarks on themes which touch directly upon what I have said already, but which really require a separate and much fuller treatment of their own. Very briefly, I should like to comment on what I take to be the differences between Kames's and Monboddo's conceptions of man, then on their respective place in the Scottish Enlightenment, and finally on their wider significance in the history of anthropological thought.

Some contrasting features of their doctrines have already been noted — among them their conflicting portraits of ancient Greece, for instance, and above all the fact that Monboddo put forward a theory of civilisation's decline since Antiquity, whereas Kames elaborated a more composite scheme, with a primeval noble savage state in Scotland, followed by decadence and then the moral improvement of mankind generally in the long passage from barbarous to commercial society. Their anthropological and historical perspectives are distinguished in many other important ways, but I pass comment here on just two points, one of which divides them and one which joins them together, while separating both men from their most prominent contemporaries in the Scottish Enlightenment.

The first point may be understood as an expression of their different temperaments and distinctive styles of composition, and it is itself encapsulated in the very contempt which each man felt for the other's company, and writings, and, above all, reputation. In an often-cited passage John Ramsay reports that when Kames asked if he had read his *Elements of Criticism*, Monboddo replied, 'I have not, my lord. You write a good deal faster than I am able to read'.[52] This exchange may be taken to express much of the spirit and character of each figure, and to reflect the essence of their respective anthropological theories. For in his account of the origins of language, Monboddo rather laboriously pieces together just one great thesis around the notion of some higher primate's apish imitation of human nature, while Kames, by contrast, racily flits through several distinct arguments about man's origins. Where Monboddo accommodates, Kames strikes out, whatever he finds at the peripheries of his model; while Monboddo regards physical similarities between creatures as providing a *prima facie* case for biological relation, Kames holds that physical dissimilarities imply biological distinction. In his definition of mankind, Monboddo aggregates and multiplies varieties so as to incorporate the orang-utan as well, whereas Kames decouples and divides races so as to exclude Americans from the same species as Europeans. In the Scottish history of eighteenth-century anthropology, in short, Monboddo appears to be the hedgehog and Kames the fox.

The second point is just a reiteration of my remarks about Buffon, who provided both Monboddo and Kames, as I have tried to show, with a common point of departure. Their concentration upon Buffon, and upon his arguments from natural history, seems to me particularly striking, when we consider the fact that for nearly all of their principal Scottish contemporaries who commented upon the history of mankind, the principal authority was not Buffon, but Montesquieu. The *Esprit des lois* towers over the Enlightenment in Scotland like a modern collosus in whose shadow so many of her leading thinkers stood in awe. Some, like Ferguson, actually wondered whether they had anything of consequence to add to Montesquieu's doctrines, and a few unkind critics have observed that very little remains of Ferguson's philosophy of man if we exclude this debt. But Kames, as has been shown, took issue with Montesquieu over his conception of the influence of climate, and in the *Sketches* he turns to Montesquieu, whom he credits as 'the greatest genius of the present age',[53] only in order to criticise and deprecate his views. Neither were Monboddo or Kames particularly impressed with Montesquieu's conception of the main currents of our societal development, or with the systems and principles of government which in his judgment corresponded with our social manners and customs.[54] Of course they agreed with Montesquieu, as against Rousseau in particular, that mankind must *always* have lived in society and *never* in isolation. But at least in their theories of human origins they were more interested in our *natural* than in out *social* history. Whereas most of their Scottish contemporaries addressed themselves to the long development of our species within society, their definitions of mankind were instead directed to the biological limits of our nature, and to the structure of the human body — in effect to the comparative study of apes and races. While their kinsmen were building upon Montesquieu to lay the foundations of the social sciences in the age that followed, Monboddo and Kames were, by contrast, contributing to the discipline of *physical anthropology*, many of whose fundamental questions over at least the next half-century were raised by these two authors.

The crucial figure in this scenario turns out to be Blumenbach, whose *De generis humani varietate nativa* — the work generally regarded as having launched the subject of physical anthropology — dates from 1775 and in fact refers to both Monboddo and Kames.[55] The essence of Blumenbach's argument was that Monboddo and others like him had been mistaken to suppose that orang-utans were human, because they had overlooked a variety of tangible dissimilarities between the two species. Orang-utans did not in fact resemble us, since they were *quadrupeds*, or rather *quadrumanes*, naturally incapable of our upright gait, while the lobes of their brains, like those of all other apes, were different in form from those of human brains. The same year 1775, moreover, also witnessed the publication of the physician John Hunter's *Disputatio inauguralis quaedam de hominum varietatibus*, a tract which similarly cites both Monboddo and Kames and was, indeed, conceived largely as a refutation of Kames's claim that the different varieties of men comprise distinct species.[56] Blumenbach's anatomical contrasts between orang-utans and humans, on the other hand, were to be further refined in the late 1770s and 1780s by other natural scientists, such as Sömmering and, perhaps most importantly, Petrus Camper, who sought to refute Monboddo's approach by locating the fundamental differences between these creatures and ourselves in more precise investigations of our disparate physical attributes and bodily structures.[57]

But even in disposing of Monboddo's arguments his critics never came to resuscitate the Cartesian and spiritualist paradigm of Tyson and Buffon which he challenged. To that extent, I believe that Monboddo marks the end of a century-long theoretical perspective by pointing to what he thought, and others seem to have accepted, was its fundamental fallacy. Thereafter, the only pertinent divisions in anthropological studies came to be those which set apart the several races *within* the human species, rather than those which separated man from ape, and the focus of researchers' attention shifted to the study of the origins of races and to the contrast between monogenetic and polygenetic approaches to this subject. My final point, then, is that while Monboddo's work brings to its close one tradition of scientific speculation on human nature, Kames's doctrine, conceived at the same time, helped to launch a second tradition which, of course in other hands, *became* the discipline of physical anthropology in its modern form.[58]

NOTES

1. William Scott, *Francis Hutcheson* (Cambridge, 1900), Ch. v and p. 257. Hutcheson was a gifted teacher and excited much enthusiasm among his Glasgow students, not least Adam Smith, in part through his informal and ebullient manner of lecturing, in English, up and down the passage at the end of their benches. As a later commentator thus remarked (see David Murray, *Memories of the Old College of Glasgow*, Glasgow, 1927, p. 144), 'We micht ca' him a Peripatetic Pheelosopher'.

2. *Boswell's Life of Johnson*, ed. G. B. Hill and L. F. Powell, V. *The Tour of the Hebrides* (Oxford, 1950), p. 111.

3. I should be most grateful to any reader who could ascribe this quotation to its proper source, which has mightily resisted all my efforts to recall it.

4. The most widely available account of Monboddo's life and thought is E. L. Cloyd's *James Burnet: Lord Monboddo* (Oxford, 1972).

5. On this subject see David Lieberman's 'The legal needs of a commercial society: the jurisprudence of Lord Kames', in *Wealth and Virtue: The Shaping of Political Economy in the Scottish Enlightenment*, ed. I. Hont and M. Ignatieff (Cambridge, 1983), pp. 203-34.

6. Hume to Smith, 12 April 1759, *Letters of David Hume*, ed. J. Y. T. Greig, 2 vols. (Oxford, 1932), i.304. For general accounts of the life and thought of Kames, see William Lehman, *Henry Home, Lord Kames, and the Scottish Enlightenment* (The Hague, 1971), and especially Ian Simpson Ross, *Lord Kames and the Scotland of his Day* (Oxford, 1972).

7. Their anthropological doctrines have not passed entirely without notice. Illuminating treatments of Monboddo's views can be found in Arthur Lovejoy, 'Monboddo and Rousseau', *Modern Philology* (1932-33), xxx.275-96; Oscar Sherwin, 'A Man with a Tail — Lord Monboddo', *Journal of the History of Medicine* (1958), xxiii.435-67; and Antonio Verri, *Lord Monboddo dalla metafisica all'antropologia* (Ravenna, 1975). For an assessment of Monboddo's contribution to the history of linguistics, see especially Stephen Land, 'Lord Monboddo and the Theory of Syntax in the Late Eighteenth Century', *Journal of the History of Ideas* (1976), iii.423-40. With regard to Kames, see Arthur McGuinness, *Henry Home, Lord Kames* (New York, 1970), Chs. v-vi, and, above all, George W. Stocking, Jr., 'Scotland as the Model of Mankind: Lord Kames' Philosophical View of Civilization', in *Toward a Science of Man: Essays in the History of Anthropology*, ed. T. H. H. Thoresen (The Hague 1975), pp. 65-89.

8. Monboddo, *Of the Origin and Progress of Language* (hereafter *OPL*), 6 vols. (Edinburgh, 1773-92), I.i.6, p. 57.

9. 'I am very happy to find, that my notions, both with respect to the original state of human nature, and the origin of language, agree so perfectly with the notions of an author of so much genius, and original thought, as well as learning', Monboddo noted (*OPL*, I.i.11, p. 141), in a commentary on Rousseau's *Discours sur l'inégalité*. See also pp. 172-73 and 176. Rousseau's general influence on Monboddo is discussed by Lovejoy in 'Monboddo and Rousseau'. The immense influence which his thought exercised over the wider Scottish Enlightenment is still in need of comprehensive treatment. Two recent introductions which point the way are Peter France's 'Primitivism and Enlightenment: Rousseau and the Scots', *The Yearbook of English Studies* (1985), xv.64–69, and R. A. Leigh's 'Rousseau and the Scottish Enlightenment', *Contributions to Political Economy* (1986), v.1-21.

10. *OPL*, I.ii.1, pp. 196-97.

11. *OPL*, I.ii.9, pp. 279-84.

12. For an assessment of Rousseau's ideas on this subject, see my 'Perfectible Apes in Decadent Cultures: Rousseau's Anthropology Revisited', *Daedalus* (Summer, 1978), pp. 107-34, and (with Christopher Frayling), 'From

the orang-utan to the vampire: towards an anthropology of Rousseau', in *Rousseau after two hundred years: Proceedings of the Cambridge Bicentennial Colloquium* (Cambridge, 1982), pp. 109-24.

13. See *OPL*, I.i.14, pp. 172-74, and, more generally, Franck Tinland, *L'Homme sauvage: Homo ferus et homo sylvestris* (Paris, 1968), especially Ch. ii.

14. *OPL*, I.ii.1, p. 196.

15. *OPL*, I.ii.4 (2nd ed. 1774), pp. 295-99.

16. I have discussed this matter in detail in my 'Tyson and Buffon on the orang-utan', *Studies on Voltaire and the eighteenth century*, CLV (1976), pp. 1-19.

17. See especially Monboddo's 'Of the Ourang Outang, & whether he be of the Human Species', Edinburgh, National Library of Scotland (hereafter NLS) Ms. 5738.109 (box 4), fo. 4; and *OPL*, I.ii.5 (2nd ed.), pp. 337-38.

18. Monboddo, *OPL*, I.ii.4 (2nd ed.), pp. 297-98.

19. See *OPL*, I.i.14 and I.ii.9 (1st ed.), pp. 174-75 and 289; and *OPL*, I.ii.4 and I.ii.5 (2nd ed.), pp. 272-73, 289-90 and 346.

20. In 'The Orang-utan as Speechless Man: Monboddo as Critic of Buffon', *Journal of the History of the Behavioral Sciences* (forthcoming).

21. See especially Peter Rodman, 'Population Composition and Adaptive Organisation among Orang-utans of the Kutai Reserve', in *Comparative Ecology and Behaviour of Primates*, ed. R. P. Michael and J. H. Crook (London, 1973), pp. 171-209; John MacKinnon, 'The Behaviour and Ecology of Wild Orang-utans', *Animal Behaviour* (1974), xxii.3-74; and MacKinnon, *In Search of the Red Ape* (London, 1974).

22. As Rodman reports (p. 197), 'The dispersion of orang-utan populations and the simplicity of social relations within them are both striking and disappointing when compared with the complexity of social structures found among other primates'. According to MacKinnon (*In Search of the Red Ape*, p. 64), the orang-utan appears to be a 'solitary nomad'. MacKinnon came to this conclusion after spending months upon months tracking down orang-utans in the tropical forests of Borneo and Sumatra, his blood drained by leeches, his strength by mud and his patience by flies. The fact that Rousseau, if not Monboddo, had been right all along in remarking upon these creatures' nomadic existence, frugivorous diet, infrequent sexual relations and essentially solitary and indolent lives, speaks well for eighteenth-century speculative primatology.

23. 'Of the Ourang Outang, & whether he be of the Human Species', NLS Ms.5738.109 (box 4), fo. 13; and *OPL*, I.ii.4 (2nd ed.), pp. 294 and 297.

24. *OPL*, I.i.14 (1st ed.), pp. 177-82.

25. La Mettrie, *L'Homme machine* (1747), ed. A. Vartanian (Princeton, 1960), p. 162.

26. Diderot, *Suite du Rêve de d'Alembert* (1769), in his *Oeuvres complètes*, ed, J. Assézat and M. Tourneux (Paris, 1875-77), ii.190.

27. Rousseau to Hume, 29 March 1766, in the *Correspondence complète de Rousseau*, ed. Leigh (Geneva and Oxford, 1965 —), no. 5129, xxix.66.

28. Kames, *Sketches of the History of Man* (Edinburgh, 1774), I.i.7, p. 267, and II.i.1, p. 379.

29. *Ibid.*, I.i.7, pp. 281-307.

30. *Boswell's Life of Johnson*, I. *The Life* (Oxford, 1934), p. 425. On Kames and Ossian, see McGuinness, 'Lord Kames on the Ossian Poems: Anthropology and Criticism', *Texas Studies in Literature and Language* (1968-69), x.65-75. On the broader Ossianic inspiration for Scottish primitivism in the eighteenth century, see Donald Foerster, 'Mid-Eighteenth Century Scottish Criticism of Homer', *Studies in Philology* (1943), xl.425-46; Foerster, 'Scottish Primitivism and the Historical Approach', *Philological Quarterly* (1950), xxix.307-23; and Roy Pearce, 'The Eighteenth-Century Scottish Primitivists: Some Reconsiderations', *English Literary History* (1945), xii.203-20.

31. Kames, *Sketches*, I.i.1, pp. 24-25, and II.ii.12, pp. 75-84.

32. Kames, *Sketches*, II.ii.12, pp. 82-83. For Buffon's treatment of this subject, in the chapter of the fourteenth volume of his *Histoire naturelle* (1766) entitled 'De la dégénération des animaux', see the *Oeuvres philosophiques de Buffon*, ed. J. Piveteau (Paris, 1954), pp. 408-13.

33. Kames, *Sketches*, I.i.1, pp. 7-9.

34. Kames, *Sketches*, I.i.1, pp. 13-15. Kames took pride in the perspicacity of these observations, and to the natural historian John Walker, for instance, with whom he corresponded at length about such matters, he remarked upon 'my great topic of different races of Men fitted for different climates'. See Kames to Walker, 12 December 1774, Edinburgh University Library, La.III.352/4. Cf. *Sketches*, I.i.1, p. 11.

35. Kames, *Sketches*, I.i.1, p. 31.

36. *Ibid.*, pp. 31-33. Some of Kames's more religiously orthodox readers were unconvinced by any of his explanations of the development of national character. David Doig, for one, Master of Stirling Grammar School, addressed two lengthy letters to Kames, stressing that 'Nations, who emerged from the Savage State, if indeed they were ever Savages, owed the blessing of Civilization' to supernatural forces (Doig to Kames, 5 November 1776, Edinburgh, Scottish Record Office [hereafter SRO] GD 24/1/578-91, fo. 18). After Kames's death Doig published these *Two Letters on the Savage State* (London, 1792), in the hope that by overthrowing Kames's hypothesis (pp. xii-xiii), 'they might be of some use to the cause of revelation'.

37. Kames, *Sketches*, II.ii.12, p. 70.

38. *Ibid.*, I.i.1, pp. 8 and 36-37, and II.ii.12, pp. 70-72.

39. *Ibid.*, II.ii.12, p. 75.

40. See Stocking, 'Kames's Philosophical View of Civilization', pp. 84-86. The theory of separate creation was to become one of the foundations of racialist, and indeed racist, doctrines in the nineteenth century, although, as has been shown with regard to his view of Negroes, it had no such implications for Kames. Nor was he the first person to conceive the idea. In the Renaissance, Paracelsus and Giordano Bruno had put forward similar notions, and perhaps its most determined proponent had been Isaac de La Peyrère, who in his *Prae-Adamitae* of 1655 contended that Adam was the first Jew, but not the first man. Americans, La Peyrère supposed, were descended from pre-Adamites, rather than, as Kames believed, from post-Noahites, though he had no doubt that the native inhabitants of the New World, as

well as other Gentiles, would partake of the resurrection. To my knowledge, La Peyrère's theory is nowhere mentioned by Kames, but it was well-known in the eighteenth century and was the subject of a commentary by Diderot in his *Encyclopédie* article 'Préadamite'. On this matter, see especially Dino Pastine, *Le origini del poligenismo e Isaac Lapeyrère*, in *Miscellanea '600*, I (Florence, 1971), pp. 127-234; Popkin, 'The Philosophical Basis of Eighteenth-Century Racism', in *Studies in Eighteenth-Century Culture*, III, ed. H. Pagliaro (Cleveland, 1973), pp. 245-62; and Giuliano Gliozzi, *Adamo e il nuovo mondo* (Florence, 1976), pp. 530-65.

41. See Edward Tyson, *Orang-Outang, sive Homo Sylvestris* (London, 1699), p. 55, and my 'Tyson and Buffon on the orang-utan', pp. 4-7. For a notable discussion of this subject in a wider context, see William Bynum, 'The Anatomical Method, Natural Theology, and the Functions of the Brain', *Isis* (1973), lxiv.445-68.

42. I suspect Rousseau may have been making tacit reference to Tyson when in note x of the *Discours* he remarked upon writers who refused to allow that such anthropoid animals could be primitive men, merely on account of their stupidity and lack of speech. His contention, too, that orang-utans might be identical with the creatures which the Ancients termed *satyrs*, *fauns* and *sylvans* recalls Tyson's suggestion that the Ancients called the same orang-utans *pygmies*, *cynocephali*, *satyrs* and *sphinges*. It has been observed, moreover, that Rousseau drew some of his reflections on the nature of frugivorous creatures in note v of the *Discours* from an article in the *Journal économique* of 1754 which reports an exchange of views on such matters by Wallis and Tyson. But I must admit that until I completed this essay I laboured under what I can now only suppose was an illusion that Tyson's name, or, as I imagined, 'Tison', was cited by Rousseau somewhere in his account of the orang-utan.

43. See the two-volume published *Catalogue of the Library of the Faculty of Advocates* (Edinburgh, 1742 and 1776). The Minutes of the Curators for the period 1751-83 (NLS Ms. FR 2) relate such matters as proposed changes in the book lending policy of the Faculty and the authorisation of the Curators to purchase books, but not to sell them. The surviving Register of the Curators (NLS Ms FR 118) reports many purchases, but of course not Tyson's *Orang-Outang*, during the period for which Monboddo shared this reponsibility with Hume and Dalrymple. Copies of the text, however, were certainly available to Monboddo elsewhere in Edinburgh. The University Library acquired two — one a presentation copy from the author early in the eighteenth century — while the College of Physicians lists the 1751 edition of *Orang-Outang* in its 1767 catalogue.

44. See especially Lyttelton to Monboddo, April 1773, NLS 5738.22.3.22; Monboddo to Lyttelton, 7 May 1773, NLS 5738.13 (box 1); Pringle to Monboddo, 29 May 1773, NLS 5738.22.3.23; and Monboddo to Pringle, 16 June 1773, NLS 5738.22.3.25. I have discussed these and other exchanges at length in my 'Monboddo as Critic of Buffon'.

45. NLS 5738.109 (box 4). This manuscript of forty-seven leaves corresponds only loosely with the two supplementary chapters on the orang-utan (Book 2, Chs. 4-5) which Monboddo incorporated in his revised text. To my mind, it remains worthy of separate publication.

46. *OPL* (2nd ed.), preface, p. x.

47. Kames, *Sketches*, I.i.1, pp. 40-41n.

48. See especially Kames's letter to Creech of 24 March 1772, SRO Dalguise Muniments, RH 4/26/1. This text has been published by Ross in *Lord Kames*, p. 335.

49. Kames to Lind, 7 March 1772, NLS 10782, fos. 113r-114v. This text has also been published by Ross in *Lord Kames*, pp. 333-35.

50. See the letter of 24 March 1772 cited above. The Kames-Creech correspondence, still largely unexplored by scholars, figures in SRO Dalguise Muniments, RH 4/26, and in some of the bundles of papers at Aldourie Castle, Inverness-shire.

51. See, De Pauw, *Recherches philosophiques sur les américains* (Berlin, 1770), ii.47-48 and 69, for instance. For a remarkable account of the nature and influence of Buffon's and De Pauw's reflections on the generally degenerate species of America, see Antonello Gerbi, *La disputa del Nuovo Mondo: Storia di una polemica, 1750-1900* (Milano, 1955).

52. John Ramsay of Ochtertyre, *Scotland and Scotsmen in the Eighteenth Century*, ed. A. A. Allardyce, 2 vols. (Edinburgh and London, 1888), i.356, n.2.

53. Kames, *Sketches*, I.i.7, pp. 226-27. Montesquieu is otherwise seldom mentioned by Kames in the *Sketches*. He takes issue with the *Esprit des lois* in II.ii.12, p. 82 and refers to it in II.ii.12, p. 96, while criticising the *Grandeur des romains* in I.i.2, p. 49.

54. It might be supposed that Kames took a different view in his *Historical Law Tracts*. But instead of praising Montesquieu in that work he pays his tribute to Bolingbroke's *Study of History* for its excellent treatment of the connection between the laws and customs of a people.

55. In the Göttingen 1776 edition, see p. 36 for Blumenbach's reference to Monboddo, and pp. 45, 53 and 64 for his citations of Kames.

56. This scarce text was later translated and edited, together with that of Blumenbach, by Thomas Bendyshe, for the Anthropological Society of London, with the title, *The Anthropological Treatises of Blumenbach and Hunter* (London, 1865). Kames was also challenged by a mocking Reverend Samuel Stanhope Smith, in an *Essay on the Causes of the Variety of Complexion and Figure in the Human Species. To Which are Added Strictures on Lord Kaims's Discourse on the Original Diversity of Mankind* (Philadelphia, 1787). That must be one of the earliest anthropological treatises to have been produced in America.

57. See especially Camper's 'Account of the Organs of Speech of the Orang Outang, in a Letter to Sir John Pringle', *Philosophical Transactions of the Royal Society* (1779), LXIX.i.139-59, and 'De l'orang-outang, et de quelques autres espèces de singes', in his *Oeuvres* (Paris, 1803), i.5-196.

58. This essay is marked by as many debts as faults, although I trust they are not owing to the same persons. Among my creditors, for reasons too diverse to recount, are Hans Aarsleff, Karen Hall, Peter Jones, Quentin Skinner, George Stocking, Charles Withers and the Master and Fellows of Sidney Sussex College, Cambridge.

9

BUILDINGS AND THE ORDERING OF MINDS AND BODIES

Thomas A. Markus

If there can be said to be any single feature of the Scottish Enlightenment which is of its very essence, surely it is the idea of order. Order in nature, capable of being captured by discovering invariant laws and classificatory taxonomies; order in society, with its fixed 'ranks' (a precursor to the idea of class); order in human thought and the operation of the mind; order in the human body and its anatomy; order in the interaction of economic forces; and order achieved through the power of totally predictable and self-governing behaviour of machines such as the rotative steam engine. These orders were held to be interlocking facets of an overall, divine and natural order which, whilst having fixed laws, governed a process which moved society towards felicitous progress.

It is not surprising that town and building design should have been based on the same ideas of order, although in the formal aspects of architecture these were made evident by means which were merely smooth and gradual transformations of the universal language of Classicism which had been evolving over the previous three centuries. Though we might regard William Adam and his sons the Adam Brothers as innovatory masters of the new style, we find no architectural equivalent here of the startling innovations of David Hume, John Millar, Adam Smith, the Brothers Hunter or James Watt. If we want to see similarly powerful shifts in architecture, which can be said to be specific to the Enlightenment, we have to look beneath the surface attributes of style. But before doing so, it is relevant to raise a question about the innovators in these other fields.

Each of them seems to be producing a double effect: on the one hand a revolutionary dislocation of a tradition and, on the other, an evolutionary development or even conservative restatement of that tradition. Although Bruce Lenman (1981) has called Hume's epistemology, with its sceptical focus, '. . . a time bomb . . . ticking away underneath it (the Scottish Enlightenment)', Hume did not see these ideas as other than leading to a general prosperity created by a liberalising 'middle class'. In fact his contemporary reputation was founded on his *History of England* which was a justification of the Glorious Revolution, a celebration of the Constitution and as conservative in its view of society as the *Treatise on Human Nature* was radical in its view of philosophy. Adam Smith's free trade doctrine and division of labour theory at one and the same time laid the foundations for the mercantile and factory systems of the Industrial Revolution (although Smith had hardly seen the beginnings of mechanised factory production, and he foresaw the application of his ideas in an agricultural economy) and defended the existing social structures in which masters continued to exercise power over labourers, servants and skilled artisans. So, in a curious dualism, the revolutionary and traditional strands were closely intertwined in the work of these thinkers, and both were used by the existing elites to reinforce their power or by the rising elites to produce new power structures.

In spite of huge intellectual advances, the immediate response to the ideas in the social and political realms was conservative, if not reactionary. This process was driven by two interlocking forces. One side of the coin was political and philosophical: the American and French Revolutions, the clearly revolutionary message of the Romantic poets and of French philosophy, notably that of Rousseau, the work of political radicals of whom Tom Paine was but the best known, and urban and rural riots centred on food, price and labour crises. The other side of the coin was production-focused, both on the land and in the new mills: clearances and enclosures, rural depopulation and emigration, the concomitant rapid urban growth, the exploitation of the new technical inventions, and the creation of a new type of labour force tied to machinery. All these challenges and threats called forth rigid, even repressive legal, political, institutional and military responses in which many Enlightenment ideas and techniques were used.

The effects on the inhabitants of towns had struck medical and social observers, such as Ferriar (1792) in Manchester, before the end of the eighteenth century. They made a connection, more than half a century before Chadwick did in his great *Report*, between poorly constructed housing, bad water supply and drainage, overcrowding, and long hours of work in damaging mill environments on the one hand and disease, crime and poverty on the other. As far as lunacy is concerned there remains an open question as to the connection between its increase, or perceived increase, and the urbanisation and industrialisation process. Scull (1979) questions the conventional view that they are closely connected; Rice (1981) on the other hand shows that, for Scotland at least, the effect was real.

In planning and architecture there is a similar intertwining of revolutionary and traditional strands, and a similar use of ideas and techniques for rigid social control. As I have indicated, the changes in Classical style, even the beginnings of its mingling with baronial and castellated, were relatively smooth developments within a strongly established tradition of order. Edinburgh's New Town, commonly held to be the major achievement of Scottish Enlightenment architecture and planning, was innovatory in its use of the grid and its spatial concepts, rather than the, sometimes drab and stilted, Classicisim of its individual terraces and buildings.

The revolution in architecture had to do, rather, with new concepts of order associated with quite new building types invented to meet the demands of the early Industrial Revolution, science, medicine, the arts and, above all, the huge new urban institutions to accommodate the sick, the insane and criminal populations. Since these developments undoubtedly had their roots in Enlightenment thought, although only reaching a peak when, under the influence of late eighteenth and early nineteenth-century utilitarianism, major urban investment took place, it is proper to regard them as Enlightenment fruits.

These new concepts of, and techniques for, achieving order are most clearly seen not in the *form* of buildings, but in their *functional programmes* and their *spatial structures*. A clarification of these three primary terms in architecture — form, function and space — will help to explain the later analysis, whose purpose is to find ways of obtaining *meaning* from buildings in terms of their effect on social relationships. Here 'social' refers to three levels of experience: the relationship of the self to self, to others and the Other (the cosmic scheme of things). *Non*-relationship at each of these levels is the alienation from self, from others and from Nature as described by Marx. What, then, is the role of buildings in the formation of these relationships?

Buildings are the major outcomes of material production. Together with nature, the *given* material world whose resources are converted to produce, amongst other things, buildings, they represent the essence of materiality. They partake of the material world's finite, limited properties. A given amount of that finite material can be divided in society in an infinite number of ways — but what one individual or group has, another cannot have. In von Neumann's language it is a 'zero sum game'. All social relationships based on ownership of or access to material resources — that is their *control* — involve relationships of power. More power here means correspondingly less power there. Social structures are power structures tied to resource control. Political science analyses these structures and the law underpins the distribution of resources. The concept of justice is used as a critique of both the law and of social structures. A building, in microcosm, reproduces this state of society. It distributes power amongst various groups, and principles of justice can be used to determine and criticise this distribution. These power relationships are tied to its materiality and, in turn, the materiality of the building is *tied* to the power relationships embedded in the rules and laws which govern its use.

There are other human relationships which are not limited by the finiteness of material resources. The more strength one person or group has, the more another related person or group has. Moreover, the greater this shared quantity, the more is available for others. The relationships are no longer governed by power-over, or domination, and principles of justice no longer apply. Such bonds are identified in poetry and religion as love and in Marx as unalienated relationships. They are described in utopian visions such as William Morris's *News from Nowhere* which act primarily as critiques of society based on the first type of relationship. The ultimate end of creation or of society is now seen as freedom, not from materiality but from its alienating relationships. Over the horizon lies a City of God without a church or social structure, or an ultimate classless society in which even the State has withered away. Both during the historical journey to that end, and, it is envisaged, when it is reached, materiality in nature, in human bodies and in objects used as gifts or sacrifices, is central. The bonds are created in and through the material world. So a building, as a major material production, plays a vital role in establishing them and in microcosm representing their universality. These bond relationships are mediated by its materiality.

The materiality of a building is experienced both directly, and indirectly, through the presence of people. Thus its forms are seen; its functions are experienced as the activities of those who are present. These activities are the outcome of a complex set of properties — such as the size of spaces, their relative location with regard to each other and to the outside, and their contents — as well as by the set of laws and rules, based on ownership, which are used to control the activities.

So the power relationships are tied to, and the bond relationships mediated by, the material properties of the building and by its control and ownership system. These are the data available for the analysis of meaning — that is, for the discovery of how the building is formative of relationships of both kinds. It is a reasonable expectation that buildings will form power relationships which are just and bond relationships which are strong and creative. This expectation is the basis for architectural criticism and historical interpretation which goes beyond mere description. The properties which are of primary interest are form, function and space, and it is in these that we can expect to find answers to questions about the meaning of buildings. But even in a period of radical change, such as the late Enlightenment and the early Industrial Revolution, one will not necessarily find equally marked disruptions in each of these fields.

The style, colour, composition, articulation, proportions, ornamentation and geometry — that is the form — of buildings, are experienced as powerful sense impressions, so immediate that there has grown up a long tradition in architectural history, theory, criticism and in the media of treating architecture as a species of large, public sculpture. (I shall suggest, in my conclusions, that there are other causes, besides the immediacy of the sense impressions, which created this tradition.) The processes by which these forms are perceived have been studied by psychologists; the study of critical judgement is at the core of the philosophy of aesthetics; and interpretation of their meaning has traditionally been the business of art history and criticism and more recently of social science.

These formal properties certainly share with art of other kinds the power of speaking of relationships not bound by material finitude and its constraining social ties. They point beyond themselves. But they also speak of power structures — the forms are those selected by someone, the designer is chosen *from* amongst others, there may be heavily laden political or ideological symbolism, certain forms or styles are censored. The formal language has always been class-related. The transformation of the Romantic impulse in late eighteenth-century Scottish Classical architecture into baronial and military elements is, in part at least, this kind of power process.

The activities that go on in a building, or which are implied by the location, form and contents of its individual spaces, are equally powerful experiences. They tell us what behaviour to expect, and what is appropriate and inappropriate behaviour by each participant. They speak of purpose or function. To *describe* these functions we use a verbal shorthand which, in a given culture, is loaded with rich and complex meanings. For instance the words 'hospital', 'museum', 'kitchen', or 'living room' carry such meanings. Texts which use such words as prescriptions, that is as instructions to the designer before a building exists, are called briefs today. In the Renaissance they may have been letters from a Pope or Prince; during the Scottish Enlightenment they were, characteristically, Acts of Parliament, Town Council resolutions and instructions to competitors in such projects as Edinburgh's New Town and the Bridewell, which is discussed later. Such language, like all language, can never be 'innocent', and analysis of vocabulary, syntax, length, structure of the text and other features reveal what explicit and implicit values and meanings are built into the statement. These 'design' the building in significant ways before the designer is even appointed.

These texts are the control system of a building. They derive from ownership and prescribe what is to go on in it, and they lead to rule systems which are used in its management.

The building's functional programme, as its form, has a dual effect. It clearly creates for its owners or sponsors a distribution of power which reproduces in microcosm their own position in making it possible for them, in the first place, to command the resources and the associated power to undertake such an investment. Therefore the way groups and individuals are defined and labelled, the relationships established between them, the amount of space and the environmental standards allocated to them — which may be selectively differentiated — the control over use and the managerial tools of ownership will all derive from wider power structures. The relationships created may be egalitarian, autocratic or bureaucratic according to the nature of ownership. Certainly principles of justice can be applied in a detailed critique of the functional programme and the building properties which derive from it. But the programme and the derived properties also mediate unbounded social relationships. They create or hinder the formation of solidarities and friendship bonds, through the way activities are defined and controlled. In the degree to which the programme leaves open or closes off role definition and the possibilities of participation in activities it will foster or suppress responsibility and awareness. Functions can be so defined that all the users' knowledge of the organisation's purpose and activities grows. Human relationships which point beyond 'technical' or structured function can be enabled; the way is open to pass over from isolation to community.

A third experience of buildings is that of the sequence and connection of spaces; we enter from the outside, find ourselves in an entrance hall which leads to other rooms, some connected by means of a tree-like, branching and ever-deepening structure, some by means of rings which connect a space to others in such a way that it is possible to find at least two alternative routes from one space to another. If all these permeabilities are represented by lines which connect dots, each of which represents a space, a diagram is obtained which in fact is a spatial map (Fig.1). If this is redrawn, so that all spaces which are the

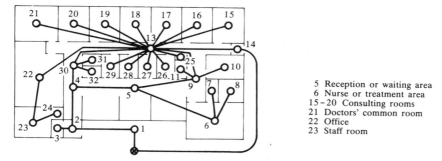

5 Reception or waiting area
6 Nurse or treatment area
15-20 Consulting rooms
21 Doctors' common room
22 Office
23 Staff room

Figure 1. Schematic plan of a health centre with permeabilities marked (after Hillier).
Source: Markus, T.A., 'Buildings as Classifying Devices', *Environment and Planning B*, 1987, Vol. 14.

same number of steps away from a given point, say the outside, are drawn on the same level, in a successive number of levels, a topological graph is obtained (Fig.2). Hillier and Hansen (1984) have shown how such maps relate to the social structure and control mechanisms of the institution or group which inhabits the building. Again we see both types of relationships being influenced by such spatial structures. On the one hand those of power-partitioning in which the relative location of groups

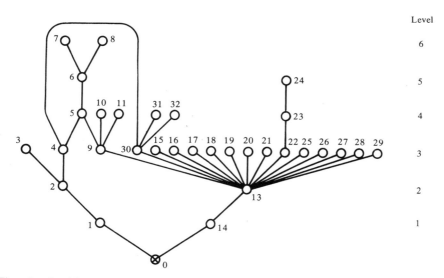

Figure 2. Spatial structure of health centre shown in Figure 1, in the form of a topological graph (after Hillier).
Source: as for Figure 1.

in space clearly establishes the control of resources and knowledge. These spatially-based structures may distribute power equally or unequally, with great imbalances between dominat*ing* and dominat*ed*. Principles of justice can be used to evaluate them. On the other hand these same spatial structures also generate, by configurations corresponding to 'next to', 'with', 'together', 'near' and 'in', unlimited, unpredictable and open bond relationships leading to development and growth in individuals and groups.

The properties of form, function and space can carry meanings at many levels. A particular property will have both power and bond meanings. They are able to work independently of each other. Thus there is no reason why a certain form should be used for a certain function. Nor why for a specific form or for a specific function one spatial structure is more appropriate than another.

In other words form, function and space are independent 'discourses' of buildings — each particular building achieving its meaning through the unique *conjunction* of the three. The common field into which these properties have to be mapped to find answers to questions of meaning is that of society itself, which we know through analytical social science and history (social theory) and through experience (social practice).

One of the salient features of social structure based on power is the underlying ordering principle. To establish and maintain stable orders involves dividing the world, people, objects and knowledge into classes. These classes can be related to each other in various, usually hierarchical, taxonomies, and then confirmed in language. Buildings translate such classification systems into concrete ordering devices. Although this classifying, ordering principle is always at work, in the late eighteenth and early nineteenth centuries it is particularly potent and interesting. It was a response to the political, social and technological revolutions already described — and was the application to production of the fruits of science and reason. It resulted in buildings which were markedly one-sided in their power structures and in which the room for achieving relationships of the bond type was correspondingly reduced. The dislocation with the pre-Enlightenment and pre-industrial tradition was enormous.

It is my purpose to examine a few revolutionary Scottish building types of this period, to demonstrate how the ordering principles were used through each of the three discourses. The types chosen are those in which there is a clear attempt to cope with *dis*order by creating models of society or knowledge based on classification, integration of the classes and their visible display.

The first group of types is that which was designed to contain those who carried what were perceived as the most serious threats to an ordered and 'progressive' society: physical, especially contagious disease; crime or 'moral disease', which threatened civic order and property; and insanity, which looked like the very negation of what the Enlightenment took to be the specific mark of humanity — reason.

All three categories diminished the pool of available and compliant labour — two through disability and one through refusal to work when crime seemed a more lucrative alternative. This unproductivity had been seen as the basic problem even in the earlier, prototypical institutions which sprang up from the sixteenth century onwards. These were unspecialised, in the sense that we find sick, aged, insane and petty criminals all together in the poorhouses, workhouses and houses of correction. These had productive labour as an important part of the regime — with three objectives. First, to produce goods which could either be sold or used within the institution, thus diminishing, but never extinguishing, its cost to its sponsors; second, as a means of discipline or punishment, in tune with the natural 'law' of work; and third, as a form of training for a possible ultimate return to useful production in the outside world. The Poor Laws and the involvement of Church and Town Councils gave these institutions a legal and municipal framework. When, during the Enlightenment, it was considered necessary to make the diffused, invisible threat to order visible, and concentrate and put under surveillance its carriers, it was these early 'houses' which became the prototypes for the new specialised institutions (these have been the subject of detailed study: Markus, 1982).

Glasgow's Town Hospital was built in 1733 on the Clyde, under the auspices of the Town Council, Merchants' House, Trades' House and Kirk Session. It not only combined the function of hospital, poorhouse, workhouse and lunatic asylum, but also had a school in which David Dale, future partner of Robert Owen at New Lanark, carried out his first experiments in the education of infants. Members of the joint Faculty of Physicians and Surgeons gave their services free, and there is evidence of clinical teaching. But the first real hospital, Glasgow Infirmary, was not built till 1792, near the Cathedral, to a design by James (and Robert?) Adam (Fig.3). Its classical, symmetrical formality was not a great departure from earlier hospitals in Edinburgh, which we will shortly examine. Eight open wards, men on one side and women on the other, with nineteen beds in each, as well as some basement 'cells' for lunatics, provided the total patient accommodation. Centrally, on the top floor under the dome, was the operating theatre with seating

Fig. 3a

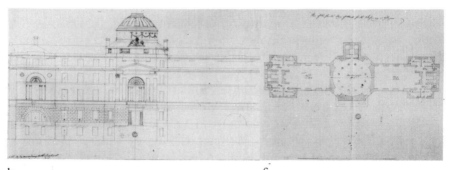

b

c

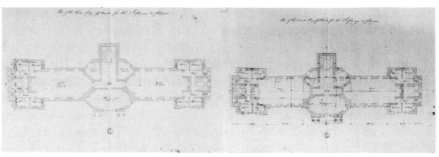

d   e

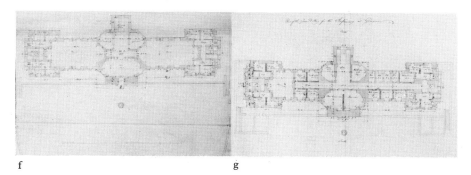

f   g

Figure 3. Glasgow Infirmary, 1792; architects, Robert and James (?) Adam.
a. Exterior view.
b. Front elevation.
c. Fourth-floor plan.
d. Third-floor plan.
e. Second-floor plan.
f. First('entrance')-floor plan.
g. Ground-floor plan.
Source: a. Joseph Swan, *Select Views of Glasgow and Environs*, Glasgow, 1829.
b–g. Sir John Soane's Museum, London.
Copyright: b–g. The Royal Commission on the Ancient and Historical Monuments of Scotland, Edinburgh.

for the astounding number of 200 pupils and observers. There was no chapel.

We need to go to Edinburgh to see the most advanced hospital design practice. As early as 1729 the Physicians had a small hospital in a converted house near the Cowgate. By this time Alexander Munro had been the first Professor of Anatomy for some seven years. The Surgeons, in competition, set up their own hospital in College Wynd, with six beds. In 1738 a new Surgeons' Hospital was designed, possibly by William Adam, in which the symmetrical, men's and women's wards opened off a central space which contained the operating theatre (Fig.4). The scheme was abandoned for, in the same year, the Physicians and Surgeons agreed on a joint Royal Infirmary venture, for which William Adam was appointed as architect. His design was the earliest British U-shaped plan — although such plans of course had been long established for large country houses, poorhouses and barracks. This solution was quite different from the great Continental Renaissance and eighteenth-century examples, all of which, to a greater or lesser extent, used central altars in long naves or Greek-cross and radial plans. The beginnings of this type go back to monastery infirmaries

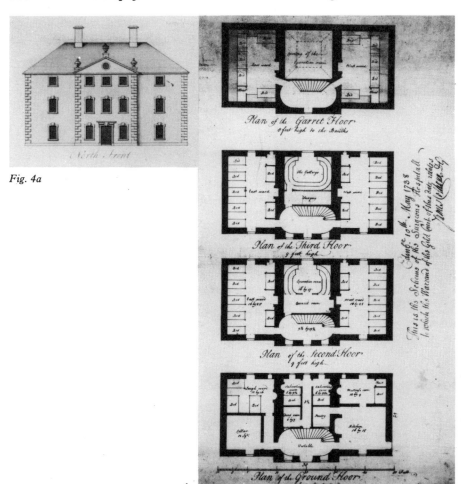

Figure 4 a–b.   Proposed Surgeons' Hospital, Edinburgh, 1738; architect, William Adam.
Source and copyright: University of Edinburgh, Department of History, History of Science
and Medicine Unit.

and medieval hospitals attached to churches (Fig.5). But undoubtedly
its most perfect expression was in Filarete's hospital for the 'ideal' town
of Sforzinda, dating from 1451-65 and built as the Ospedale Maggiore in
Milan (Fig.6). Prior to Edinburgh the British experience was to be found
mainly in the London hospitals such as St. Thomas's. These consisted of
various agglomerates of courtyards and wings, except St Bartholomew's,
for which in 1729 James Gibbs laid out four, detached blocks around an
open quadrangle.

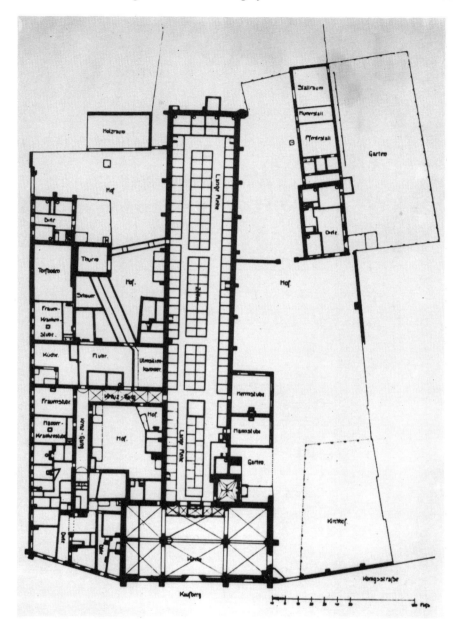

Figure 5. Hospital of the Holy Spirit, Lübeck, 1287.
Source: Dieter Jetter, *Geschichte des Hospitals*, Band 1, *Westdeutschland von den Anfängen bis 1850*, Franz Steiner Verlag, Wiesbaden, 1966, Figure 11, *after* Gustav Schaumann, *Das Heiligen-Geist-Hospital (in Lübeck), in Bau- und Kunstdenkmaler der Hansestadt Lübeck*, Lübeck, 1906.

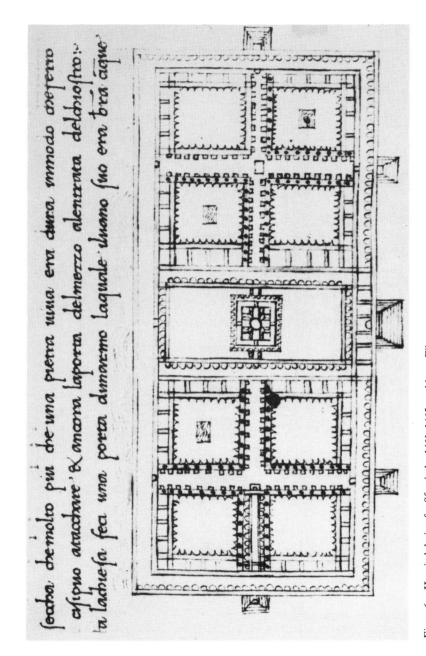

Figure 6.   Hospital design for Sforzinda, 1461–1465; architect, Filarete.

Source: Filarete, *Treatise on Architecture*, trans. and with an introduction by John R. Spencer, Yale University Press, New Haven and London, 1965, Book XI, folio 82v.

In the Edinburgh Infirmary (Fig.7) there were beds for 288 patients on four floors and in a garret, and 'cells' for twelve lunatics in the basement. On the top floor a central operating theatre was designed to be used also as an observatory and, on Sundays, as a chapel — a peculiarly Scottish Enlightenment response to the established European practice of locating an altar, chapel or church at the centre of the hospital as an expression of cosmic unity. Here, instead, practical clinical function was combined with religion and science, in an economic and 'progressive' manner!

The prototype established by William Adam was soon to be followed in other parts of Britain, such as Boulton Mainwaring's 1740 design for the London Hospital and, in the same year, Tully and Halfpenny's scheme for Bristol Infirmary. By the end of the eighteenth century the form was well established, as seen in Manchester's 1793 Infirmary. But, though the form seemed static, the spatial structure was undergoing rapid development; this can be clearly seen by comparing the successive spatial graphs of these three hospitals.

Adam's scheme located patients at various depths, and was free of all corridors; staff, patients and visitors all passed through wards of one set of patients to get access to those of another (Fig.8a). In the London Hospital (Fig.8b) the central block had corridors, but the two wings were still without. But all the patients are now at the 'deepest' part of

a

Figure 7 a–b.   Edinburgh Royal Infirmary, 1738; architect, William Adam.
a.   Front elevation.
b.   Floor plans.
Source and copyright: as for Figure 4.

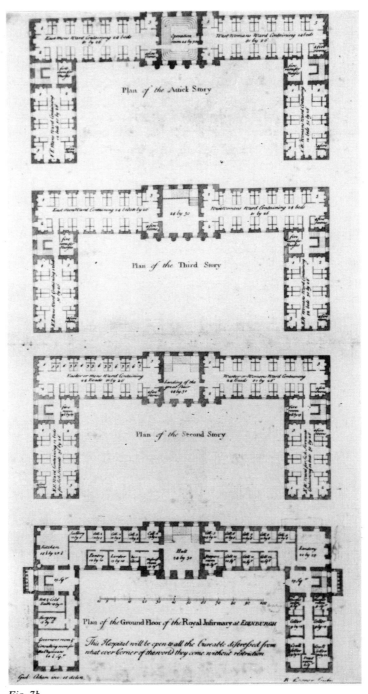

Fig. 7b

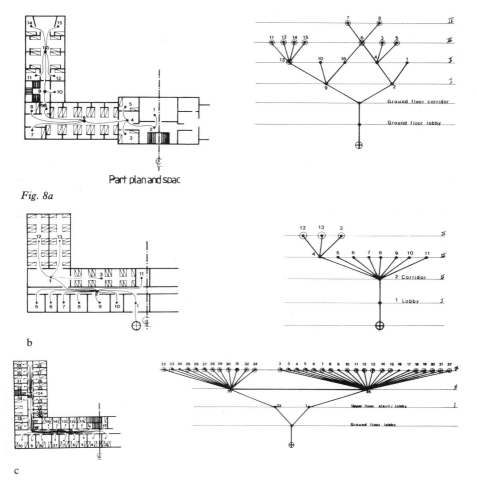

Part plan and spac

Fig. 8a

b

c

Figure 8.   Spatial development of the U-shaped hospital plan in the eighteenth century. Schematic half-plans and spatial structures of:
a.   Edinburgh Royal Infirmary, 1738; architect, William Adam.
b.   The London Hospital, 1742; architect, Boulton Mainwaring.
c.   Manchester Royal Infirmary, with 1793 extension; (architect?).

the tree structure and depth is reducing. In the Manchester case (Fig.8c), the three wings are entirely accessed by corridors, the wards are much smaller and all are the 'deepest' layer of an otherwise 'shallow' plan. One of the main effects of this type of spatial structure, once patient areas are on the tips of tree-branches and the only communication between them is through rings near the 'surface' of the building controlled by the staff, is that patient solidarity in the form of information flow, and hence the possibility of participating in making or resisting others' decisions, is eliminated. This, from the eighteenth century onwards, develops into a deliberate spatial and managerial policy in all institutional buildings. The change in spatial structure we have noted is a clear example of how institutional, social and medical practice makes fundamental alterations to buildings which nevertheless leave formal, in this case geometrical, characteristics relatively stable over long periods of time.

The second type of this first group is that for dealing with criminals — the houses of correction, prisons, gaols and bridewells. Glasgow had its house of correction near the Cathedral, in a converted manse, established under a seventeenth-century Act. After several short-lived attempts to house prisoners in various converted buildings, a new large Bridewell was built in 1795 in Duke Street, according to designs by Paterson and Horn (Fig.9). The plan, which very soon became U-shaped by the addition of two lateral wings, contained individual cells in a double-banked corridor

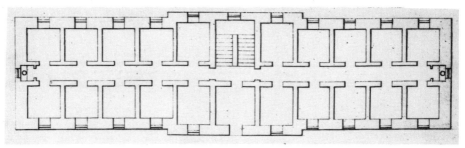

Fig. 9a

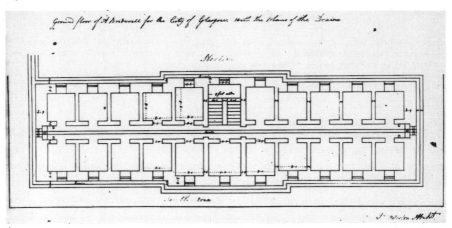

b

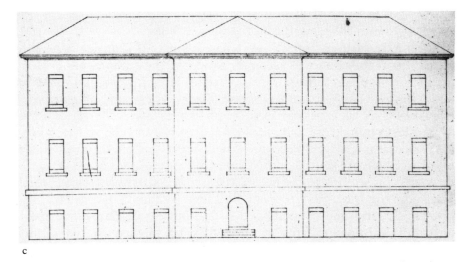

c

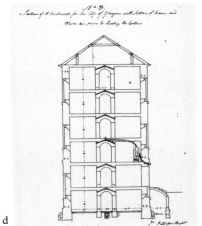

d

Figure 9.   Glasgow Bridewell, 1795; architect, John Paterson.
a.   Ground-floor plan.
b.   Drainage plan.
c.   Front elevation.
d.   Cross section.
Source and copyright: Strathclyde Regional Council Archives.

system; the six floors were expressed on the exterior as three storeys by means of split windows which served two floors. The scale and image of a typical classical country house were thus maintained in spite of the cellular enlargement of the interior and the multiplication of its floors. Sophisticated drainage and ventilation systems appear — a start to the separation-with-hygiene obsession which was to last right through the nineteenth century and well into the present one.

By 1809 Glasgow required a new complex of Law Courts and Gaol to replace the inadequate cell accommodation in the seventeenth-century Tolbooth. Three architects were invited to submit designs — Robert Reid, David Hamilton and William Stark. Each submitted several alternatives, all in Classical form, with courts and cells arranged in more or less symmetrical complexes of courtyards and connecting wings. A typical example is Reid's second design (Fig. 10). Here the magistrates' and main courts are central on two floors, with other courts and offices in the wings; then a bridge connected these to a courtyard, around which three sides of the three-storeyed building contained the felons' and debtors' day and night rooms, whilst the fourth side had the keeper's apartments at its centre, with windows from his kitchen overlooking the open courts, and a chapel above. On the same central axis, further back, was the execution platform. So, aligned with the new Saltmarket Bridge was the sequence of entrance, judgment (court), surveillance, worship and death — thus mapping out a unified and inevitable chronology and cosmology.

The architect chosen for the scheme was William Stark, who produced a similarly formal, but less complex plan, again with the gaoler's quarters separating the two prison courtyards, thus giving a

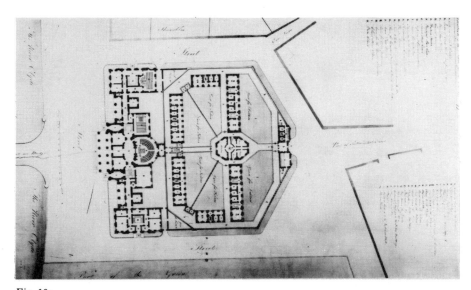

Fig. 10a

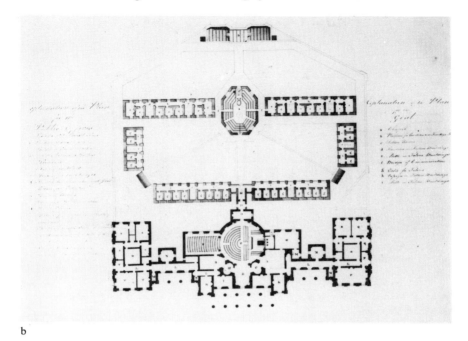

b

c

d

Figure 10.   Glasgow Judiciary Buildings, 1809; second design by Robert Reid, architect.
a.   Ground-floor plan.
b.   First-floor plan.
c.   Front elevation.
d.   Alternative front elevation.
Source and copyright: as for Figure 9.

rudimentary surveillance possibility (Fig.11). Above, on the centre, was the infirmary and above that the chapel — still maintaining the centralised cosmic location of God, healing and surveillance.

As in the case of hospitals, so for prisons — it was in Edinburgh that the most advanced thinking was taking place. As early as 1782 a remarkable plan was produced (Fig.12) by Lord Provost David Steuart and Archibald Cockburn (Steuart and Cockburn, 1782). Whilst they acknowledge their debt to John Howard, the first edition of whose major book on prisons was published five years earlier, they are four years ahead in their thinking of Britain's first *executed* radial prison, built at Ipswich in 1786 according to designs by John Blackburn. They developed a detailed strategy for separation by sex, age and type of crime so that no moral contagion could take place. 'Moral' was taken in more senses than one as analogous to 'physical' so that prevention of both kinds of contagion could be achieved by the same design devices: classification, separation of individuals and classes, separate exercise yards, and location of cells to give distance for easy ventilation as well as preventing visual and speech contact. The

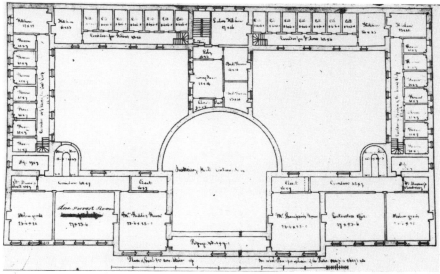

Fig. 11a

b

Figure 11. Glasgow Judiciary Buildings, 1809; executed design by William Stark, architect.
a.   Ground-floor plan.
b.   Annan photograph of front, ca. 1900, before 1910 substantial alterations.
Source and copyright: a.   As for Figure 9.
b.   As for Figure 3b–g.

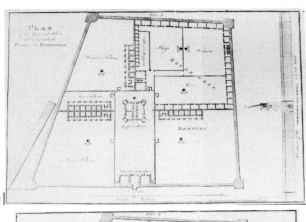

Fig. 12a

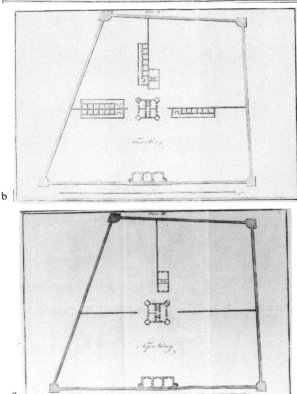

b

c

Figure 12.   Proposed Edinburgh Prison and Bridewell, 1782; designers, D. Steuart and A. Cockburn.
a.   Ground-floor plan.
b.   First-floor plan.
c.   Top-floor plan.
Source: Steuart, D. and Cockburn, A., *General Heads of a Plan for Erecting a New Prison and Bridewell in the City of Edinburgh*, Edinburgh(?), 1782.
Copyright: Trustees of the National Library of Scotland, Edinburgh.

four-armed cruciform plan was the solution. Centrally placed was the gaoler's house for surveillance of all the yards. Swivel guns were to be placed on each of the four corner turrets, to shoot outwards *or* inwards! They suggest that such a design might have avoided the Gordon Riots of 1780 and the consequent burning down of Newgate. They also draw attention to the reduced number of warders such a centrally surveyed prison would require. This too is a prophetic foretaste of the calculus of economy upon which Jeremy Bentham founded his design for the centrally surveyed circular Panopticon prison published in 1791.

Steuart and Cockburn's project was not built and it was 1791 before the Act of Parliament for a new Bridewell, to be erected on Calton Hill, was passed. The radial idea was now popular — one four-armed version was submitted for the competition by Baxter; another, of six separate radiating blocks whose axes met at the altar of the central chapel in a block which also contained the gaoler's house, was submitted by Wardrop of Glasgow. In the event it was Robert Adam who was chosen as architect. His first two submissions were much grander than these, with extensive wings for a Bedlam and an infirmary (neither of which had been asked for in the brief as set out in the Act). They were not radial but based on palatial courtyard planning (Fig.13).

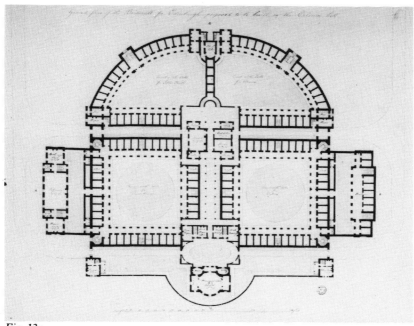

Fig. 13a

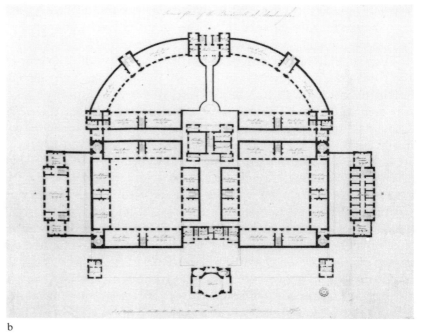

b

c

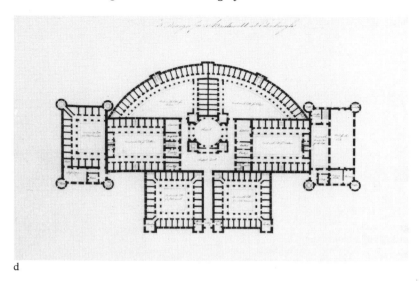

d

Figure 13.   Edinburgh Bridewell, 1791; architect, Robert Adam.
a.   First design, ground-floor plan.
b.   Ditto, first-floor plan.
c.   Ditto, rear elevation.
d.   Second design, ground-floor plan.
Source and copyright: as for Figure 3b–g.

But the publication in that year of both Bentham's *Panopticon* and its further development in his *Postscript* proved irresistible to Adam. Perhaps he accepted Bentham's claim that here was a solution for any institution in which a person of skill or power had to supervise a large number of unskilled or weaker persons — as in a factory, school, hospital or asylum — and believed that the successful architectural development of the new type would give his practice an entry into a rapidly growing field. He prepared three new designs in quick succession, but each used the *half* circle as its basis (Fig. 14). In the third, which was built, but shorn of its lateral wings, the central annular space was separated from the cells on the outer periphery by a corridor and inward-facing day/work rooms. This change, which blocked the inspection tower's view of the night cells, was a bitter disappointment to Bentham who saw it as undermining the 24-hour surveillance regime on which the whole moral authority of the 'unseen eye' depended. But he was unable to persuade either Robert, or his brother James who took over the project upon Robert's death in 1792, to revert to the original idea. So the lighting system to achieve one-way vision became mostly

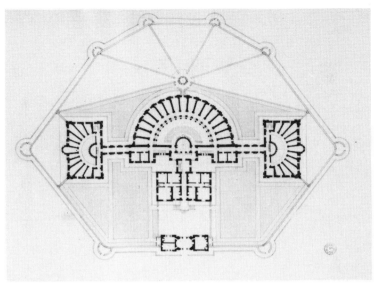

Fig. 14a

b

c

d

e

f

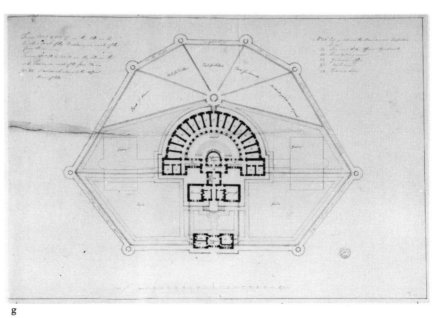

g

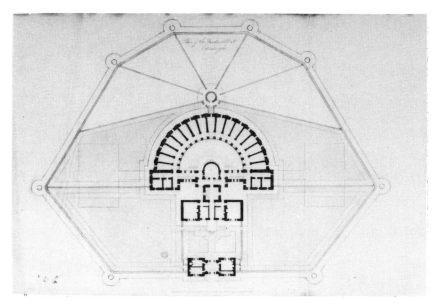

h

i

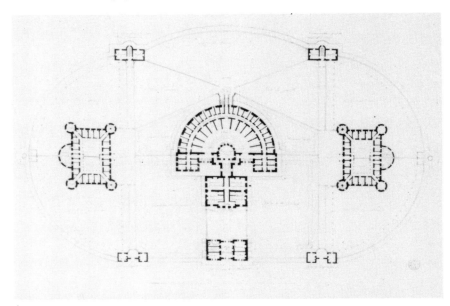

j

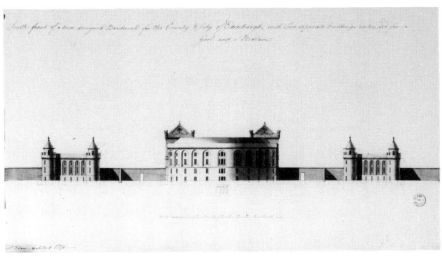

k

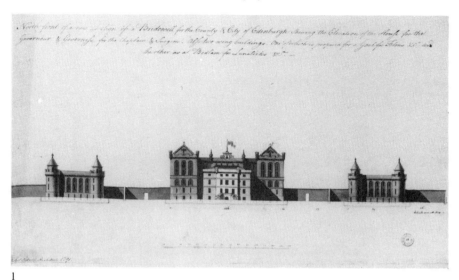

l

m

H

n

Figure 14.   Edinburgh Bridewell, 1791; architect, Robert Adam.
a.   Third design, ground-floor plan.
b.   Ditto, section.
c.   Ditto, section.
d.   Ditto, rear elevation.
e.   Ditto, front elevation.
f.   Fourth design, basement plan.
g.   Ditto, ground-floor plan.
h.   Ditto, first-floor plan.
i.   Ditto, section.
j.   Fifth design, ground-floor plan.
k.   Ditto, rear elevation.
l.   Ditto, front elevation.
m.   Ditto, scheme as executed, front view by Shepherd, 1831.
n.   Ditto, scheme as executed, rear view by Shepherd, 1831.
Source and copyright: a–l. As for Figure 3, b–g.
Source: m. and n. *Modern Athens! Displayed in a Series of Views: Edinburgh in the Nineteenth Century*, James & Co., London, 1831.

superfluous nor did Adam ever intend to incorporate Bentham's listening tubes, to give one-way hearing, since he must have realised that the laws of acoustics would defeat him. Nevertheless it is significant that in spite of a lifelong propaganda campaign in England, France, Ireland, Russia and America the only example of what Gertrude Himmelfarb (1968) has called Bentham's 'haunted house' should have come into being in late Enlightenment Edinburgh.

It is interesting to examine the spatial structure of one of the three panoptical schemes — number two (Fig.15). The two surveillance points are the central inspection tower and a similar one for the

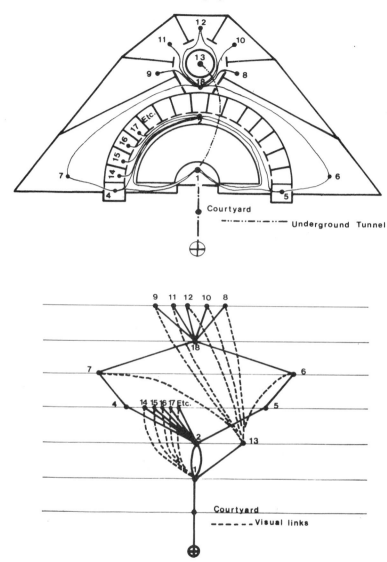

Figure 15.   Schematic plan and spatial structure of Robert Adam's fourth design for the Edinburgh Bridewell.

supervision of the external exercise yards. It was necessary to connect these two directly, without the prisoners being able to see the gaoler passing along the communication link. The only means of doing this, that is of overcoming the adjacency limitations of a planar graph, was to make a link at another level. This was precisely what was done—a subterranean passage links the two towers, thus bringing the second much closer to the 'surface' of the spatial structure. If dotted lines are drawn to represent direct visual connections between the two towers and the cells and exercise yards, and this diagram is superimposed on the normal one showing spatial permeabilities, all the control mechanisms are displayed simultaneously.

The third type of this first group stands, in several respects, between hospitals and prisons. This is the lunatic asylum. At this time there was considerable ambiguity in the perception and treatment of the mentally sick and disabled.

On the one hand by the 1790s, under the influence of doctors such as Pinel working in the Bicêtre in Paris and Tuke at the York Retreat founded in 1796, 'moral' treatment was beginning to gain the upper hand. Control was not by chains or physical restraint, and hardly any purgatives, bleeding or drugs were used. Instead the regime depended on two chief principles: a salutary feeling of fear and an appeal to the patient's 'self-esteem'. The former was encouraged by the threat of *social* punishment — punitive isolation — and the latter by promise of *social* reward in the form of interaction with keepers and in groups with other patients. The notion of 'family' appears in the descriptive literature of the time, as it does, surprisingly, in mid-nineteenth century descriptions of vast workhouses! The pastoral idyll was consciously used as a counter to the internal disorder of the patient which was seen as a mirror of the chaos in the rapidly growing cities — hence the emphasis on farms, gardens and rural views from windows and over the walls. The regime emphasised recreation, music, dancing and work-therapy.

On the other hand the chains and punishment regimes of the earlier eighteenth century still survived, and the buildings in Scotland reflected this duality. The Montrose Asylum founded by Susan Carnegie in 1784 was nearer to and anticipated the York model and regime; but in Glasgow, in 1807, a new asylum was designed by William Stark, which even in its day was criticised for being too prison-like. Nevertheless aspects of the 'moral' regimes are built in, such as the emphasis on garden scenery.

It had four wings radiating from a central observation tower capped by a dome with all its conventional cosmic and sacred associations (Fig.16). Stark (1807) saw the dilemma of reconciling freedom for patients to move about 'without interference or controul (sic)' and the 'classing of patients . . . which the more minutely it is pursued, the more it increases the difficulty of preserving the individuals from that degree of confinement which is both irksome and injurious'. Whilst this shows a sensitive appreciation of the problem, his solution was the creation of Europe's most classified, ordered and centrally controlled asylum. By classifying the patients, and giving direct access for each class to its own outdoor 'inclosure', he allowed curative nature ('air and recreation') to play its part, without any loss of surveillance. It was 'completely out of their power (for patients) to go beyond their own boundary, or to meet with, or even see, any individuals belonging to other classes'. They would be 'constantly in view of their keepers, and the superintedent, on his part, will have his eye both on the patients and keepers'. The orderly will be less aware of surveillance, whilst the disorderly 'will be aware that an unseen eye is constantly

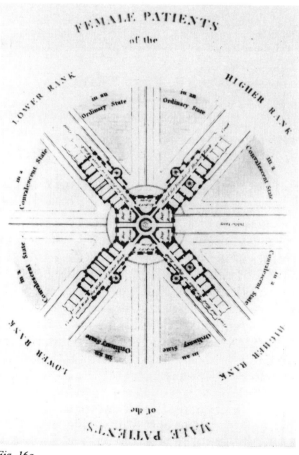

Fig. 16a

b

Figure 16.   Glasgow Lunatic Asylum, 1807; architect, William Stark.
a.   Ground-floor plan.
b.   Exterior view by Joseph Swan, 1829.
Source: a.   Stark, W., *Remarks on Public Hospitals for the Cure of Mental Derangement etc.*,
Edinburgh, 1807.
b.   Joseph Swan, *Select Views of Glasgow and Environs*, Glasgow, 1829.

following them, and observing their conduct'. Basic to the strategy was rigid classification, and the hierarchy from the most disorderly patients, through convalescent and the keepers to the superintendent reproduced perfectly the mechanically-based hierarchies of workers, overseers and mill managers of the nearby cotton mills.

But the most interesting feature of Stark's design process is the way he presented the brief he was either given or developed by discussion with the promoters. The patients were classified by sex, economic means (of the 'higher rank', i.e. able to pay, and the 'lower rank', i.e. pauper patients from the surrounding counties), and by clinical diagnosis — 'frantic', 'incurable', 'convalescent' and 'in an ordinary state'. The hierarchical decomposition of this three-layer classification was set out by Stark on a page with the spatial consequences in terms of storey location, front and back, left and right and distance from the centre, set out on a matching part of the table (Fig.17). This is, first, an extremely clear example of the close connection between language, form, function and spatial structure. Secondly, it is interesting to see

General View of the Plan of Classification, and of the Distribution of the Classes in the GLASGOW LUNATIC ASYLUM.

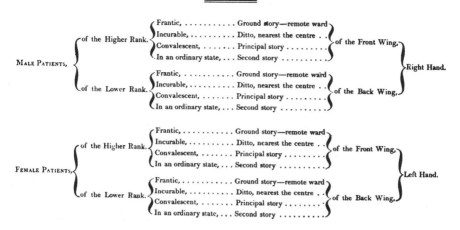

Figure 17. Glasgow Lunatic Asylum: Stark's hierarchical table of patients and his matching hierarchical locational table.
Source: as for Figure 16a.

that each of the three categories used for classification represents degrees of productive capability.

Just before he died in 1813 Stark embarked on two other asylum designs; one in Gloucester in 1811, which was a formalistic exercise based on a semicircular block connected to a rear (paupers') wing (Fig.18) and another at Dundee in 1812, where he designed an H-shaped, low, cottage-style building which contemporaries likened to a farm (Fig.19). In this project there was a considerable shift from his rigid 1807 position. He seems to be reacting against the formal Classicism of his life's work and groping towards a naturalistic Romanticism, at least in form and scale. Together with his reaction against the rigid Classicism and grid of Edinburgh New Town (Reed, 1982) it signifies a profound inner revolution. But he died within a year and this will always remain a matter for speculation.

In 1807, too, Edinburgh's Morningside Asylum was built according to designs by Reid; it represented no radical departure from the conventional, courtyard plan, but did have a central inspection tower for surveying the four gardens, with access from the keeper's quarters by four sunken passages. There was the same triple classification as at Glasgow. Aberdeen and Perth also had asylum foundations at this time;

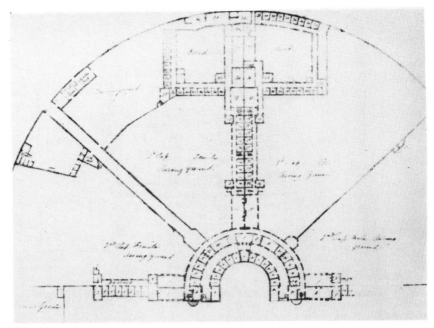

Fig. 18a

b

Figure 18.   Gloucester Lunatic Asylum, 1811; architect, William Stark.
a.   Ground-floor plan.
b.   Exterior view.
Source and copyright: a.   Gloucestershire County Council Archives.
b.   The Royal College of Psychiatrists.

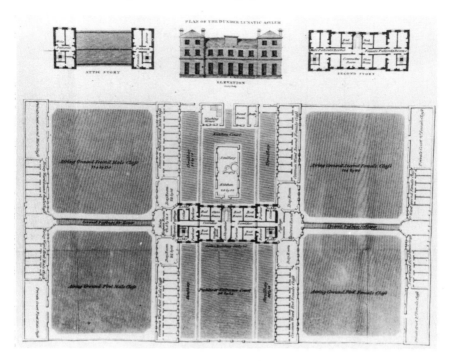

Figure 19. Dundee Lunatic Asylum, 1812; architect, William Stark. Ground-floor plan.
Source: *An Account of the Dundee Infirmary etc.*, Dundee, 1815.
Copyright: Dundee City Council, City Library.

the buildings were derivative of the U and H-shaped blocks we have already seen.

It is worth looking at a very late example, since it shows the persistence of many late Enlightenment features. The new Asylum in Dumfries was not built till 1834, according to the designs of William Burn (who also completed Stark's design at Dundee), and was still based on two huge Greek-cross, radial blocks, one for men and the other for women (Fig.20). Only one half was built. Backward-looking and penal as this design was, the first superintendent was Dr. W. A. F. Browne, who came from Montrose, and established a 'moral' regime which far surpassed any earlier ones in its completeness. He describes an idyllic, Utopian setting, which suggests that Genet's parallel between a prison and a palace in the *The Thief's Journal* is not outrageous:

> Conceive a spacious building, resembling the palace of a Peere, airy and elevated, and surrounded by extensive and swelling grounds and gardens. The interior is fitted up with galleries and workshops, and music rooms.

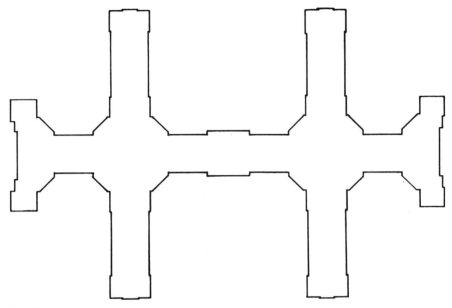

Fig. 20a

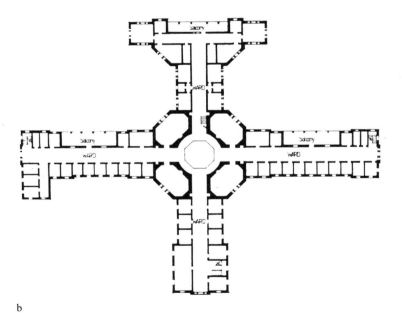

b

Figure 20.   Dumfries Crichton Royal Asylum, 1834; architect, William Burn.
a.   Block plan of original proposal.
b.   Reconstructed half ground-floor plan.

The sun and the air are allowed to enter in every window, the view of the shrubberies and fields and groups of labourers is unobstructed by shutters or bars; all is clean and attractive . . . The inmates all seem to be actuated by a common impulse of enjoyment, all are busy, and delighted by being so. The house and all round appears a hive of industry. All are anxious to be engaged, toil incessantly, and in general without any recompense than being kept from disagreeable thoughts and pains of illness. They literally work in order to please themselves . . . There is in this community no compulsion, no chains, no whips, no corporal punishment, simply because these are proved to be less effectual means of carrying any point than persuasion, emulation and the desire for gratification. (Browne, 1837)

The whole spirit of the enterprise is symbolised by images of rural peace, order and quiet; above all space, light and fresh air. When the phrenologists, at the very end of the eighteenth century and well into the nineteenth, constructed spatial maps of the brain, each of whose zones housed particular affections or abilities, they located, at the very front, zones of light, fresh air and space (Fig.21); moreover some of them held, like Browne, that only an environment possessing these corresponding features could satisfy human beings. In this they were merely anticipating le Corbusier and the CIAM Group, who, in the 1933 Athens Charter, propounded an identical philosophy in the 'four functions' model. George Combe made Edinburgh the stronghold of phrenology, and the connections between this 'science', psychiatric medicine and the rational principles which grew directly from Enlightenment ideas, made that city its natural home.

To finish this analysis of Enlightenment ordering principles in building design a single case of a quite different type — buildings designed to house objects which represent the classification of knowledge — will be considered. Eventually these became what we now know as art galleries, museums and libraries. But in Renaissance Europe, and still in eighteenth and early nineteenth-century Scotland, the distinction was not so clear. Collections often included paintings, drawings and sculpture, coins and medals, antique fragments, pottery and weapons, natural history and geological, fossil and crystal specimens, ethnographic curiosities collected on travels, and machinery or tools. Where the collector had special interests or skills in medicine or surgery, anatomical specimens and examples of diseased organs were included. The attempt was made not only to invest in objects of beauty, rarity, curiosity and value, but also to arrange and display them so as to give a comprehensive view of nature, human skill, archaeology and history. The collectors had, in addition, more or less specialised libraries of manuscripts, incunabula and printed works.

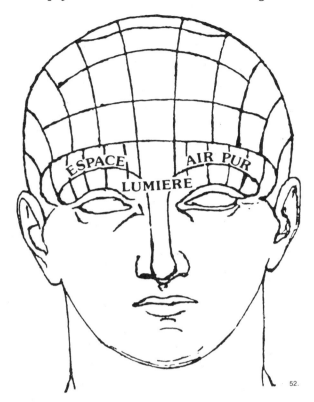

Figure 21.   Nineteenth-century phrenological head.
Source: J.-B. André Godin, *Solutions Sociales*, 1871.

To arrange library books on shelves, paintings in galleries, or
objects in cabinets, required the existence or creation of a global
definition of the field, its subdivision in a hierarchical and systematic
manner, and a consecutive order which governed the sequence of the
sections. In the case of a library, the global field was nothing less than
all human knowledge, and its subdivision was one of the major tasks
of philosophers. For centuries variations and developments of Bacon's
scheme were dominant. Some philosophers were called upon to organise
a library — such was the case with Leibniz who was responsible for
the Duke of Brunswick's library at Wolfenbüttel in the seventeenth
century. They were then faced with the basically architectural problem
of translating a theoretical taxonomy into spatial organisation.

By the late seventeenth century special buildings were designed for housing such mixed collections. An outstanding example was the Ashmolean Museum in Oxford designed to house Ashmole's and Tradescant's collections, and also to accommodate scientific lectures and experiments. Throughout the late eighteenth and early nineteenth centuries large and small, public and private museums of this kind were built or fitted into existing, converted buildings. The best Scottish example is Hunter's Museum, or the Hunterian (see Markus, 1985) founded by William Hunter who, with his brother John, was one of the outstanding surgeons, 'man-midwives' and anatomy teachers in London. He was also an ambitious collector of books, pictures, coins, medals, natural history specimens and, of course, anatomy specimens for his classes. He used a number of premises for teaching, and in 1763 proposed to the Government that an anatomy school be built, with a demonstration dissecting theatre, its own library and museum (of specimens) with an attached house for himself (Fig.22). As nothing came of this proposal he eventually bought a house in Great Windmill Street in 1766 and by 1768 had had it converted by the Scottish architect, Robert Mylne.

A comparison of his 1763 sketch and the Mylne design of 1768 (Fig.23) shows remarkable similarities; they contain the same basic elements, in the same spatial relationship to each other, and the anatomy theatre, which is separately entered by students from a lane off Great Windmill Street, was probably intended to be entered similarly in the 'ideal' plan. A spatial analysis of the 1768 scheme (Fig.24) shows that the three core elements — the anatomy theatre, the picture gallery and the library-with-museum — all occur at the third level, and are linked via shallower spaces at level two. The library-with-museum at ground level, and the picture gallery at first level, act as the connections between Hunter's residence and the anatomy school.

Contemporary descriptions make it clear that in the organisation of objects in the museum Hunter tried to represent not only the connection between medical practice and teaching, scholarship and art but also his ideas about nature and knowledge itself. He subscribed to the theory that all objects, animate and inanimate, formed, in Pope's words, a 'Chain of Being'. This was based on Aristotle's notion of continuity and gradation, and Plato's principle of plenitude — according to which all possible kinds of things exist, in a continuous and graduated chain which extends from stones, through plants and zoophytes, to mammals, man, angels and eventually God. The extinction of a species seriously undermined this theory and hence the great scientific battles of the times over certain animal skeletons which had to be treated either as remains of an extinct species, or of a rare, but surviving one. There is plenty of

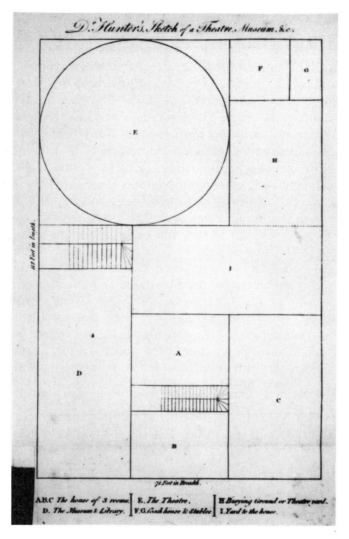

Figure 22.   William Hunter's sketch plan for his proposed school of anatomy, house, library and museum, 1763. Published posthumously 1784.
Source: *Two Introductory Lectures etc.*, London, 1784.

evidence that both Hunter brothers (John's museum was in Leicester Square) arranged their specimens so as to tell the story of the Chain; moreover, in William's museum the more global relationship between the spaces for science and medicine, art and knowledge also betrays similar conceptual structures.

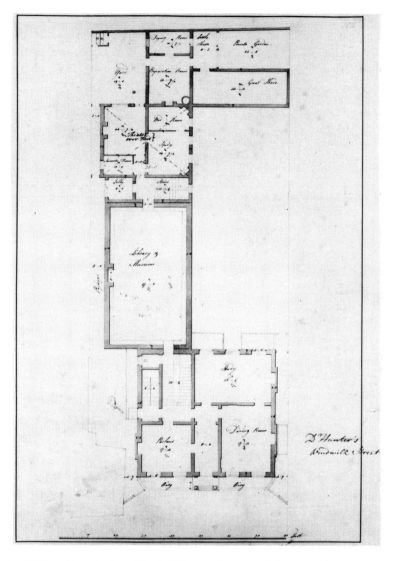

Figure 23.   William Hunter's Great Windmill Street Museum and Anatomy School, London, 1768; architect, Robert Mylne.
Source: Drawing in possession of Glasgow University.
Copyright: Wellcome Institute for the History of Medicine, London.

To Hunter the human body was also a continuous, interconnected system of all its parts, organs and tissues. Special interest focused at this time on inanimate material found in the body such as calculi, or stones,

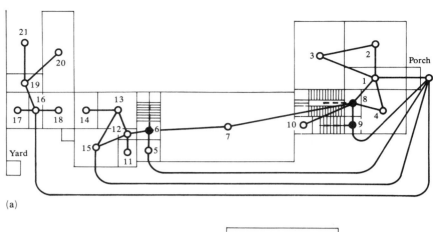

(a)

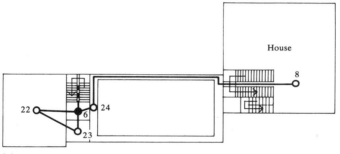

(b)

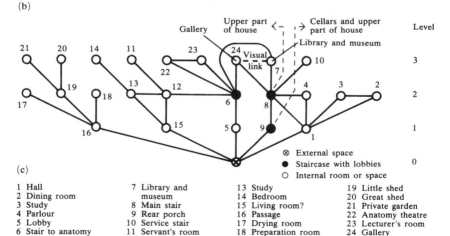

(c)

1 Hall	7 Library and	13 Study	19 Little shed
2 Dining room	museum	14 Bedroom	20 Great shed
3 Study	8 Main stair	15 Living room?	21 Private garden
4 Parlour	9 Rear porch	16 Passage	22 Anatomy theatre
5 Lobby	10 Service stair	17 Drying room	23 Lecturer's room
6 Stair to anatomy	11 Servant's room	18 Preparation room	24 Gallery
theatre	12 ...		

Figure 24. William Hunter's Great Windmill Street Museum and Anatomy School.
a. Schematic ground-floor plan.
b. Ditto, (reconstructed) first-floor plan.
c. Spatial structure.
Source: as for Figure 1.

which were often held to grow in an organic manner, and formed major exhibits in all anatomy collections.

Within a week of its foundation, in 1768, Hunter became the first Professor of Anatomy to the Royal Academy. There he lectured and demonstrated regularly, using skeletons and *écorché* figures — wax models of 'muscle men' stripped of skin. He maintained the superiority of nature over art and insisted that only by the most minute imitation of nature could the artist hope to produce the empathy in a viewer which resembled the power of nature itself. Anatomy was, to him, the clue to this study. In an interesting and analogous way his teaching anticipates the three 'discourses' of architecture with which this essay starts. Anatomy concerns structure and location of organs — analogous to spatial organisation in buildings. Physiology is concerned with function; whilst the artist is concerned with outward form.

On Hunter's death in 1783, his collection and a sum of money were left to Glasgow University to build a special Museum. There were long delays, caused by legal, financial and organisational problems. It was not till 1797 that the first moves were made to find an architect. Mylne was early on the scene and produced a design which has recently come to light (Fig.25). Its spatial structure (Fig.26) is remarkably like that of its London precursor — for instance the three major elements of anatomy theatre, museum and library all, again, occur at the third level — although formally it is entirely different.

Other architects were approached — David Hamilton, Peter Nicholson and William Stark. Hamilton produced a large number of solutions, but ultimately it was again Stark who was successful (Fig.27). He was asked to exclude the anatomy theatre on the grounds that riots against anatomy teachers and body snatchers might endanger the collections. The spatial structures of one of the two slightly different surviving designs (Fig.28) show a number of interesting phenomena. First, that art and knowledge (paintings and books) are far deeper into the building than nature and medicine (natural history and anatomy). Second, that the central dome acts on both the main floors as a transitional space, where there is a movement from the visible, or surface phenomenon, to the invisible or underlying one. This is achieved by the domed space (shown on the diagram by a dotted circle) becoming the junction of a three-pronged fork — the two side prongs in each case having the same functions as the root, and embracing the central prong which represents deeper penetration, both actually, in space, and metaphorically, in concept. Thus on the ground floor we move from the natural philosophy of visible objects to the anatomy of invisible structures; on the first

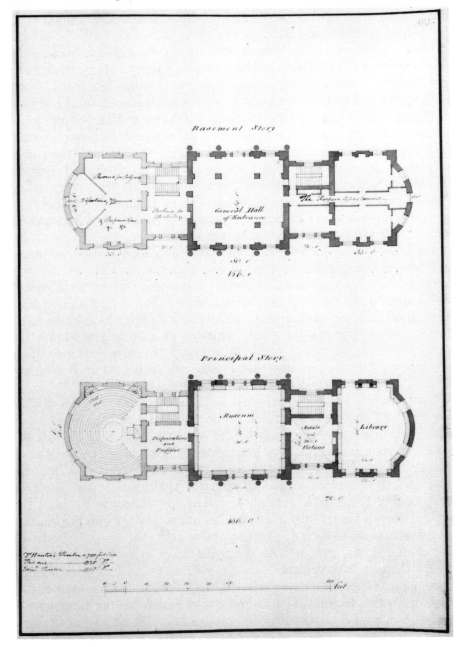

Figure 25. Proposal for the Hunterian Museum, Glasgow, 1799; architect, Robert Mylne.
Source: Drawing in possession of Glasgow University.

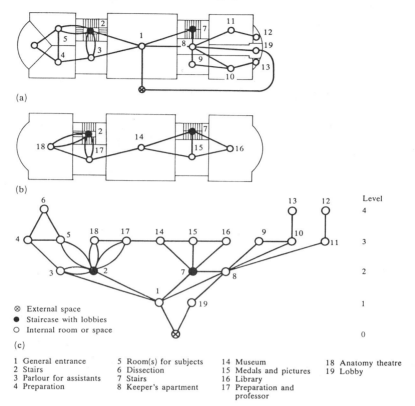

(c)

1 General entrance	5 Room(s) for subjects	14 Museum	18 Anatomy theatre
2 Stairs	6 Dissection	15 Medals and pictures	19 Lobby
3 Parlour for assistants	7 Stairs	16 Library	
4 Preparation	8 Keeper's apartment	17 Preparation and professor	

Figure 26. Mylne's 1799 proposed design.
a.   Schematic ground-floor plan.
b.   Ditto, first-floor plan.
c.   Spatial structure.
Source: as for Figure 1.

floor from visible art (painting) to invisible knowledge (books). It is no coincidence that a central dome — the dominant *motif* of cosmic unity in European architecture from Hadrian's Pantheon onwards — should have been the formal means to accompany the functional and spatial devices used to express this complex idea.

In these great institutional buildings, as well as in the museum, we see clearly how buildings are used as control devices. The relationships are those of power, and power which is asymmetrically distributed. In the institutions every device is used to create isolation, prevent communication and solidarity, classify and keep under surveillance. In the museum it requires substantial investment by the owners to

Fig. 27a   b

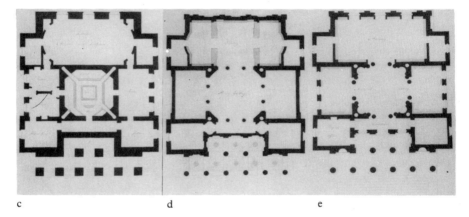

c   d   e

Figure 27.   Hunterian Museum, Glasgow, executed design, 1803–4; architect, William Stark.
a.   Front elevation.
b.   Side elevation.
c.   Basement plan.
d.   Ground-floor plan.
e.   First-floor plan.
Source and copyright: Scottish Record Office, Keeper of the Records, Edinburgh.

collect the objects which are then classified and grouped in a manner which reproduces both the owner's wealth and his knowledge base. The observer responds to the objects on these terms. The most evident property of the buildings which survive, or the designs for unexecuted ones, or the archaeological evidence for those which have been destroyed, is their power to exert control over bodies and minds.

To reduce the realisation of such alienating power was one of the important functions of the continuing use of the well-established

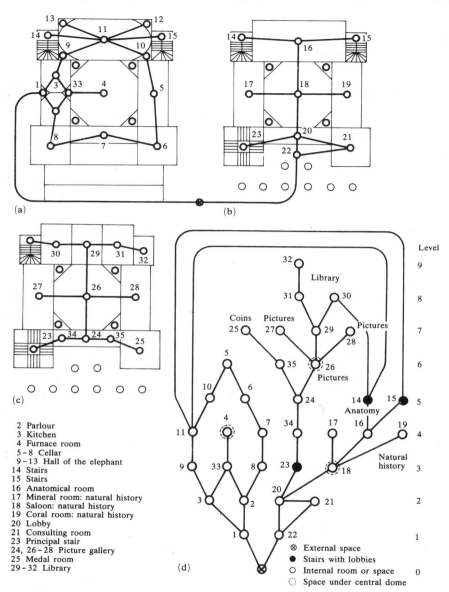

2 Parlour
3 Kitchen
4 Furnace room
5-8 Cellar
9-13 Hall of the elephant
14 Stairs
15 Stairs
16 Anatomical room
17 Mineral room: natural history
18 Saloon: natural history
19 Coral room: natural history
20 Lobby
21 Consulting room
23 Principal stair
24, 26-28 Picture gallery
25 Medal room
29-32 Library

⊗ External space
● Stairs with lobbies
○ Internal room or space
◌ Space under central dome

Figure 28. Stark's executed design.
a. Schematic basement plan.
b. Ditto, ground-floor plan.
c. Ditto, first-floor plan.
d. Spatial structure.
Source: as for Figure 1.

Classical style. More generally, whether style is traditional, thus hiding underlying changes, or radically innovatory, thus focusing attention onto itself, it is one of its functions to act as camouflage. And to divert critical attention to formal issues is the purpose of that kind of scholarship,

Figure 29.   Plate V, first version, of Piranesi's *Carceri.*
Source: G.B. Piranesi, *Carceri,* 1745(?).

criticism and teaching which locates architecture into the art discourse. When building design became a more pluralistic enterprise in the late Enlightenment and during the Industrial Revolution it was no longer safe to assume shared values between sponsors and designers. Form was released into the realm of artistic freedom, and architecture-as-art ensured that other properties remained undebated and thus beyond argument.

The building types and the period of history in this essay have been deliberately chosen to create a conjunction of unique strength. But the ability of these buildings nevertheless to carry other meanings embeds in them the tragic paradox which is at the heart of all architecture: the mode of production of buildings requires them to reproduce power but the same material speaks of a world of alternative relationships over the horizon. Piranesi, in his *Carceri* etchings, which have nothing obvious to do with prisons, is I believe exploring this paradox (Fig. 29). The dark underworld of impossible perspective, unbounded space, undefinable functions, unruly forms and primitive technology, is weighed down from above by a world of light, reason, Classical order, spatial division, clearly stated function and rational technology. The contrast could not be more extreme. That upper world, of the rule-governed architecture of power, is the true prison. The late Enlightenment exploited this architecture to the full.

REFERENCES

W. A. F. Browne, *What Asylums Were, Are and Ought to Be* (Edinburgh, 1837).

John Ferriar, *Medical Histories and Reflections* (Caddell and Davies, London, 1792).

W. R. G. Hillier and Julienne Hansen, *The Social Logic of Space* (Cambridge University Press, Cambridge, 1984).

Gertrude Himmelfarb, *Victorian Minds* (Weidenfeld and Nicolson, London, 1968).

Bruce Lenman, *Integration, Enlightenment, and Industrialisation: Scotland, 1746-1832* (Edward Arnold, London, 1981).

Thomas A. Markus, *Order in Space and Society: Architectural Form and its Context in the Scottish Enlightenment* (Mainstream, Edinburgh, 1982).

Thomas A. Markus, 'Domes of Enlightenment: Two Scottish University Museums', *Art History*, 8, 2, June 1985, pp.158-177.

Peter A. Reed, 'Georgian Edinburgh', in Markus, 1982, *op. cit.*

Francis Rice, Madness and Industrial Society: a Study of the Origins and Early Growth of the Organisation of Insanity in Nineteenth Century Scotland c. 1830-70, PhD Thesis, University of Strathclyde, Glasgow, 1981.

Andrew T. Scull, *Museums of Madness: The Social Organisation of Insanity in Nineteenth Century England* (Penguin Books, Harmondsworth, 1982. First published Allan Lane, London, 1979).

William Stark, *Remarks on Public Hospitals for the Cure of Mental Derangement etc.* (Edinburgh, 1807).

David Steuart and Archibald Cockburn, *General Heads of a Plan for Erecting a New Prison and Bridewell in the City of Edinburgh* (Edinburgh?, 1782).

INDEX

Aberdeen 207
Aberdeen Town Council 57
Aberdeen University Marischal College 4
  King's College 10
Adam, J. 156, 166n, 167n, 177, 195
Adam, R. 193, 195
Adam, W. 169, 179, 183
Aether 70
Agriculture 102ff
Akhar, M. A. 140n
Albert of Saxony 10
Americans, native 152, 153–156, 159, 166n
Amery, G. D. 114n
Andalousia 117
Anderson, G. M. 142n
Anderson R. R. W. 90n
Angoulême 117
Anthropology 145–163
Antient Metaphysics 145
Antwerp 117
Architecture 5
Aristotelian categories 146
Aristotle 9, 213
Asylums 5
Atheists 26, 29
Avignon 117

Bacon, F. 42, 70–71
Baker, K. 101n
Bannerman, Sir A. 56
Barbeyrac, J. 20–21, 23, 24–25, 28, 30–34,
  35, 36, 37, 38
Bayle, P. 4, 20–23, 26, 27–28, 29, 31, 34,
  36, 37, 38
Beattie, J. 40, 62n, 64n
Beattie, W. 18
Becker, J. 107
Beckman, M. J. 140n
Bendyshe, T. 168n
Bentham, J. 193, 195, 202
Bérard, J. E. 78
Bernard, J. 22
Berthelot, M. 100n
Black, J. 68, 71, 72, 75–77, 78, 79, 80, 81,
  82, 83, 85n, 102
Black, R. D. C. 141n
Blackburn, J. 190
Blair, H. 2
Bleaching 57
Blumenbach, J. F. 162, 163, 168n
Board of Manufactures 51
Boas, G. 99n
Boece, Hector 10
Boerhaave, H. 70–72, 75, 82, 107
Bolingbroke, H. 168n

Botanical Garden, Aberdeen University 63n
Bower, T. 45, 46, 61n
Boyle, R. 41, 69, 70, 76, 106, 107
Bracken, H. 34
Braidwood, Dr. 151
Brain, human 163
Bristol 183
Broadie, A. 18, 19
Browne, W. A. F. 209–211
Bruno, G. 166n
Brush, S. G. 99n
Brussels 117
Buffon, G. L. L. 5, 58, 150, 153, 154, 155,
  156, 157, 158, 160, 161, 162, 163, 165n,
  166n
Bulloch, J. M. 63n
Buridan, J. B. 10
Burnett, J., *see* Monboddo
Bute, Lord 51
Bynum, W. 167n

Cadiz 117
Calvinism 26
Cambridge, University of 67
Cameron, Hon. Lord J. 1
Campbell, G. 53, 56, 64n, 65n
Campbell, N. 114n
Camper, Petrus 163, 168n
Cantillon, P. 122, 123
Cardwell, D. S. L. 68, 84n
Carmichael, G. 21, 32
Carnegie, S. 204
Carnot, S. 67–68, 82, 83, 84n
Castaglione, D. 38n
Castlehill Observatory, Aberdeen 51, 63n
Caton, H. 142n
Causation 73
Chadwick, E. 170
Chalmers, P. 41
Chambers, W. 56
Chamley, P. 118, 140n, 142n
Charleston 159, 160
Charron, P. 23
Cheyne, G. 70
Chitnis, A. 59
Christie, J. R. R. 74, 76, 85n, 113
CIAM 211
Cicero, *De Republica* 20
Clarke, S. 28, 53
Clausius, R. J. E. 67
Cleghorn, W. 79
Clerc le, J. 20, 22, 23, 30, 36
Climate 152, 154, 159, 160, 162
Cloyd, E. L. 164n
Cockburn, A. 190, 193

Cohen, I. B. 85n
Combe, G. 211
Commissioners of Supply 44
Comte, A. 97
Conant, J. B. 99n
Condorcet, J. A. N. de C. 57, 97
Congar, Y. M. J. 99n
Conrad, S. A. 64n
Cook, Captain J. 159
Copland, P. 45, 51, 52, 57, 61n, 63n, 66n
Coqueret, College of 9
Cordoba 117
Coventry, A. 111–112
Crab, G. 9, 11–13
Cranston, D. 9
Crawford, A. 78, 80, 81, 85n, 86n
Creech, W. 158, 159, 168n
Crichton 9
Crousaz, J. P. de 20–22, 23, 28–31, 35, 36, 37, 38
Cullen, W. 39, 71, 72–74, 75, 76, 77, 82, 83, 85, 102, 107
Culture 88ff
Cumberland, R. 21
Curricula, university 47–52

Daiches, D. 1
Dale, D. 177
D'Alembert, J. le R. 118
Dalrymple, D. 167n
Dalton, J. 79, 86n
Darwin, C. 159
De generis humani varietate natura 162
Delaroche, F. 78
De Lisle 55
Deluc, J. A. 80, 86n
Denzer, H. 35
Dérathé, R. 35
Desaguliers, J. T. 43, 45
Descartes, R. 41, 69, 157, 163
Desmaizeaux, P. 23, 36
Diderot, D. 4, 151, 165n, 167n
Dijksterhuis, E. J. 84n
Discours sur l'inégalité 148, 157, 164n, 167n
Disputatio inauguralis quaedam de hominum varietatibus 163
Dodgshon, R. A. 114n
Doig, D. 166n
Donaldson, A. 53
Donaldson, J. 104, 113, 114n, 115n
Donovan, A. 73, 85n, 98n, 99n, 101n
Douglas, F. 49, 63n
Douglas, G. 8
Downey, G. 99n
Duff, W. 61n
Dunbar, J. 47
Duncan, R. 21–22, 35
Dundas, H. 58
Dundee, 207, 209
Duty 28

Edinburgh 1, 2, 39, 43, 71, 72, 102, 104, 105, 174, 177, 179, 183, 193, 207, 211
Edinburgh Agricultural Society 108
Edinburgh International Festival 1, 2
Edinburgh, Royal Society of 102, 105
Elements of Criticism 161
Emerson, R. L. 40, 66n, 99n, 114, 155n
Enterprising Scot 2
Epistemology 8
Esprit des lois 162, 168n
Essay on the Causes of the Variety of Complexion and Figure in the Human Species 168n
Essays on Natural Religion 146
Europeans 154–155, 159
Explanation 68
Eyles, J. M. 114n
Eyles, V. A. 114n

Fabian, B. 65n
Faculty of Advocates, Library of 157, 167n
Fahrenheit, D. G. 71
Fenton, A. 114n
Ferguson, A. 2, 125, 147, 152, 154, 162
Ferriar, J. 170
Fideism 22
Findlay, A. 64n
Fingal 158
Fire 71
Fischer, M. M. J. 99n
Fisher, N. 99n, 114
Foerster, D. 166n
Forbes, D., co-founder of club in Aberdeen 53
Forbes, D., on Hume 31, 37n
Forbes, Sir W. 64n
Fordyce, D. 43, 45, 52, 60n, 64n
Forth and Clyde Canal 131
Fourier, J. 83, 86n
Fox, R. 86n
France, P. 164n
Frankfurt 117
Franklin, B. 74–75
Franklin, T. B. 114n
Frayling, C. 165n
Freind, J. 70
French, G. 56, 64n
French Revolution 57

Galbraith, R. 9
Galileo, G. 76
Gassendi, P. 69
General Assembly of the Church of Scotland 110
Genet 209
Geoffry 73
Gerard, A. 40, 56, 62n
Gerbi, A. 168n
Gibbs, J. 180
Gillispie, C. G. 101n

Glasgow 39, 43, 131, 177, 186, 188, 204, 207, 217
Glasgow University 8, 10, 67, 72, 75, 77, 78
Gliozzi, G. 167n
God (Providence) 156, 160
Gombrich, E. H. 98n
Gordon, T. 48, 53, 62n, 63n
Gordon Water Report 57
Grandeur des romains 168n
Gravity 70
Greeks 146, 152, 153, 158, 161
Gregory, James 51, 53
Gregory, John 40, 50, 54, 55, 56, 59n, 75n
Greville, R. K. 114n
Groeningen 21–22
Granada 117
Grotius, H. 21, 25, 29, 33, 38
Guerlac, H. 76, 81, 84n, 100n, 101n
Guinea, natives of 153

Halley, E. 43, 60n, 61n
Hamilton, D. 188, 217
Hamilton, R. 57
Handler, R. 99n
Handley, J. E. 114n
Hansen, J. 175
Harpe, J. E. de la 35n
Harris, J. 147
Hauksbee, J. 43
Heat 68, 75ff, 78, 79ff
Heathcote, N. H. 76, 85n, 86n
Heilbron, J. L. 100n
Helmholtz 67
Henderson, G. 109
Hermes 147
Hillier, W. R. G. 175
Himmelfarb, G. 202
Hirschman, A. O. 133
Histoire des Animaux 157
Histoire Naturelle 153, 157
Historian, social 2, 3
Historical Law Tracts 168n
History of America 154
Hobbes, T. 36
Holmes, F. L. 98n, 100n
Home, F. 113
Home, H., *see* Kames, Lord
Home, R. W. 100n
Homeric epics 153, 158
Homme machine, L' 151
Hont, I. 138
Hooke, Robert 41
Hope, J. 2, 63n, 102
Horace, 29, 33
Hospitals, 5, 177ff
Hotbed of Genius 1
Howard, J. 190
Huguenots 20, 25–26

Hume, D. 1, 2, 4, 16, 18, 31 on politics, 33 on justice, 34, 37, 38, 40, 118, 120, 122, 136, 138, 141n, 145, 146, 152, 154, 164, 165n, 167n, 169–170
Humphries, W. R. 64n, 65n, 66n
Hunter, J. 163, 169, 213ff
Hunter, W. 169, 213
Hutcheson, F. 2, 33 Hume on justice, 38, 145, 163n
Hutton, James 39, 58, 102, 114n

Idea 14, 15, 28
Improvement 104
Innes, Cosmo 62n
IPSE 1
Iroquois 153
Irvine, W. 77–78, 79, 80, 81, 85n

Janson, P. L. 99n
Johnson, D. 1, 65n
Johnson, Dr. Samuel 145, 153, 164n
Johnston, G. 114n
Jones, J. 1
Jones, P. 114
Joule, J. P. 67
Jurisprudence 21, 24, 32
Justice 33

Kames, Lord (Henry Home) 145–147, 152–168
Kames 2, 4, 5, 102, 105, 113
Keill, James 70
Keill, John 43, 70
Keohane, N. O. 36
Kindleberger, C. 142n
King, M. D. 99n
King's College, Aberdeen 4, 39–52, 59n–64n
King's College, Aberdeen, Natural History Museum 39–52, 63n
Kirwan, R. 79, 80
Knox, J. 9
Kobayashi 137, 142n
Krieger, L. 35
Kuhn, T. 90, 93, 95, 99n, 100n

Labrousse, E. 22, 25, 35–36
Lakatos, I. 93, 99n
La Mettrie, J. O. de 151, 165n
Land, Stephen 164n
Language 32
La Peyrère, Isaac de 166n, 167n
Laplace, P. S. 80–82, 83
Latour, B. 98n
Laudan, L. 60n, 93, 98n, 99n
Laudan, R. 99n
Lauderdale, J. M. 138
Lausanne 21
Lavoisier, A. L. 4, 5, 78, 79ff, 82, 86, 88, 94ff, 99n

Law, 21, 23, 28, 30, 33
Lehman, W. 164n
Leibniz, G. 212
Leigh, R. A. 164n
Lenman, B. 169
Leslie, P. D. 82, 86n
Letwin, S. 31 on Hume, 39
Leyden 117
Leyden, University of 70
Liebermann, D. 164
Liddell, J. 8
Liège 117
Lind, J. 159, 168n
Lindeboom, G. A. 71, 84n
Linnaeus, C. 72, 73, 102, 148, 150
Linnekin, J. 99n
Livingstone, Dr. W. 56
Locke, J. 16–18, 24, 30, 32, 33, 36, 147
Logic 8, 10
Lokert, G. 9, 13 — notions
Love, R. 71, 84n
Lovejoy, A. 164n
Lyons 117
Lyttelton, Lord 158, 167n

McCann, H. G. 100n
McClellan, J. E. 65n
McCosh, J. 60n, 64n, 65n
McElroy, D. D. 54, 65n
McGuinness, A. 164n, 166n
McKail, M. 41, 59n, 61n
Mackenzie, H. 116n
Mackie, C. 22
McKie, D. 76, 85n, 86n, 101n
MacKinnon, J. 165n
Maclaurin, C. 39, 41, 43, 60n, 61n, 64n
Macleod, R. 62n
Macvicar, S. 114n
Madrid 117
Magellan, J. H. de 78–79, 80, 86n
Mainwaring, B. 183
Mair, J. 7, 8, 9, 12–13, 16, 17, 18, 19
Malebranche, N. 27–28
Man, nature of 161
Manchester 183, 185
Manderston, W. 10
Mandeville, B. 28
Mankind, different races of 152, 154, 155, 159, 160, 162
Marcus, G. E. 99n
Marischal College, Aberdeen 39–52
Marischal, C. 4
Marshall, G., on Hume 31, 37n
Marx, Karl 137, 153, 171, 172
Maxwell, J. Clerk 67, 68
Maxwell, R. 113
Mead, R. 70
Medick, H. 35
Meek, R. L. 140n, 142n

Memis, Rev. R. 63n
Mercia 117
Metzger, H. 71, 84n
Meylan, P. 35
Milan 180
Millar, J. 169
Mind 15
Mirabeau, H. G. R. 123, 128, 140n
Molesworth, Lord 42, 60n
Monboddo, Lord 2, 4, 5, 145–152, 156–168
Montaigne, M. de 23
Montesquieu, C. de S. 5, 128, 138, 154, 162, 168n
Moral philosophy 10
Morrell, J. B. 66n
Morris, R. J. 81, 86n
Morris, W. 172
Moses 156
Munro, A. 179
Murray, D. 163n
Musgrave, A. 99n
Mylne, R. 213, 217

Nantes 20, 25
Naturalist 107
Naudé, G. 23
Negress 155, 166n
Neumann, V. 171
New World, The 154–156, 166n
Newman, J. H. 98n
Newton, Isaac 4, 41, 42, 43, 46, 58, 60n, 69–70, 73, 75, 76
Nicholson, P. 217
Nicole, P. 27
Norton, D. 34, 38
Notions 9, 10, 11, 14

Ogilvie, W. 49, 50, 52, 55, 56
Old World, The 154–156
Orang-utan 149–152, 156–158, 165n, 167n, 168n
Origin and Progress of Language, The 145, 147–152, 156, 157, 158, 164n
Ortner, S. B. 99n
Ossian, poems of 153, 166n
Othmer, S. 35
Owen, R. 177
Oxford 213

Paine, T. 170
Paisley 131
Paracelsus 166n
Paris 8, 9, 10, 117, 136
Parry, M. L. 114n
Pastine, D. 167n
Paterson, J. 186
Patterson, W. 62n
Pauw, C. de 159, 160, 168n
Pearce, R. 166n

Pelikan, J. 99n
Perelman, M.
Perrault, C. 157
Perth 209
Peter, the mute 148
Petty, W. 139, 140
Phillipson, N. 39, 59
Philosophers 2, 3
Picardy 117
Pinel, P. 204
Pitcairne, A. 61n, 70
Plato 213
Platonic forms 146
Playfair, J. 102
Plummer, A. 107
Polignac, Cardinal de 151
Politics 30, 31
Polygenesis, theory of 156
Ponting, B. 59n
Pope, Alexander 213
Popkin, R. 20, 35, 167n
Popper, K. 89
Porter, R. 102, 114n, 115n
Postlethwayt, M. 127
Priestley, J. 69, 84n
Pringle, Sir J. 158, 167n
Prisons 5, 186ff
Pufendorf, S. 21, 24, 25, 29–30, 31 — and
    Hume, 32–33, 34, 35, 38
Pulteney, W. 108, 111, 135
Pyrrhonism 20, 23, 28

Quadrumanes 162
Quesnay, F. 123

Rait, A. 46, 59n, 60n, 62n, 63n
Ramsay, C. 28
Ramsay, J. of Ochtertyre 64n, 161, 168n
Rankine, W. J. M. 67
Rappaport, R. 101n
Raschid, S. 142n
Reed, P. A. 207
Regnault, H. V. 67, 82
Reid, J. S. 63n, 66n
Reid, R. 188, 207
Reid, T. 4, 6, 11, 14–18, 39, 47, 48, 51,
    52, 53, 54, 55, 56, 59n, 62n, 64n, 65n,
    145
Recherches philosophiques sur les américains
    159
Representation 11–14, 16, 17
Rétat, P. 20, 35
Rice, F. 170
Richards, S. 116n
Richter, M. N. 98n
Rights 25, 26, 30
Ritchie, J. 102, 114n
Robertson, W. 2, 154
Robinson, B. 72

Robison, J. 57, 75–76, 88n
Roche, D. 54, 65n
Rodger, E. H. B. 64n, 66n
Rodman, P. 165n
Romans 146
Rome 117
Ross, I. S. 164n, 168n
Ross, J. 53, 55
Rothkrug, L. 36
Rotterdam 117
Rousseau, J.-J. 147, 148, 151, 156–158,
    162, 164n, 165n, 167n, 170
Rowbottom, M. 60n
Royal Commissions 41
Royal Society of Edinburgh 102, 105
Royal Society of London 54
Russell, J. L. 59n
Russian peasantry 153

St. Andrews, University of 9, 10
Sade, Marquis de 160
Sahlins, M. 99n
Savage, R. 1
Say, J. B. 127, 141n
Scepticism 14, 16–18, 31
Schneewind, J. B. 35
Schofield, R. E. 71, 72, 84n
Scholar, literary 3
Schumpeter, J. 117
Science, impact of, on Scottish
    Enlightenment 40–58
Scotland 152, 153, 161
Scotland, Royal Museum of 1
Scott, H. 103, 114n
Scott, R. E. 48, 57, 62n, 63n, 66n
Scott, T. 69, 110
Scott, W. 163n
Scull, A. T. 170
Sen, S. R. 141n
Shapin, S. 103, 104, 114n, 115n
Shaw, P. 84n
Sheep scab 109
Shepherd, C. M. 59n
Sher, R. B. 59n
Sherwin, O. 164n
Shils, E. 99n
Signification 12–13
Simson, R. 55
Skene, A. 53
Skene, Dr. D. 50, 53, 54, 55, 56, 57, 65n
Skene, F. 48, 61n, 62n
Skene, G. 45, 48, 54, 65n
Sketches of the History of Man 152–154,
    158–160, 162
Skinner, J. 64n
Slater, T. R. 114n
Smallwood, W. M. 114n
Smellie, R. M. S. 114n

Smith, Adam 2, 4, 5, 40, 118, 120, 125, 126, 134ff, 145, 146, 147, 152, 163n, 164n, 169–170
Smout, T. C. 114n
Snow, C. P. 67, 84n
Societies 33, 52, 53, 54, 56, 58, 60, 64n, 65n
Society in Scotland for Propagating Christian Knowledge 110
Sömmering, S. T. v. 163
South Carolina 159
Spain 117
Spavan, J. 31–32
Spreull, I. 60n
Stahl, G. E. 107
Stanhope, Rev. S. 168n
Stark, W. 188, 204ff, 209, 217
Statistical Account of Scotland 63n
Steuart, D. 190, 193
Steuart, J. 4, 5, 117ff
Stewart, D. 137
Stewart, John 40, 52, 54, 55, 56, 59n, 64n, 65n
Stewart, M. A. 60n
Stocking G. W. 164n, 166n
Swinbank, P. 61n

Tassie, J. 1
Taylor, G. 102, 114n
Thackray, A. 65n
Thermodynamics 69ff
Thimon 10
Thomson, J. 85n
Thomson, S. P. 84n
Thomson, W. 67
Tinland, F. 165n
Tollison, R. D. 142n
Torlais, J. 100n
Tradition 90ff
Trail, J. W. H. 63n
Trail, R. 54
Traill, W. 65n
Tübingen 117

Tuke, S. 204
Tully & Halfpenny 183
Turgot, A. R. J. 97
Turnbull, G. 42, 43, 53, 56, 60n
Turnock, D. 114n
Tyson, E. 149, 150, 151, 157, 158, 163, 165n, 167n

Understanding 14
University education and society 48
Utrecht 117

Valencia 117
Valentine, J. 64n
Vayer, La Mothe le 23
Venice 117
Verona 117
Verri, A. 164n
Voltaire 4, 34

Walker, Rev. Dr. John 4, 5, 48, 53, 62n, 102ff, 166n
Wallace, A. R. 158
Wallis, J. 41, 167n
Waterston, C. 114
Watson, J. A. S. 114n
Watt, J. 67, 77, 82, 83, 169
Weights and measures 57
Whiston, W. 43
Whittington, G. W. 114n
Whyte, I. 114n
Wight, A. 106, 113
Wilcke, H. C. D. 80
Williamson, Capt. C. 109
Winch, D. 133, 139
'Wise Club' (Aberdeen Philosophical Society) 54–56
Wodrow, R. 22, 35
Wolfenbüttel 212
Woolgar, S. 98n
Wren, C. 41
Württemberg 117